EXECUTIVE
RESILIENCE

EXECUTIVE
RESILIENCE
Neuroscience for the Business of Disruption

Jurie G. Rossouw

With

Pieter J. Rossouw

Jurie G. Rossouw
Pieter J. Rossouw

RForce Pty Ltd
Level 13, 333 George St
2000, NSW
Sydney, Australia
ISBN 978-0-9942412-3-8

A catalogue record for this
book is available from the
National Library of Australia

For more information, please contact us through:
www.rforce.com.au – info@rforce.com.au

driven books

"I do not think there is any thrill that can go through the human heart like that felt by the inventor as he sees some creation of the brain unfolding to success... such emotions make a man forget food, sleep, friends, love, everything."
Nikola Tesla

One hundred years later, Telsa's words came to fruition. Today, innovation is so desired in business that a great many people sacrifice their own wellbeing in order to instigate another disruption.

Resilience provides a way forward—sustainability and thriving for the human spirit in an age of uncertainty.

Contents

Introduction

Now's not a good time.

There's a lot of change right now.

We're in a middle of a restructure.

Think back—how frequently are you saying this? How frequently do people say it to you when talking about a new initiative? Is there any organisation right now that's not in the middle of some big change or restructure?

These days, corporate change triggers cascading disruptions that seem to only have a middle—no beginning or end. Change morphs and permeates organisations, tearing through with endless aftershocks. Yet somehow we still hold on to the belief that some mythical time will come when there is no change and we can calmly sip a peppermint tea while considering new initiatives with clear minds and full budgets.

'Let's talk about it when things have settled down.'

Does it ever settle down? Even if the calm seems to come, there's the magma of another disruption building below our feet, ready to erupt with pyroclastic flow enveloping our calendars. Surely, soon the smoke will clear to reveal free days where we can finally get all those bearings we keep talking about.

In simpler times, big businesses worried about what their big competitors were doing. There was clarity in what to look for and where to look for it. The players were familiar and there was time to react. On a calm morning we could read the newspaper, on actual paper.

Now in calm, we find only stagnation—the slow death of competitive edge. Our competitors obsess about disruption. Change is not enough anymore. We need to shake the very foundations to be notable. These disruptions can come not just from established competitors, but from tech behemoths or invisible start-ups.

We don't even know where to look. We've left the age of information. We are now in the age of information overload. We no longer face constant change. We now face accelerating disruption. This weighs on us, more than we tend to admit. The mental impact is becoming like a global tax on society as we try to ignore the psychological impacts of this fast pace. But like a tell-tale brain beating in our heads, it refuses to be ignored.

What do we do with this? Do we learn to cope—to survive?

Survival does not help. It creates a state in the brain that supresses our ability to be strategic and design our own disruptions. A state that pervades culture and immobilises innovation. Exactly the gap that competitors need to storm the podium. It's not about survival.

Rapid change and disruption won't be leaving us any time soon. This is our new reality. A reality that makes it harder than before to find a sense of wellness. Therefore, we must explore a different path. A path that allows us to embrace an ever-changing world. A state of mind that creates clarity in the chaos. This is the path of resilience.

Resilience is not just about bouncing back—it is so much more. Resilience is about purpose, preparation, access to strategies, and the constant advancement of ourselves and our world. Resilience contains the mechanisms needed for our achievement of wellness and by extension, the very means through which we realise our purpose.

We should not fear change, nor should we grit our teeth and hold on with white knuckles while another round of restructures rip through. We should revel in these times, confident in our preparation, agility, and ability to transmute any situation into fuel for our personal drive.

We must learn to value the potential destruction of what we know... and trust in our ability to reassemble the shattered pieces in mid-air into something even better. There's no time to wait for our feet to rest on the ground. Humanity isn't walking anymore—we are running. There's no sign of slowing down. If we choose to fight for relevance and leap the boundaries of business, then we need to embrace this reality.

Resilience teaches us a mindset that is hard to embrace, but infinitely rewarding. It is the fundamental disruption of our own values. We then learn to look away from the blinding lure of happiness—after all, pursuing happiness directly brings anything but. Resilient people find what is truly of value is struggle, learning, challenge, growth. This fundamental re-evaluation of values brings exhilaration and excitement even in our toughest moments. We gain a surge to our sense of purpose far greater than what the pursuit of happiness could ever bring.

No longer would we need to wait for things to 'settle down'.

Now is always the right time to consider the value of an idea. *Now* is always the right time to adapt programs and integrate what might be the critical innovation that's needed to advance. Constant change can become an additional happy place, with resilience the prerequisite for this mental agility. However, we cannot expect this flexibility without resilience education.

Fortunately, neural structures are ready to be rewired for resilience. Like an old house, the wiring starts out hidden and confusing. With time, effort and investment, the old house becomes a modern masterpiece. The discovery of neuroplasticity shows us that no one is too old or too young to change. This ability to change, combined with our inherent social nature, means we can all work on this together. The growth to be achieved is not only worth striving for, it's quantifiably necessary for the future. We are heading towards one trillion dollars lost each year due to poor mental health—resilience is necessary.

How much more could we accomplish together if we collectively embrace the biggest challenges ahead? Resilience removes fear. A veritable vaccine against intolerance. It opens the pathway for us to fully embrace each other and our differences. Imagine the depth of compassion we can reach through the collective struggle of diverse people towards meaningful, shared goals.

Forget survival—to truly live in the world that we are running into, we need to build our collective resilience. Organisations, more than any other, need to develop cultures of resilience. Through an integration of neuroscience, psychology and management knowledge, we can transform our global culture.

This is the goal of Executive Resilience.

Jurie Rossouw

1.

The resilience imperative

As with planting trees, the best time to develop resilience was 20 years ago. The second best time is now. Yet few of us ever consider that we really need to improve our own resilience. Surely we are strong enough already, right? It's only once we finally face an inevitable, life-changing event that we learn if we can actually cope—a very precarious strategy. Humans have a natural tendency to avoid the type of voluntary challenges that test our limits. It takes a pinch of humility and a cup self-awareness to proactively act on our own betterment. This is why so many people turn to books about resilience only after they have squared off with great adversity. Soon enough, many of us find ourselves not coping, at which point we realise that, yes, we could be better.

Most troubling about this aspect of human nature is that it drags down our mental health. It drains the joy we get out of life, and it reduces our productivity and progress towards our goals.

The impact of this is about to be magnified, as we are hurtling towards a world of ever-increasing automation... an avalanche of disruption just starting to roll towards our mental safe zones. Artificial intelligence is no longer a topic for science fiction—it is real and already changing the nature of work. Traditional jobs are disappearing. A recent study at Oxford University indicate that in the UK alone, 1.3 million jobs in the administrative sector alone will most likely be automated by 2030—74% of all jobs in transportation, 59% in wholesale, and 56% in manufacturing will most likely disappear.

As these changes materialise, it falls on the leaders of organisations to consider their place in the future. Undoubtedly, in order to stay competitive a key component of this is to consider concepts and ideas that will be highly disruptive. It's not only about disrupting the market itself, but also about ideas that will disrupt your own business practices, landing on your own staff with particular impact. The nature of increasing change and challenges in society calls for a unique display of human capacity—resilience.

A brief history of workplace disruptions

To understand where we are heading and what is both similar and different compared to what we have faced previously, let's take a brief tour of the major historical disruptions to the workplace over the last few centuries.

Starting off, we got an appetiser to workplace disruption during the first industrial revolution, when factories initially appeared (between the mid-1700s and mid-1800s). Factories required more capital investment than what most people had access to, resulting in larger organisations owning factories, increasing the need for factory workers. At the same time, agricultural mechanisations pushed workers out of farms and into the factories that now offered jobs.

In many cases, people had to leave behind longstanding agricultural and cottage industries that had been in their families for generations. This took away the personal autonomy of running these small businesses, requiring workers to specialise. This furthered the 'division of labour' concept (dividing a job into many specialised parts) popularised by Scottish philosopher, Adam Smith's work, 'The Wealth of Nations' (1776). He reflects on concepts such as division of labour, productivity and free markets. Apart from the impact of this concept on world economics, the underlying message of the impact on human capacity is evident. It points towards the inter-relational nature of human capacity and society—and their combined

---

[1]   Smith, Adam (1776). An Inquiry into the Nature and Causes of the Wealth of Nations. 1 (1 ed.). London: W. Strahan.

need for resilience to thrive.

Change happened rather gradually during the first industrial revolution as the conception, design and physical construction of factories took many years. These machines were new, bespoke and required time-consuming, manual effort to build. In a world of snail mail, ideas and know-how spread slowly. Nearly a hundred years after the revolution began, change started to slow... until later in the 1800s when steel became more readily available.

Standardisation of tools and machinery also became more commonplace. This, combined with the increased availability of steel, meant factories could be built faster and more ambitious projects could be undertaken—longer bridges, railroads, and taller buildings, to name a few. Eventually, the invention of the telegraph drastically closed the distance between cities, increasing the availability of information.

These radical phases of the industrial revolution changed the nature of the human race—from autonomy of control (the craftsmen)—to being part of a larger mechanical system (the factory). This had a significant impact on our neurobiological need for safety[2]. No longer were we primarily self-sufficient. Instead, we became highly dependent on machinations outside of our control.

About the early 1900s, metropolitan areas became more densely populated and living standards improved. Increased mechanisation of agriculture meant that food production was finally able to keep up with population growth. Yet this also meant that many more people were displaced into cities, far away from their familiar surroundings. This shift forced generations of people to find a new sense of meaning, often as specialised components of large corporate machines, leaving behind the days of independent work, farming, and small business ownership.

During this time, the services industry started to show growth, though still far behind in size compared to the agricultural, minerals and manufacturing industries. The increased complexity of sophisticated processes, specialised functions and the new wave of information flowing in through telegraphs required more complex operational, financial and legal

---

[2] Rossouw, P. J. (Ed.) (2014). Neuropsychotherapy: Theoretical underpinnings and clinical applications. Mediros Pty Limited.

management. Increases in living standards also meant a greater availability of doctors and medical specialists. Railways increased the need for hotels and fuelled the hospitality industry. Indeed, the services industry created a growing middle class, generally better off than factory workers, who themselves faced volatility due to innovation.

As our ability to harness and mobilise power—such as waterwheels—became more commonplace, a constant flow of improvements made non-services industries increasingly efficient. These increases in efficiency enabled us our first real glimpse of automation.

New machinery had the capability of wiping out entire swathes of jobs, and after Nikola Tesla ignited the modern age with the spark of AC electricity and the induction motor in 1887, the stage was set for the biggest revolution yet. Power stations, the electrification of offices, factories and homes gradually spread through countries. Telephones appeared and the business world sped up. Still, process automation required long lead times, extensive research, development and time to operationalise. In a relative sense, there was still certainty in most jobs that they wouldn't disappear quickly, giving people long careers of performing similar tasks. What's more, constant economic growth meant that living standards continued to improve and increased complexity created more middle-class jobs than ever before.

But the trend wasn't always positive. The growing availability of quality steel meant that bigger and more destructive weapons could be made, resulting in some countries feeling more confident than ever in their military might. This, along with growing international tension, led to the First World War.

The widespread impact of the war left a strong psychological mark on the people at the time. Beyond the tremendous toll on life, the war ended the unprecedented growth in spending power and living standard increases caused by the previous two industrial revolutions. The unbridled optimism of the 1920s was gone. The Great Depression of the 1930s followed, deeply testing the resolve and resilience of hundreds of millions of people. Particularly affected during the Depression were factory workers, who experienced far more job losses than those employed in people-related services. Soon after, the concept of mass production found new life; the Second World War required vast amounts of military equipment to fuel the war effort. This unlikely source of investment revitalised the world economy.

As the war came to an end, investment turned towards rebuilding the infrastructure and factories of cities that fell victim to the war. The world economy recovered, though after the war it became clear the sort of destruction that industrialisation has rendered us capable of. An uneasy truce followed during the Cold War, though businesses were free to return to normal operations.

As the military force returned to the workforce, factories were the first to see a new type of mass production, particularly in countries such as post-war Germany and Japan. There, factories were generally refitted for military equipment, making them targets for the Allies. This meant that most factories in these countries ended up being destroyed during bombing runs. Mazda, for example was, and still is, located in fated Hiroshima.

After the war, recovering businesses took the initiative to invest in new production techniques, none more so than the German and Japanese car manufacturers. These invested in machinery that were more flexible and faster to adapt to required changes. This meant faster response times to market needs, better quality, and less reliance on workers. The remaining workers in these factories were able to operate more types of machinery compared to the high specialisation of traditional mass production methods. Efficiency was further improved through the pursuit of standardisation and simplification, making it feasible for workers to expand their workplace versatility.

In contrast, automotive factories in America were generally left unscathed after the war, meaning there was no immediate need to retool or change manufacturing methods. This was a similar case in the UK, where they escaped most of Germany's highly-inaccurate V2 rockets. While the countries rebuilding invested in new machinery, factory workers in America and the UK returned to the same old machines and manufacturing techniques that they used before the war. Bolstered by the confidence of victory, few took seriously the new techniques being adopted elsewhere.

This attitude of sticking with 'tried-and-true' methods resulted in a growing gap of competitive advantage that would only be felt many decades later. The once-bustling automotive capital of Detroit is now being likened to a ghost town. Meanwhile, Volkswagen and Toyota came to dominate the automotive world, despite conducting manufacturing in countries with relatively higher costs of employment.

Throughout this time, the level of complexity required to run these large factories contributed to the ongoing growth of the services industry. This growth provided an avenue of employment for laid-off factory workers ousted by increased factory automation. A desire for further education increased, as it gave more people a shot at ascending towards middle-class professions in finance, law, medicine and the like. So far, the services industry had seen little disruption of any significance beyond continued growth. However, a curious contribution from the Second World War set the wheels in motion to change all that.

The third industrial revolution

Enigma, the machine used by Germany to encrypt messages to the naval fleet, presented a specific challenge to the Allies due to its sophistication. Decrypting these messages in a timely manner required something of even greater sophistication. Alan Turing and his team provided the answer in the form of the Bombe machine. A big, hulking metal box full of wires and spinning wheels, the Bombe is now seen as the first-ever general-purpose computer. Turing's contribution to computational science set the stage for what is sometimes referred to as the third industrial revolution—the digital revolution.

Electronics had already made its way into the industrial and manufacturing world, allowing even greater automation of highly-repetitive processes. The specificity of industrial and manufacturing processes meant that the shift from analogue to digital machinery from the 1950s onwards was a natural part of the endless drive for efficiency.

Workers who had been in the manufacturing world for generations came to see that this type of change was part and parcel of their chosen occupation. More successful workers aimed to stay abreast of what was coming in and be part of the new advances, thus avoiding redundancies. Those left behind looked for work in the services industry, while others moved to manufacturers that had not yet implemented computer automation, sometimes postponing the inevitable. Some never truly found a way back into the workforce, adding to a growing contingent requiring welfare. People left without employment options had few positive thoughts to spare for the corporate world.

Around the mid-1900s, mainframe computers started to make its way into offices, generally taking the shape of large punch-card machines used for back-office financial processing. From colossal machines taking up large rooms, computers slowly shrank towards something that could be placed on a desk without breaking it. But miniaturisation took decades and few people imagined then that they would ever have access to one themselves. Although, as the first desktop machines started to appear in the '70s and '80s, the increased ability to do word-processing, number-crunching and managing schedules meant that they quickly became ubiquitous in business.

However, it didn't take long for the demographics of computer users to change. Computer programmers and operators at the time were mostly female. Advertisements in the '60s and '70s centered on how women could accomplish many more tasks by using computers. Mirroring the earlier shift in manufacturing—from specialised manual labour to fewer generalists operating multiple types of machines—office workers now faced the same change. Businesses needed fewer people to do the same tasks, particularly so for office clerks and secretaries. The women's now familiar role as computer operators grew throughout the '80s, though at the time few managers and executives were using computers themselves. This changed in the '90s as computing became so accessible that all office workers started to get their own computers. Managers no longer needed secretaries to dictate messages since they could now simply type it out themselves in a word processor. They could even manage their schedules and communicate through internal networks themselves. This demographic shift brought layoffs—a prelude to times ahead.

As we've seen in industrials and manufacturing, whenever there's a sophisticated new way to automate, an increase in complexity duly comes along. The complexity of the digital revolution brought with it the rapidly-growing Information Technology industry, ready to absorb the portions of population no longer required by the traditional manufacturing and services sectors.

However, young people who grew up around technology were far more likely to enter the IT world than older generations laid off due to industrial automation. As people from the business world mingled with the IT world, the ability to program a computer ignited our collective imagination. Finally, an accessible tool was available to businesses in the services industry to perform complex processes that previously had to be done manually.

As the Internet began connecting the world, ideas spread faster than ever before, not least of which were ways to do more with less. The cycle of change and innovation sped up through 2000 to 2010. The volume of information and data available grew to an enormous scale, adding further complexity, information that needed people to manage it and to try to make sense of it all.

Around 2010, we had already started to see factories that are almost entirely unstaffed, foreshadowing what is in store for businesses now. In the services sector, smaller organisations popped up that are primarily digital, while larger organisations pursued process optimisation to require less human interaction. Old skill sets, particularly related to repetitive office tasks, were routinely replaced with programs and systems which themselves required different skills to manage. Though at this point, most services jobs were still considered to be relatively safe as long-term careers. Doctors, nurses, lawyers, bankers, advisors, and so on studied in their fields with a reasonable sense of confidence that this will be their occupation for decades to come. Even though computing reduced the need for people doing menial work in offices, these were generally replaced with more 'thinking' jobs to manage the increased sophistication. It seems every time a process is made more efficient, the added complexity requires additional staffing elsewhere, though in sum the overall increase in productivity makes it worthwhile.

Why resilience now?

Arriving at the present day, what is the same and what is different compared to where we've come from? Also, why is the need for us as employees to be resilient any different now than before?

Starting with what is the same, the main familiar theme is that there has always been change and disruption, and while some people grew and advanced through it, others found themselves left behind. The global economy continually grew, while living standards around the world improved for many.

However, the digital revolution also made offshoring easier than ever. While a boon to growing economies, many mature people in first world countries who lost their jobs due to outsourcing and automation had little chance to reskill and find a new place in the working world. Here we find a growing segment of people who feel abandoned in the wake of incessant technological progress. Combine that with offshoring and the misconception that migrants are undercutting low-wage jobs, and we find a recipe for serious discontent.

Desperation may lead them to unite with political groups that promise the type of change they want. While this segment of people has been growing through hundreds of years of industrial automation, they are now reaching a proportion where they can influence global politics. We have seen this recently through the shock decision of the United Kingdom to leave the European Union, followed by an even bigger shock as the United States elected Donald Trump as their next president.

As the gap between rich and poor widens, businesses and politicians have ignored the working class, and the out-of-work class, to their peril. Just as factory and industrial workers have faced this fate over hundreds of years, laid-off service workers may add to the discontent contingent. Governments and businesses rarely bothered to build soft skills in workers to help them weather these disruptions. The result is that together we face the consequences through growing global political uncertainty. However, an even bigger challenge is yet to come.

As manual and repetitive work jobs were replaced, the added sophistication of techniques and processes creates new, though less, 'thinking' jobs to understand the added complexity. The humourist author Douglas Adams joked that should the exact purpose of the universe ever be discovered, it would immediately be replaced by something even more bizarre and inexplicable—and that this might already have happened. Arguably, the same could be said of financial products and many business practices. Management of this continual addition of complexity has always been the domain of humans, but what if technology is finally catching up with us to the point that it can manage complexity better that we can?

This is where we find differences compared to the change we've faced before. Previously, 'thinking' jobs were generally exempt from automation, while now the sophistication of our algorithms and machines are starting to rival human cognitive capabilities. For the first time, we are seeing robotic lawyers, digital doctors and automated advisors. Professions that were once seen as rock-solid career paths now suddenly have the potential to be digitised and automated. In the offices of large businesses, processes requiring complex decision-making can now be automated, as machines learn from observing humans.

To help us understand the significance of this change and why resilience is becoming more important than ever, let's explore a few key innovations that is set to transform the workplace in the next decade.

Robots love processes

While industrials and manufacturing have long ago adopted computer-controlled robotics to automate production lines, service organisations have struggled with process variability and a requirement for flexibility. For example, manufacturing a car is more standardised than processing an application for a home loan, since all parameters for the car can be set in black and white, while the loan application might require some fuzzy judgement calls. While some parts of the home loan process can be easily automated, many exceptions still pop up that must be managed by humans. People must take into consideration the most recent policy guidelines, regulations, rules, targets, unclear information provided, and other variables that often change too quickly to realistically program into a set of rules to automate the process.

Many touchpoints and handovers may exist between departments and systems, at each step requiring some input, transformation or validation by a human. What adds to the challenge for businesses is that systems used to run these processes are often provided by large third party developers, such as SAP, Oracle, and so on. This results in prohibitively high costs to develop integrations between suppliers and redevelopment of old legacy platforms, meaning that even the proverbial low-hanging fruit is still far out of reach. However, a relatively new innovation provides an alternative.

Robotics Process Automation, or RPA for short, has been around in various guises for decades now but in recent years has become incredibly powerful. Yet it's surprisingly simple to put into operation. The concept is different from normal process automation, which is usually built into the software itself where software developers and programmers are needed to create the automation. RPA, in contrast, functions like an employee. The RPA robot is a software application that uses the existing interfaces that employees use, and performs tasks just like an employee does, by using a virtual keyboard and mouse. The robot is also trained by observing a human trainer, the same way that a human would be trained. Rules and procedures to handle variation can easily be added and updated as required, thus reducing the retraining requirement of a large group of employees. Quality, consistency and speed increases. Significantly different here is that no programming skills are required, overcoming the problems of integrating large third-party applications.

RPA has finally matured to a stage where even the largest organisations now have the confidence to implement it to reach short-term gains in productivity. On a human level, RPA is often promoted as an avenue to free people from repetitive work so that they can spend more time on more valuable tasks. Many do not see this as a threat to people employed in these jobs currently, though it is clear to see where this will go when competitive pressure mounts.

New jobs will be created to oversee and maintain these robots, though as is always the case, these jobs will be more complex, require different skills, and be fewer than the number previously employed. Speed is also a major difference here. In the manufacturing industry, robots are physical machines, picking up, modifying, and placing parts. These machines take time to design, build and put into operation. In contrast, RPA robots doing knowledge work are entirely virtual, meaning they can rapidly be put into place and in infinite numbers. This will result in sudden disruptive shocks to employment, once again impacting service workers who aren't generally used to this type of disruption.

The machines are learning

The ability of RPA robots to learn without being programmed stems from the ability of an algorithm that can recognise patterns and make predictions, called machine learning. Machine learning is particularly useful for processes such as our home loan application, where the answers are not always black and white. This mirrors human cognitive functioning—which is often fuzzy—resulting in the eventual judgement call of whether the home loan application should proceed or not. Let's say that in this particular loan application, the applicant had a gap in employment recently. Our human may look at employment consistency prior to that, consider from experience if home loans with similar situations have defaulted, and make a judgement call based on experience. Machine learning functions in the same way. In this instance, the machine learning-enabled robot would be 'trained' by looking at previous home loans, their variables, and default rates. Based on this, the robot builds a model to which it compares a new home loan to predict how likely it is to be repaid, and approves or denies it based on those decisions. The difference here is that our robot can consider millions of home loans, weigh thousands of variables at once, predict with greater accuracy, do it instantly, and never get tired.

Machine learning provides computers with the potential to understand complex concepts that would be far too time-consuming to program directly. Although here our robot is making predictions without a broader understanding of *why* it is doing what it's doing. So again there is a need for humans to oversee and maintain these robots to make sure they don't run off into some unintended direction, perhaps deciding to grant free home loans to all, due to a misinterpreted variable. This possibility has already occurred in high-frequency trading algorithms using machine learning;

these sometimes spiral down in a vicious circle of stockmarket destruction when unforeseen circumstances arise. For quite a while, human oversight will be required, again requiring fewer people with a different set of skills.

What is interesting is that there are many different types of machine learning. One example is the distinction between *white box* and *black box* machine learning, which is of interest because it also relates to how humans think. White box machine learning can take the shape of a decision tree. Here, you can open the box and see the specific sets of rules through the branches of the tree to work out exactly how it made a particular decision. From time to time, you can open the box to see how the rules are being updated as the robot learns. This is useful for relatively simple situations. Perhaps most of our home loan application can be processed this way.

Black box machine learning is where, when you open the box, you have no way to tell why the robot made a certain decision. When you look inside the box, you see an absurd number of nodes connected to each other in a seemingly nonsensical way—a jumbled mess that mysteriously results in a precise decision.

These jumbled connections are generally called *artificial neural networks*, and are called such because they resemble what we see in the human brain. That's right, humans are also black boxes. No amount of looking at the neurons of a human—as yet—can allow us to explain exactly why a person made a certain decision.

In addition, humans do not have direct access to understand exactly what is going on in their brains, so they also cannot explain exactly what their reasoning for a decision was. We do have the ability to rationalise decisions and point out why we think we made a decision, but this does not reflect all the subconscious processing that the brain did.

Taking a simple example of reasoning with our home loan application, it might have passed the white box phase, but now we pass it to the black box robot to verify the signature. This robot rejects it. If we opened up the box, we couldn't tell which neurons made this choice. If we asked why, maybe the robot could explain that there was a line it didn't like, but even the robot doesn't know exactly why it didn't like it. This is important, because this simple example hints towards the future, where black box solutions will be required to make highly-complex decisions. When this happens, no one, not even the robot, will be able to explain why it made a certain decision. And if the robot makes a choice that seems illogical to us, would we trust it because it's considering more factors than we are? We already trust all the biological black boxes around us that we call our colleagues, so perhaps we can.

Look who's talking (it's the robots)

The human brain has a few million years of evolutionary development behind it which has slowly allowed us to become very adept at interpreting language and using words to express ourselves. Our ability to recognise patterns and relate meaning to those patterns have so far been way beyond the capability of computers. What has held computers back so far from being able to understand language is quite simply that language is incredibly complex to program.

Advances in machine learning provides a way to teach a computer how to talk in a similar way that humans learn—not only to understand written words, but also spoken words. Already we are seeing these natural language robots appear in call centres where you can speak instructions instead of dialling options. These are still very rudimentary, though the foundations are there to build more sophisticated robotic agents.

Most call centres have been recording customer calls for decades, usually for training purposes. Few in the '90s would have predicted that these recordings would eventually be used to train computers to talk directly to customers. This treasure trove of data is available, allowing robots to be trained using millions of real-world customer calls. As technology such as natural language processing and voice recognition improves, businesses are realising what they can do with it and the eventual increase in efficiency and service that can be achieved.

IBM's Watson (a machine-learning computer system) can understand natural language well enough to beat the best Jeopardy players. In 2016, Google's DeepMind team demonstrated a leap forward in producing a natural-sounding synthesised voice, to the point that it's hard to tell that it wasn't spoken by a human. These technologies are converging to create a digital person that can be spoken to in natural language and can speak back to you in natural language. Add to that the ability to access company systems, follow policy rules and complete tasks on request through robotics process automation, and you have a complete digital worker.

Back in 2000, this might have seemed unlikely. Now, many large companies have already kicked off this gradual transition from human workers to digital workers. Some companies have worked out that they don't even require sophisticated digital workers; they're now replacing point-of-sales staff with digital terminals, as can be seen at some McDonalds restaurants. The Henn-na hotel in Nagasaki is staffed entirely by robots. The Royal Bank of Scotland (RBS) has just rolled out a smart chatbot called Luvo.

Improvements in self-service capabilities may remove the need for many people to dial into a call centre in the first place. Call centres performing overdue invoice collections have found that most of their calls can be avoided by sending an automated message, capturing many accounts that were overdue simply because people forgot to pay. Soon, digital workers may handle most customer interactions, with only the most complicated cases passed on to the remaining human specialists.

Overall, this growing ability to understand human language is helping computers to cut deeper into traditional knowledge and 'thinking' jobs. While call centre jobs and those of agents have been a mainstay of employment, we now see a shift towards a smaller set of people with new skillsets managing groups of digital workers.

Artificial intelligence—The last great invention

These innovations are part of what feeds into the larger goal of artificial intelligence (AI), or more accurately, artificially created intelligence. There are many different ideas of what AI can be, and we are already seeing many forms of 'specific AI', which is AI created to solve specific problems. A hugely disruptive example of *specific AI* is self-driving cars. This will change the entire transportation industry and how we move ourselves. The first self-driving taxis and trucks are already on the road today, spelling the end to tens of millions of professional driver jobs worldwide over the next decades.

The disruptive effects do not end there. Also impacted will be smash repair shops, facing a drop in demand due to lower numbers of accidents.

Insurance companies are set to no longer insure drivers, but mechanical failures instead. The value of parking spots may dwindle as shared vehicles that constantly roam the roads may become the new norm.

As this form of AI improves, it may eventually even become illegal for a human to operate a vehicle in public, as human driving will be considered too dangerous and unpredictable compared to self-driving vehicles. In a way, this is still an example of a simpler form of AI.

More complex forms of specific AI are those that can perform tasks that we previously thought only humans could do. The game of Go was for a long time considered to be beyond computers since the amount of options within the game is far too great for an AI to find the best move. Google's AlphaGo program changed all that in March 2016 when it beat one of the world's top Go players in four out of five matches.

Specific AI is what we'll be seeing more commonly in businesses, performing repetitive tasks that are still too complex to complete, such as the judgement calls in our home loan application. Robotics process automation, natural language processing and machine learning all factor in, bringing us closer to the realisation of 'general AI'. The concept of this form of AI is one that exhibits intelligence in the same way that a human does— it can learn on its own, decide the best course of action to achieve a goal, and even decide what its own goals should be.

General AI may be our single greatest achievement as humans. It may also be our last great achievement... as any great future achievements would likely come from the AI itself. To see why, it's useful to think of the human brain, which has taken millions of years to develop to its current form, with little improvement in the brain's processing power in the last few thousand years. In contrast, in just the last few decades, we have made huge strides towards the creation of general AI, going from a blank slate through to eclipsing human ability in complex tasks in less than a century. The potential of general AI is far beyond what humans can ever hope to accomplish, because AI can easily upgrade and scale up, while we are limited to our biological hardware.

Traditional rock-solid career choices are suddenly on the line for automation. We are now even seeing the first robot lawyers, providing legal advice to common questions. Virtual doctors are appearing that are more accurate in diagnosing illnesses than their real-life peers.

The implication for business is profound, as AI will one day drive the most complex decisions of all—how to run the business. While our analytics tools now help us choose between options, AI would actually come up with the options themselves. As scandals of fraud and bad business practices continue to appear, many customers may come to prefer dealing with digital workers and automated businesses rather than humans, due to the perception that a digital worker will be unbiased and not act unscrupulously.

This is the future we need to prepare for—one where we as the doers gradually shift to become caretakers of robots, digital workers and AI. Though this caretaker role will certainly not be as easy as it sounds—we must keep pace with fast-moving advances to maintain competitive advantage.

The accelerating pace of change

The last few hundred years have shown us how the pace of change relentlessly accelerates. Especially as the digital age matures, businesses are getting access to increasingly powerful tools that are faster and simpler to deploy. This contrasts with the manufacturing industry, which still needs to physically build robots to perform tasks, putting some limit to how quickly they can automate processes. Also in contrast, manufacturing has had to contend with ongoing automation for far longer than the services industry. The result is that the services industry is in for much more turmoil in a shorter period. Essentially, what manufacturing did in a hundred years, services will do in ten.

To some extent, people in the services industry have experienced occasional layoffs due to economic downturns and recessions. Though in these cases, jobs often returned as economic conditions improved. Redundancies due to automation are different in that the jobs do not return—instead, people have to quickly learn new skills to remain relevant and find new opportunities. As we have seen, many are left with lower quality of life, or do not find employment again at all. Meanwhile, the services industry consists of a large segment of the population who are even more unprepared for large scale disruptions. Especially disruptions that result in fundamental change.

What we are seeing now is that options are appearing to automate longstanding, previously secure careers. In their place we find new, yet fewer, jobs to program and maintain digital workers, often in technologies that come and go; creating jobs and destroying them soon after as the technology changes. Programming languages also rise and fall, sometimes due to a better option appearing, other times due to the language being axed by its developer. As new technologies come and go and the pace of change accelerates, we will reach a point where entire career paths pop into and out of existence in less than a year.

This is a dramatic shift in mindset as it moves away from the idea of studying a field for a few years, then launching into a decades-long career in the chosen field. Instead, we are moving to an era of constant re-learning. Once in a chosen field, a person will constantly have to learn new technologies and skills to program and maintain an automated work environment. This is not to say that the requirement to study a specific field would fall away. For example, an accountant would still need to study accounting, even though most processes are automated.

This relearning will be necessary in case modifications are needed, or complex maintenance is required, or when things eventually go wrong. Essentially, people will move from repetitive tasks to tasks requiring higher cognition—complex thinking tasks that computers can't yet do. Therefore, more subjective occupations, such as user experience design, may experience an increase in demand for employment. In this example, even though user experience design can be enhanced through increased data and machine learning analysis, the result will be more subjective complexity, putting these decisions further out of reach of digital workers.

Subjective complexity takes the form of trade-offs to be made. For example, ongoing optimisation of a mobile banking app might show several possible ways to restructure the app interface based on user research. One option favours retail customers, which make up most app users, while reducing the user experience of the smaller number of stock investors.

Another option favours increases in loan applications, but results in a reduced experience for retail customers. As additional data becomes available, it's easy to fall into analysis paralysis, requiring larger teams of user experience designers to put the data in context of the business strategy and work through the subjective complexity to make the right trade-offs. Meanwhile, other banks all push for experience optimisation and so speed to market will be the key to determine competitive advantage.

This change of pace is evident in many areas, though particularly in programming. In previous decades, the de rigueur method to plan and roll out a system change was the 'waterfall' approach. *Waterfall* is where every single requirement is thought out and planned in advance, often requiring years for larger projects. Once all the requirements are finalised, development work starts from front to back and everything is built. The waterfall approach has fallen out of favour since early 2000, as an 'agile' approach to development came to prominence.

The concept of *agile* is centred on fast, iterative planning and development so that functional systems can quickly be deployed, tested and improved. This has seen change cycles drop from years to months, even in the largest organisations. Even here, working in this type of rapid-development environment requires a change in mindset—an extraordinary emphasis is placed on mental flexibility, adaptability, and being able to quickly evolve concepts and revise preconceptions. Often people are thrust into an agile environment where their new roles and statuses are not immediately clear. Without having the right mental state to adapt, this shift not only results in lower productivity, but increased stress, feeling overwhelmed, and a reduced level of engagement.

Large companies face an even tougher environment as they find themselves caught between shifting tectonic plates. On the one side is an increased requirement to be able to quickly innovate, iterate, and disrupt your own business practices faster. On the other side are increased compliance requirements, more stringent risk and regulatory pressures, and an increasingly inflexible internal legal landscape. As these tectonic plates scrape against each other, shakeups occur and fissures open up. Either your business can use these as opportunities, or another nimbler competitor will fill up the cracks.

The increase in internal complexity is a natural result of organisational growth and maturation, yet the accelerating pace of change requires faster adaptation and a willingness to take on risk—not just financially, but also operationally. A large organisation may recognise that it needs to innovate and encourage innovation in its employees, however if employees are constantly having their efforts stifled by increasing difficulty to actually do something innovative, then a culture of innovation will not develop. Every day, great ideas get crushed by well-intentioned bureaucracy.

As we look at these trends, it becomes clear that the world is changing, and the speed of change is about to hit a blistering pace. This rapid change brings with it a continual state of uncertainty, which results in a need for extraordinary adaptability.

Achieving adaptability

Increased personal resilience enables an individual to not only be adaptable and handle challenges and uncertainty, but to flourish in this tumultuous environment. Thrivers will continually be uncovering opportunities and driving change themselves in order to achieve goals. So, the way to manage the challenge of our evolving workplace is through increasing the capacity of people to be resilient.

Resilience is often thought of purely as how we bounce back from difficult situations. However, this definition doesn't provide enough clues as to the true depth of resilience skills and their benefits. To uncover these depths, we can modernise the definition of resilience as *advancing despite adversity*. The key shift in focus is away from simply 'bouncing back', which implies returning to the status quo. Instead we shift towards 'advancing', meaning continual growth and the ongoing achievement of your goals and the goals of your organisation.

Naturally, there can only be advancement if there exists a goal to advance towards. This highlights the critical need to have clarity of purpose as a driving force. We can contrast this concept of 'goal-oriented resilience' with another type of resilience, which we shall call 'nihilistic resilience'. Nihilistic resilience is when some may appear resilient, not because they have developed resilience skills, but instead because they do not care enough to be invested in any particular outcome, and therefore is not affected by adversity in general. This distinction is important, as not all forms of resilience are equal and one is clearly more constructive than the other.

Advancing despite adversity

Continuing our refinement of the definition of resilience, another change is adding the word 'despite'—but why *that* word instead of 'because' or 'through'? The subtlety of the word 'despite' is an aspect of resilience that is often neglected, namely proactivity. A highly proactive person who learns from the mistakes of others may be able to avoid many forms of adversity and advance regardless. Here the point of using the word 'despite' is to clarify that for the truly resilient person, adversity is not a prerequisite to advancing towards their goals. Similarly, we cannot wait for adversity before we grow and finally pursue resilience. As Otto von Bismarck said, perhaps somewhat harshly, 'Only a fool learns from his own mistakes. The wise man learns from the mistakes of others.'

Along with this comes the other critical aspect of resilience that is nearly universally ignored—resilience should be developed ahead of time, *before* facing a major crisis. So often people flock to books about resilience only *after* they have faced a traumatic event, looking for something to help them through their emotions. However, here individuals would have been far better served by working on resilience proactively as a necessary skill for successful living, which would then help them deal with whatever situation arises along the way.

The idea of advancing despite adversity helps to clarify that resilience is something we need to work on throughout our lives. Eventually all of us will face adversity, both large and small. It's not a matter of *if,* but *when.* Resilience education and development should therefore be mandatory as a key factor to build resilience into our society itself through resilient people. This has important global implications, as increased resilience can constructively guide the efforts of the discontent towards more effectively improving their own situations and to elect more enlightened leaders.

'Adversity' in the context of resilience is not only the big life-altering events, but also includes the small challenges of everyday life. From heavy traffic on the way to work, to the ever-noisy neighbour, to dealing with onerous compliance processes, through to personal challenges you set for yourself, small annoyances can add up to large emotional reactions eventually. So much time and energy can go into fretting about things that we cannot readily change, resulting in fruitless distractions that take energy away from advancing towards goals.

This aspect is particularly relevant in organisations, where employees may become fixated on small annoyances in processes, compliance requirements, or imperfect technology, to the point that it distracts them from the mission of the organisation. This is an easy trap to fall into as there are often many sources of sympathy that validates an employee's frustration. This is most visible in large multinational companies with highly-structured processes and compliance requirements that take a mammoth feat of coordination to improve. The glacial pace of change in large organisations, combined with a vast number of concurrent changes, can simultaneously create a paradox: a perception of rigidity mixed with being arbitrarily alterant.

As is evident from the millions of people employed by large organisations, the majority of people can *survive* in the corporate world. However, comparatively few manage to truly succeed while also enjoying the challenge of working in a multinational. Being able to take all the everyday challenges—as well as larger, disruptive events—in your stride, is a skill that is not natural to everyone. Importantly, it is also not a skill that develops automatically when facing adversity. This is important to realise— throwing someone into the deep end does not guarantee they will learn to swim. Some simply sink.

Worryingly, resulting effects are anxiety, depression, or nervousness. These in turn often lead people to seek relief by consuming excessive amounts of alcohol, indulging in other unhealthy habits, or by retreating from the corporate world. The annual impact of stress in the Australian economy alone is estimated at over AU$14 billion, equating to a 1.36% loss of employee productivity—a massive cost that is only projected to increase in the coming years.[3]

In the United States, the World Health Organisation (WHO) has estimated the cost of stress to be nearly US$300 billion per year, or 2.6% of the GDP.[4] The WHO further estimates that depression alone causes an US$800 billion impact globally, which is expected to double by 2030[5], and so they're naturally calling for increased investment in mental health programs.[6]

The resilience imperative

As a society we have developed a large network of mental health support services, such as coaches, counsellors, psychologists and psychiatrists. However, these services are usually only activated when a personal situation has significantly worsened and is having a major impact in that person's life. These services are rarely proactive: they don't reach out to you before something happens. We don't have door-to-door psychology salesmen trying to convince households to invest in resilience.

Psychology as an industry is primarily focused on pathology—the practice of diagnosing what is wrong and then fixing it. Essentially, it's bringing a person back to the status quo. In contrast, there is little interest in changing the status quo itself, and from what we've seen with the increasing trends in workplace disruption and the global impact of poor mental health, it is precisely the status quo that needs to be improved. If businesses and governments are not proactive by developing resilience, then they will increasingly face the wrath of voters who are angry because they

---

3   Econtech. (2008). The cost of workplace stress in Australia. *Australia: Medibank Private Limited.*

4   Brun, J. (2006). Work-related stress: Scientific evidence-base of risk factors, prevention and costs. Retrieved October 9, 2016, from http://www.who.int/occupational_health/topics/brunpres0307.pdf

5   World Health Organisation. (2014). *Out of the Shadows, Making Mental Health a Global Development Priority.* Retrieved from http://www.who.int/mental_health/WB_WHO_meeting_2016.pdf?ua=1

6   World Health Organisation. (2013). *Investing in Mental Health: Evidence for Action.* Retrieved from http://apps.who.int/iris/bitstream/10665/87232/1/9789241564618_eng.pdf

were ill-prepared to deal with the effects of innovative disruptions.

Research already singles out resilience as being a critical protective factor against mental health disorders[7]. Increased resilience is universally beneficial to every single person on this planet. There is no one to whom resilience does not apply. Some learn aspects of resilience naturally, while others never truly gain this skill.

Meanwhile, extraordinarily few people ever receive any structured education on this critical skill. Parents pass on some wisdom to their children, but only to the extent that they themselves understand. Usually parents are not resilience experts, so the level of resilience education could certainly be better.

Only a miniscule few forward-looking schools and universities have effective mental wellbeing programs in place, with most missing a key opportunity to ready children for the world they will soon face. Governments might have the resources to provide wide-scale training, but no such training is proactively supplied, instead deferring to pathology-based treatment. Our friends are often who we turn to when facing adversity, but they are also not resilience experts. Businesses who invest in resilience training and coaching often only do so for higher levels of management and top-performing employees, skipping over the masses of lower-level employees who may well need resilience training the most.

Resilience is a skill that needs to be taught, however it seems no one is actively preparing people for the coming environment of rapid disruption. No sector has clearly taken up the mantle to drive a wider improvement in the status quo of resilience and mental wellbeing. Yet the potential benefits are profound and wide-ranging, just as the status quo of neglect can erode global stability.

Everyone stands to benefit from increased resilience in people:

- Marriages and romantic relationships need resilience to stand the test of time.
- Parents need resilience to provide a caring environment for children

---

[7] Edward, K. L. (2005). *Resilience: A protector from depression*. Journal of the American Psychiatric Nurses Association, 11(4), 241-243.

while coping with lack of sleep and unrelenting demands from everyone around them.

- Family relations and friendships need the ability to manage small annoyances and to be there for each other when facing greater adversity.
- Individuals need resilience skills to achieve a sense of purpose and keep working towards personally important goals.
- Patience and understanding fostered by resilience training will help diverse communities overcome tension and become more empathetic, building a supportive society—the kind of environment that can overcome deeply-ingrained cultural tensions and wars.
- Resilience in the voting public helps with focussing on important issues such as climate change, adding to forward-looking governments, stable countries and constructive global relations.
- Organisations benefit from people who are more engaged, productive, and focused on broader goals. Measurable improvements can materialise through lower incidents or compensation claims, less absenteeism and more presenteeism, as well as through increased productivity and retention. More importantly, businesses stand to benefit most directly from a workforce that can innovate, readily adapt to change, and keep pace with disruption by thriving, even through growing uncertainty.

While businesses have much to gain, they also contribute strongly to the need for resilience in the first place. Often identified as a major contributor to stress is the demands businesses place on employees. Given the new environment of constant disruption and uncertainty, reducing demands on employees is not an avenue that can realistically be explored. To the contrary, as change accelerates, competition will become fiercer, disruptions will be felt more intensely, impacts of change will be more widespread, and demands on employees will increase. This is a natural consequence of our increasing advancement as a society.

Therefore, investing in resilience is the most realistic and effective long-term solution available. A resilient workforce can not only cope in this increasingly challenging environment, but can thrive in it. However, this is not to say that productivity is purely up to the resilience of the individual. A crucial factor is management practices that provide welcome challenges and are conducive to employee wellbeing. If your organisation maintains a caustic culture, then asking employees to be more resilient will not yield productive results. Indeed, you will foster nihilistic resilience instead in those that stay, while the truly innovative employees will leave. If there isn't a clear indication that the organisation cares about the wellbeing of its employees beyond minimal lip service, then no constructive change will take place.

Similarly, it would not be fair for the organisation to expect high levels of performance through uncertainty if no effort had been made to provide a healthy environment, alongside universal resilience training. There is a symbiotic relationship between the organisation and the individual when it comes to developing resilience, largely because the organisation itself is a key contributor to the need for resilience in the first place. Any one-sided attempt at change is doomed to fail. There has to be a collective effort to improve. From above, a healthy culture must flow down from the executives and leaders of the organisation. From below, education and development programs help employees develop and hone resilience skills. In the middle, management connects cultural leadership guidelines with strategy and facilitates resilience development in their employees.

Executives, leaders and managers need to develop their own resilience to be willing to consider challenges from employees to change the business itself—and this might well be the disruption that the company needs to survive. Goal-oriented resilience means that there will be different views in how to best achieve the goals of the organisation. This diversity in views, and the willingness of individuals to fight for and invest in the best ideas, is what the organisation will need to succeed.

As a leader, you need to build a culture and an environment where recognition of ideas and investment in them can take place more rapidly than ever. This is where businesses have the greatest opportunity, as they not only stand to gain the most, but also have the best infrastructure through which to facilitate resilience development. Through the structure of teams—with managers, support staff and training systems—the workplace effectively stands out as the last bastion for universal resilience training. No other societal structure is as ideally placed as business to measurably impact the status quo of resilience and mental wellbeing.

Here then, we arrive at the resilience imperative:

Global collaboration to build resilience is imperative for the sustainable advancement of our civilisation.

The resilience imperative applies to leaders, educators and service providers in all sectors. However, it falls with particular impact on business leaders to take action. Businesses have a critical role via empowered positions to build cultures of resilience, cultures through which people can advance despite increasing uncertainty and disruption.

This is especially true in the services sector, where people are generally less prepared for the scale of coming disruptions through robotics and automation. Investing in resilience preparation is the responsibility of the business, not only to its people, but to its shareholders as an investment in its very ability to stay competitive. Even beyond the corporate world, there is a global responsibility to do this as we are now feeling the impact of those left behind by automation in the workplace. Likewise, voters grasp at any promise of hope to improve their standing.

Industries such as mining and manufacturing particularly need resilience training, due to the relatively lower level of soft skills development when compared to the services industry. Their 'tough it out' culture result in a high percentage of people who develop and hide mental health problems instead of seeking help. Resilience training here increases emotional intelligence and reduces the stigma that holds back help-seeking.

On one hand, providing resilience education is an altruistic venture to contribute to the stability of our society, while on the other hand, your organisation stands to directly benefit from this very venture. Not only would the organisation benefit, but increased resilience is crucial to the long-term survival of the business itself.

The flipside of resilience is fear—i.e. patterns of resolve that focus on one option only: survival. This leads to patterns of avoidance, disengagement and detachment—building walls and predicting the end is near. What is more remarkable is that these patterns of fear, through the absence of resilience, are visible patterns in the brain, just like the patterns of thriving (resilience) are visible neural networks. More about this later.

Considering the workplace, one needs to ask if people are fully equipped and trained to thrive in a time of more frequent change and growing uncertainty? Does a particular workplace culture truly have an advantage over those of competitors, not only to innovate more rapidly and stay ahead but also to facilitate personal growth and capacity?

2.

Understanding the neuroscience of resilience

Neuroscientist, Richard Davidson, describes resilient people as people who not only withstand certain kinds of stressful events, but benefit from them, and turn adversity into advantage. Other concepts that he links with resilience are *recovery period, higher developed left-brain capacity* and *increased hippocampal functioning.*[8]

Many neuroscientists focus in their research on the concept of *neural plasticity*—the ability of the brain to establish new neural networks. This plasticity is closely aligned with resilience. At its core, it points to neural activation and the development of new connections—to assist with the process of living and ultimately to enhance higher levels of existence—in other words, the neural concept of *thriving*. Resilience is part of every breath we take and every step we make—from the most primitive patterns of survival in the brain, fighting neural deterioration due to the degeneration of dementia—to high levels of problem-solving and social interaction.

---

[8] Begley, S., & Davidson, R. (2012). The emotional life of your brain: How its unique patterns affect the way you think, feel, and live-and how you can change them. Hachette UK.

To be able to effectively enhance resilience, we need to have an understanding of what it is and the components it consists of. Fortunately, developments in neuroscience helps to uncover what underpins resilience, providing more concrete ways to improve and measure resilience skills.[9,10]

Resilience on a neurobiological level can be described as the process of enhancing neural connectivity towards increased domains of capacity.

Advancing despite adversity is a simple way of summarising these highly-complex thought processes and patterns within the brain. The human brain itself is the most complex device we've ever come across, with over 100 billion neurons and over 100 trillion synapses connecting them all. This is far more complex and integrated than any supercomputer that we've ever developed, yet the brain is remarkably adaptable and resilient in its own sense.

To appreciate the uniqueness of the brain, it helps to compare it with a device of our own design that aims to rival human cognition—the computer. A computer has two main constructs that make it work. One construct is hardware, including processors, hard drives, transistors and the wiring connecting everything. In the broader sense, the hardware itself is unchanging from moment to moment—a wire isn't about to spontaneously rewire itself to some other component. The other construct is software, including the operating system, drivers and applications. Software is primarily changeable and uses the foundation of the hardware to perform useful functions. In contrast, the brain consists of neurons and synapses, which are like a combination of hardware and software, making it changeable 'wetware'.

The wetware of the brain is incredibly unique as a biological computer and is still much more advanced than what we've been able to create through our silicon computers. For example, while the human brain has 100

---

[9] Kandel, E. R. (2007). In search of memory: The emergence of a new science of mind. WW Norton & Company.

[10] LeDoux, J. E. (2003). Synaptic self: How our brains become who we are. Penguin.

billion neurons, our largest computer processing units have around ten billion transistors. This might seem like computing is catching up quickly, but the difference is that a neuron is far more complex than a transistor. A neuron is not binary and can distinguish between much more than simply 1 and 0.

Another aspect where computer power lags far behind is in the 100 trillion synaptic connections between neurons. The connection patterns between neurons is the code of our very personalities and consciousness— a naturally-evolved programming language so complex that even after hundreds of years of study, we still don't know exactly how it works.[11] These synaptic patterns are not fixed though, as they constantly create new connections and break old ones. New neurons are born and others die through natural processes. This means that the very code of who you are constantly changes and adapts.

When your body has an injury, the brain will try to rewire so that it becomes functional again and regains lost abilities. While groups of neurons can perform highly-specialised activities, they are also highly generalised and can be repurposed as needed. This incredible adaptability, fault tolerance and general resilience of the brain itself is far beyond what we've been able to make. Even our most hardened computer systems still need to be restarted now and then when things break. For the brain, this inherent resilience is necessary as it doesn't have the option of someone swooping in to restart it when malfunctioning. Instead, the neural networks that lead to the best outcomes for survival were passed on to the next generation. So, over millions of years of evolution, the brain slowly learnt which neural structures were useful and which weren't.

Interestingly, over time it also became clear which areas of the brain should be more changeable than others. For example, you don't want the part to change that keeps your heart beating or lungs breathing. Certain functions became 'baked in' and come as standard with every brain, while others areas are set up to rapidly learn and structure accordingly to suit the environment.

[11] Kandel, E. R. (2007). In search of memory: The emergence of a new science of mind. WW Norton & Company.

Ancient brain, modern world

For millions of years the brain has been evolving and adapting to an environment filled with constant danger. A world where we were part of the food chain and certainly not the most powerful beings to contend with. Back then, the most common solutions were to run or fight—primal instincts that helped survival. This meant that the brain wired itself towards making these primal instincts as accessible as possible. For example, if a snake is coming toward you, you shouldn't have to take a few moments to consider what action to take; you should just run.

In contrast, the brain hasn't had nearly as much time to adapt to the world we live in now, a world of relative safety where complex thought is more valuable than primal instincts. The work of neurologist and researcher, Paul D. MacLean, pointed towards the development of the neural networks, from the primitive (*survival brain*) to the advanced (cortical regions—the *paleomammalian brain*).[12] He wrote of a hierarchy of development—survival first and then higher-order connectivity—thriving. Taken in the context of societal development, the brain architecture shares its deepest narrative: it is geared toward survival, but it has the capacity to thrive. However, thriving is only possible when survival is well and truly taken care of. Herein lies the secrets of the pathway towards resilience.

This concept is significant—to realise that we live in a modern world with primitive brains. Relatively speaking, the brain is not used to the world we live in now and doesn't instinctively know what is always appropriate. Knowing about the brain therefore helps us to successfully operate the intricacies of our minds in a changing environment. The brain easily reverts back to primitive styles of existence when it perceives danger, except that in the modern world these impulsive (survival) actions are rarely useful. At best, it enhances survival, but these impulses also increase patterns of avoidance and as a result have a detrimental effect on neural connections.

---

[12] MacLean, P. D. (1990). The triune brain in evolution: Role in paleocerebral functions. Springer Science & Business Media.

Let's consider someone experiencing a crisis at work. It's a situation of intense pressure accompanied by a great deal of ambiguity. Meanwhile the impact of the crisis is spreading and time is adding pressure. Higher brain activation is needed to operate at peak efficiency to solve the problem. Unfortunately, in this situation the brain has a natural tendency to increase norepinephrine, corticotropin-releasing factor, adrenaline and cortisol (the stress response), and activate the fight-or-flight response. This reduces serotonin flow and impedes activation of higher order cortical functioning—the reasoning skills. The result is quick thinking—patterns to enhance immediate survival and the accompanied pattern of avoidance. This person may experience the situation as overwhelming, unable to think clearly and provide answers, leading to eventual retreat.

So, resilience is the capacity to maintain whole brain activation and requires higher-order, solution-focused neural networks.

Responding constructively to challenges does not come naturally. Even as children we learn behaviours that are useful to us, rather than behaviours that are constructive. This is why a young child is more likely to scream until it gets that chocolate, rather than ask for it politely. (Why? A less advanced neural network capacity resulting in little or no emotional regulation—an essential part of one of the domains of resilience—more about these domains later). Throwing a tantrum is not constructive, but it works.

There are little behaviours like this that we carry around through much of our adult lives without being challenged on whether they are constructive and help us achieve our goals. Many businesses already feel these effects through unconscious biases and beliefs that people bring with them to the workplace. Often it is in the workplace where people are first confronted by the negative effects of these subconscious beliefs. People finally come face to face with the consequences of old neural pathways. Without thinking, this lead to behaviours that might have been useful before, but are not constructive now.

Lucky for us, we are not victims of default neural networks. The unique nature of our brain architecture allows us to use our own capacity to change our neural structures and pathways. As mentioned, neuroplasticity is now a widely recognised aspect of the brain, which states that the brain can change and adapt at any age. The classical research of Donald Hebb (1949), describing the process of neural affinity, is often summarised as *'neurons that fire together, wire together'*.[13] Later this was enhanced and elaborated with the reverse, stating that *'neurons that fire apart, wire apart'*.[14]

Together they mean that we can both build neural pathways and break them apart. This adaptability gives us the opportunity to change how the brain works, moving towards something more constructive and breaking free from primal problem-solving methods. Though again there are some aspects of the brain that are easier to change than others, with some areas highly resistant to change.

When we set out to change thinking, it helps to understand what aspects are more hard-wired, so we can learn how to work with those, rather than fight against them. This will then free our efforts to focus on what kind of thinking can be changed more readily. As we look further into the neuroscience of resilience, we can start to gain the wisdom to know the difference between what can be readily changed, and what can't.

A tale of two brains

To appreciate why some neural structures are more hard-wired than others, it helps to know how the brain developed. After all, homo sapiens didn't pop into existence with their complex brains fully formed. Instead, as we evolved from simple organisms through to the complex beings we are today, so did the brain undergo key stages of development. Just as the history of automation in industry helps us to understand the challenges we face ahead, learning about the evolution of the brain helps to understand our own behaviour and the behaviour of others in the organisation.

---

[13] Hebb, D. O. (2005). The organisation of behavior: A neuropsychological theory. Psychology Press.

[14] Bao, S., Chang, E. F., Woods, J., & Merzenich, M. M. (2004). Temporal plasticity in the primary auditory cortex induced by operant perceptual learning. Nature neuroscience, 7(9), 974-981.

Life first appeared around four billion years ago, but it wasn't until about half a billion years ago that the first brain-like structures appeared. This first structure, often called the *reptilian* brain, was highly mechanical and unchanging, mainly taking care of basic functions such as breathing and keeping the heart beating—thus ensuring the progression of the species. All these functions are located in the brain stem region—a section that we share with all living organisms that have a central nervous system 'cluster'—a *brain*.

Around 250 million years later, a new neural network evolved on the posterior part of the primitive network that included areas now known as the amygdala and hippocampus. This network (structure) enabled faster learning and controlled the fight-or-flight response, increasing survival through one of the most powerful emotions of all—fear. Generally found in early mammals, this structure is often referred to as the *limbic brain/network* and is somewhat more adaptable than the reptilian brain. Interestingly, the process of evolution does not significantly alter older brain structures, but instead adds to them while keeping the original structures mostly intact. As more complex structures develop, the reptilian brain and limbic system stay in place in the genetic footprint, due to their critical role to ensure basic survival.

Surprisingly, it was only fairly recently, in the last two to three million years, that the neocortex developed. It was the *third layer* of the neural networks. This layer drastically expanded the capacity of the brain to grasp abstract concepts and adapt to different circumstances. The neocortex allowed us to create complex language, develop ideas, and rapidly rise above all other animals.

However, compared to the four billion years it took us to get where we are today, we've spent extraordinarily little time in the digital age. Given that the old structures of the brain are still intact and functioning in the ways they did millions of years ago, it's easy to see why they still play such an active part in our daily lives. While we may *feel* in control, the primal structures always stand ready to kick in at any sign of trouble to help us 'survive' in same way they did millions of years ago.

From a psychological perspective, Seymour Epstein provides clarity through his Cognitive-Experiential Self-Theory[15]. This theory has evolved over the last 40 years and provides a particularly useful view of the two main ways in which the brain operates. On the one side, Epstein identified the *'experiential system'*, which functions on a preconscious level, meaning that it is the first to receive what you see and hear. The experiential system is automatic, effortless, fast and emotional. It generally directs behaviour towards what is most likely to result in a pleasurable experience.

Outputs from the experiential system are emotions, however the desire for pleasurable experiences doesn't mean that pleasurable emotions will always be produced. For example, following a loss, sadness may be produced out of a desire to be comforted. Still, it is through this desire for pleasurable experiences that the experiential system determines which experiences and interpretations to integrate into the neural structure. Emotional and instinctive, on a neural level you may see how this corresponds with the limbic and reptilian brain.

Epstein highlighted aspects about the experiential system that was significantly different from previous theories, including that of Sigmund Freud's view. What he pointed out is that the experiential system *is inherently adaptive and remains adaptive*. This is critically important to us, as it means we can change how our preconscious interpretation of experiences work. If long ago the experiential system has assimilated an experience in a negative and maladaptive way, we could employ the rational system to reinterpret that experience and improve our future responses. Someone may automatically react with anger to a change at work, but this instinctive reaction can be changed through the second system that Epstein identified.

The *'rational system'* is what corresponds to the neocortex, specifically the prefrontal-cortex where our higher thinking occurs and the personality resides. The rational system is conscious, meaning that it contains the words and images we play in our mental theatre. It takes effort to employ, is relatively slow, uses language and numbers, and is analytical. Interpreting highly abstract concepts is what the rational system particularly excels at.

---

[15] Epstein, S. (1994). Integration of the cognitive and the psychodynamic unconscious. *American Psychologist*, 49(8), 709.

For example, 'tax' is a very abstract concept with additional levels of abstraction below it, such as 'money' and 'income' and 'government'. Though if you say 'tax' to someone, the rational system would quickly be able to access those abstractions and know what you're talking about.

Meanwhile, the experiential system might produce an emotional response, such as anger, if there's a strong belief the tax rate is unjustified. Through the rational system, beliefs about the tax rate can be challenged with new information or new thinking. This can override how the experiential system interprets the concept of tax preconsciously, thus producing a different emotion.

All animals have an experiential system and can function perfectly well without anything more, however it is the second system that gave humans an advantage. It allows us to look beyond the surface of what we experience and understand how the world works (from our perspective) and use that information to do more. For example, income taxation is certainly something that doesn't appear naturally, but it is a powerful concept that allows us to achieve great advancements for our society.

That's not to say that the rational system is inherently better than the experiential system. In fact, we cannot function without the experiential system as it allows us to process massive amounts of sensory input and boil these down to emotions that motivate the rational system.

Both the rational and experiential systems build an internal model of the world. This internal model is how we understand the world to work; it's what we compare ideas against to determine the feasibility of solutions and how we should react to events. Naturally, none of us fully understand how the world works, so the internal model always contains flaws. The experiential system starts building its implicit model of the world from infancy, and does so automatically as we experience the world. Later in life as the rational system develops, we start to develop an additional explicit model of the world based on our conscious understanding of the rules of the world and our rational interpretations.

At the top of this model of the world sits the broad generalisations of existence, such as whether life is meaningful, whether people are good, and if the world is a just place. These are very deeply held beliefs that influence a great many beliefs below them, and is what forms the major biases that people bring to the workplace. Changing these beliefs has a profound impact on all the connected beliefs and can have a major effect on how a person behaves. In contrast, lower level beliefs are far less connected and may have little impact if changed. These can be seen as building knowledge about the world. For example, changing your view on the usefulness of taxes is unlikely to change your personality itself.

We have inherited the experiential system through hundreds of millions of years of evolution, and the rational system through the last few million years. Each have their own powerful neural networks, however, the experiential system has more fundamental and baseline connections, established over a much longer timeframe in a much smaller neural network. As a result, it is genetically programmed to activate much quicker for a solitary purpose—to ensure survival. On top of the powerful activity of this system, it has another 'advantage'—it operates on all senses and is supported by a multi-sensory process.

The rational system, on the other hand, operates much slower and has arrived quite 'recently' to the neural network process. It evolved to be more powerful than even the experiential system, but it is dependent on certain variables (like cortical blood flow, good hippocampal functioning and downregulation of the stress chemicals and networks). So, we can identify two systems of resilience—survival resilience and thriving resilience. This is beautifully demonstrated in Daniel Kahneman's bestseller, *Thinking fast and slow.*[16]

Nobel laureate in economic science, Kahneman basically identifies two *systems of thinking*—system 1—the fast system and system 2—the slow system. In his work, system 1 refers to the activation of the amygdala and the HPA-axis. The hypothalamus-pituitary-adrenal system activates the fight/flight stress network to ensure survival[17]. The *slow system* (system 2) is linked to the hippocampus PFC networks—the longer neural network devoted to rational thinking and problem-solving.

---

[16] Kahneman, D. (2011). *Thinking, fast and slow.* Macmillan.

[17] Rossouw, P. J. (Ed.). (2014). *Neuropsychotherapy: Theoretical underpinnings and clinical applications.* Mediros Pty Limited.

These networks are what we will describe later as the networks of *thriving*—the resilience networks. The focus of modern research is on the latter—to such an extent that speakers on resilience even refer to our *survival* patterns as the opposite of resilience.

> *Thinking fast and slow—Resilience and the 'Linda problem'*
>
> *In the (now famous) Linda-experiment, participants were introduced to an imaginary woman, Linda. Linda is single, outspoken and when a student was deeply concerned with issues like discrimination and social justice. Participants were asked which was more probable: 1. Linda is a bank teller, or 2. Linda is a bank teller and is active in the feminist movement.*
>
> *The respondents overwhelmingly indicated '2' as most probable— despite '2' blatantly violating the laws of probability. Even at Stanford Business School, where students were trained in laws of probability, 85% opted for option '2'.*

The reality is, the *fast system* is powerful, tends to override the slow system, and unless well-trained, we are all prone to follow the fast network. Thriving resilience is the capacity to activate the whole brain—a comprehensive neural network with vast opportunities and outcomes—but we need to control the beast—system 1.

Of particular interest are the basic needs of us as humans and how they relate to the two systems. For simplicity, from here onwards we will refer to the rational system and prefrontal cortex as the 'smart brain', while the experiential system, limbic and reptilian brain we will call the 'impulsive brain'. It is the relationship between these two that holds the key to resilience.

The basic human needs

As the brain evolved, there were certain behaviours and desires that proved to be instrumental in the success of the human race and its individuals. Without these adaptations, we would not be where we are today. Because of this, these behaviours and desires were embedded deep within the brain.

Their significance is obvious, as each of us bring them to the workplace where, knowingly or not, we try to fulfill these basic needs.

As organisations, we can achieve greater levels of staff engagement and wellbeing when these human needs are met in meaningful ways. Though, interestingly, extraordinarily few organisations and leaders know what it is at the very base level of their people's needs that seek to be fulfilled. A further complication is that few people truly understand these basic needs themselves, with exploratory discussions with staff yielding low levels of insight into the true problems. Meanwhile, organisational actions address symptoms rather than causes. This results in wild goose chases and scattershot approaches that are rarely as effective as targeting the basic needs directly.

Many researchers explored these needs, including Sigmund Freud around 1900 and Abraham Maslow back in 1943 with his famous hierarchy of needs. Maslow and others presented a good starting point, though this was purely from a psychological perspective. Back then, there was a limited understanding about how the structures of the brain fit into the picture. As the field of neuroscience developed, more nuanced theories appeared about what exactly the basic needs are and how they fit together. At this point, four basic needs have been identified as follows:

- the need for connection and attachment to others,
- the need for control and orientation,
- the need for motivation by maximising pleasure and minimising pain, and
- the need to enhance self-esteem (which is a 'meta-need', as it feeds off the enhancement of the other basic needs).

These needs were also included in the work of Nobel laureate Klaus Grawe, as he amalgamated psychology and neuroscience into the growing field of neuropsychotherapy[18].

Once again, Epstein provided an insightful view by bringing together 100

---

[18] Grawe, K. (2007). Neuropsychotherapy: How the neurosciences inform effective psychotherapy. Lawrence Erlbaum Associates Publishers.

years of theories on basic needs. Epstein's insight was that there is not just one basic need, but that each of the basic needs are important and are interactive with each other. If an individual meets one need at the expense of the others, then the other needs become more demanding in order to return a sense of balance between them. However, achieving balance between the needs does not necessarily result in a sense of wellbeing. Instead, if all needs are equally unmet, then the individual will experience a sense of distress.

Unlike Maslow's pyramid, these needs are not hierarchical. Instead, they function together, often simultaneously, while at other times one will be more pressing than the other. Understanding these needs in more detail will help us understand more clearly how to increase resilience in a world set for rapid digital change.

Connection

We have evolved as social creatures, using the power of connected communities to survive in a harsh world. Looking at the animal world, we can see how species differ in their desire for connection. Some species, like snakes and spiders, are inherently 'loners', preferring to live and hunt alone. Other species have found strength in numbers, such as sheep and buffalo, where individual behaviour is very much affected by group behaviour. More advanced species, like chimps and apes, form complex communities with a hierarchy, a leader and various roles. Complex communities allow for better protection of the group and its individuals, thus increasing survival.

This is how we have evolved as well, resulting in a deeply ingrained desire for connection with other people. In fact, the brain is strongly wired for connection with others, seeking secure relationships where we can trust those around us. The 'bible' for neuroscientists—the monumental work of Erik Kandel, James Schwartz, Thomas Jessel, Steven Siegelbaum and A.J. Hudspeth—*The Principles of Neural Science*[19] can be summarised with four words: principles of *neural connection*. Everything in neural science—from

---

[19] Hudspeth, A. J., Jessell, T. M., Kandel, E. R., Schwartz, J. H., & Siegelbaum, S. A. (Eds.). (2013). *Principles of neural science*. McGraw-Hill, Health Professions Division.

our genetic makeup, to the activity of neurons and glial cells, to the production of neural chemicals—point to one key function: managing and maximising connections for the organism to (first and foremost) *survive* and ultimately to *thrive*. And resilience is the science that explores these patterns, from survival to thriving.

Early life experiences have a strong influence on the way that we naturally connect with others. This is because of subconscious beliefs and expectations about others that are set automatically as we start to experience connection with others. The deep belief regarding connection is mainly about whether people are generally trustworthy and helpful, or if they are untrustworthy and dangerous[20]. When we lean towards a belief that people are dangerous and can't be trusted, then it naturally leads us to behaviour where we avoid being around people and collaborating with others.

The problem is that the need for connection does not go away. Instead it becomes an unmet need that weighs not just on our sense of self-worth, but also on our ability to achieve our personal and career goals. After all, much of our success in organisations is about building and maintaining productive relationships.

Located within the impulsive brain is the amygdala, a small structure that plays an important role in recognising danger in the environment. The amygdala constantly scans the environment for any threats, and compares situations to previous experiences, producing a signal of avoidance if danger is detected. Where our experience with people has been generally positive and secure, then an approaching person would not be registered as a threat by the amygdala.

On the other hand, if previous experiences with people have generally been perceived as harmful, then fear or anxiety is produced. Of course, these emotions are preconscious, meaning they kick in before the smart brain becomes aware of the thinking, and serves to guide the thinking of the smart brain. However, if we consciously recognise that our inherent way of perceiving people is not necessarily accurate, then we can start to rewire

[20] Epstein, S. (2003). Cognitive-experiential self-theory of personality. *Handbook of psychology*.

how the impulsive brain thinks about people, in the preconscious process.

In the work context, our ability to connect is often impacted by unreasonably high expectations of how people should act, which naturally leads to feeling disappointed by colleagues. This is more prevalent at lower levels in the hierarchy, while more senior management have already had many years to hone their expectations of people, through experience, to be more realistic. The challenge being that a larger portion of the workforce feels an unmet need of connecting in the workplace, but instead seeks connection outside of work. While not necessarily wrong, this does lead to a feeling that work is not as fulfilling because one of their basic needs are not met.

The increasingly digital workplace may also negatively effect this interpersonal connection, where staff have less face-to-face contact with colleagues and customers. This also has a direct impact on resilience, since our ability to rely on a support network plays a major role in working through adversity. A hallmark of resilience is to be willing to ask for help when you need it, though this presupposes that you have built a network that you can rely on in times of need. Finding ways to both set realistic expectations while also fostering connections at the workplace is therefore an important step to building engagement and resilience.

Control

The need for control and orientation is a higher order need of humans, a more advanced species that do not simply rely on instinct to function. Essentially, we have a very deep desire for a sense of purpose and meaning to our lives. In addition to this sense of purpose, we want our internal model of the world to make sense and feel that we can control the pursuit of our purpose.

The internal model that we build of the world includes all our perceptions of what the world is like and how it works. This plays a crucial role in our ability to see opportunities and have a sense of the options available to us. If we cannot see any options to pursue our goals, then we feel like we don't have any control. This does not mean that we necessarily want to control everything all the time. Different people certainly have different ways in which they express their need for control, but at our core we want to have a sense that we have chosen the path we are on. Even if we hand control of an aspect of our lives over to someone else, this is still an act of control as we have made that choice ourselves, rather than it being forced on us.

In the workplace we maintain a basic sense of control, since technically we can leave any time we want to if we disagree strongly with company behaviour. Our ability to leave at minimum distinguishes modern society from times of slavery. Naturally, this doesn't completely satisfy the extent of our need for control, though businesses are already working on many levels to provide an increased sense of control. For example, offering flexible working arrangements and employee participation in development planning.

Factors that disrupt a sense of control include restructures and relocations, as well as changing how and what an employee does. Change brings uncertainty, and uncertainty disrupts control. We've all seen how some deal with change constructively, while others are very negative about change, resulting in anxiety, anger and disengagement. These emotions are produced by the impulsive brain in response to previous negative experiences with change. In this state, change is often experienced as a disruption, or a personal crisis. Overcoming this response to be inherently constructive requires the smart brain to be activated and over time rewire the emotional response of the impulsive brain.

Developing resilience helps employees reinterpret change towards something that is both expected and an opportunity. Being able to see change as an opportunity largely comes from how well we can connect it with our own sense of purpose.

The 'need for control' inherently implies that we desire to drive outcomes in a certain direction. After all, there's no need for control if you have no desire to achieve a particular state of affairs. This direction we desire is our sense of purpose, meaning and personal goals. Unfortunately, the meaning of life isn't exactly printed in the manual of living, so it is up to each of us to define our own purpose. Few explicitly do this, but most implicitly define their purpose through their chosen career path and by doing more of what they seem to enjoy.

In a way, organisations provide a sense of purpose in that people form part of something larger, something that needs their input and effort. Similarly, if a person cannot see how their efforts contribute to a useful outcome, then they may feel the job is pointless. If effort doesn't lead to a meaningful outcome, then again there is a loss of control.

The inherent need for control does not imply the need for things to *never* change. It actually implies change, due to increasing neural activation and new neural connections. However, the need is closely aligned with the need to need to effectively manage these changes. Grawe describes this as the need to have the maximum number of options available.

Consider being diagnosed with Type ll (or the more significant Type l) diabetes. This is a life-changing event—our maximum number of options (i.e. diet) is no longer available, resulting in big adjustments. The need for control is compromised and the neural system can move in two directions. Option 1 is to give up and fall victim to the illness—life comes to a standstill and one deteriorates quickly. Patterns of avoidance kick in and more signs of un-wellness present—depression, anxiety, relationship difficulties and so on. Option 2 is to deal with the challenges—adjust to the reality and make the best of options still available. This activates both new neural networks and patterns of increased connectivity (despite adversity).

This is the essence of resilience. Trauma, losses and disasters can be described in terms of this need as more extreme violations of the need for control. The loss of a loved one forces the brain to establish new neural networks because existing options are no longer available. Normally, the first responses are all aligned with option 1—patterns of avoidance (avoiding the reality of the loss) and resulting distress (the risk of neural loops where we are unable to establish new neural connections). We label this distress as depression and anxiety, and in severe cases, dissociation.

Moving towards option 2 is the process of healing—the ability to reconnect and form new pathways—this is evident in the neural networks of all those who experience significant violations of the need for control—from stroke patients, to moving to another city, to being retrenched.

When we feel that we have no clear sense of purpose, it's easy to feel lost and indecisive. Where we cannot see a realistic way to pursue our goals and sense of purpose, we may feel out of control. This is particularly relevant in a rapidly-changing digital world, where a faster pace of innovation introduces a higher degree of uncertainty than ever before. It is precisely this uncertainty that has the potential to strongly undermine our fundamental need for control, resulting in anxiety, distress, depression and disengagement.

This is why the resilience imperative is so important, now more than ever. Through developing the resilience skills of employees, a new sense of control and purpose can be found within a world of uncertainty. The key is in focusing our goals and purpose on conceptual ideals that lie beyond the concrete world being constantly disrupted.

Motivation

Somewhat unsurprisingly, we have a fundamental need to do more of what we enjoy, and less of what we don't. In a sense, it is about maximising pleasure and avoiding pain, but what really brings this to life is motivation. This comes from the primitive evolution of the brain, where pain and fear developed as a mechanism to avoid danger, such as poisonous foods or the sight of a predator. Pleasure developed as a mechanism to identify things useful for survival, such as energy-rich foods, or mating.

Each of these primal emotions pushes us to take some type of action, for example to eat more, or run away. The way that the brain motivates us into action is through a number of neurotransmitters, like dopamine, serotonin, endorphin and norepinephrine. One of the most important activators of motivation, however, is the chemical *dopamine*. We will specifically focus on the activation system through this chemical.

The term *motivation* can also be activated in various situations. We can be motivated to run away from danger (survival), or not go to the dentist or pay a bill (patterns of avoidance). The brain can even become trapped in these patterns and eventually we see the onset of unhelpful behaviour (like gambling, obsessive-compulsive disorders etc.). This is the result of ongoing activation of the dopaminergic system. We become *motivated* (read: *trapped)* in ongoing patterns of behaviour—the link between ongoing dopamine activation and addiction. Dopamine keeps the system firing!

In terms of unhelpful patterns, psychologists often refer to this as clients becoming *comfortable with their discomfort* (the dopaminergic loop). Dopamine is often misunderstood as a feel-good neurotransmitter, yet dopamine is a motivator that pushes us towards actions which are perceived to bring the greatest rewards.

As we just discussed, it does not mean that dopamine always motivates us to take constructive actions, as some behaviour that is rewarding to the brain can be damaging to the person. Dopamine would just as easily motivate one person to perform well at work as it would motivate someone else toward excessive alcohol consumption.

Here the concept of having an ancient brain in a modern world becomes important, as there are many patterns the brain finds pleasurable that are not necessarily constructive. Major industries and organisations have developed around these basic desires of the brain, such as food companies producing products high in sugar and fats. This tasty combination is highly preferred by the brain because of its extreme scarcity in ancient times, but in excess it is also the worst combination for our brain and body health. At a basic level, the brain hasn't realised that these types of food are no longer scarce and it should instead find nutritious foods (like vegetables) to be more tasteful now. Instead, it still craves something —even though it's since become destructive to the body.

When the brain realises that a certain action would lead to a likely reward, dopamine is released to motivate you to take that action. Dopamine only releases before you take an action, not during or afterwards—it is a motivator. Interestingly, dopamine activation is strongest when there is about a fifty percent chance that you will receive a reward. If reward is guaranteed, it is not as interesting for the brain, but if chance is involved, then we are more willing to take a risk. Which huge industry do we know that is all too aware of this quirk of the human brain? Casinos with games of chance like roulette and craps, where the odds are just below 50% for a win, are perfect to get dopamine going. In fact, the motivation from dopamine can get so strong that addiction follows, powerfully urging someone to go just one more round.

Fortunately, we also have a smart, rational brain that can change our motivations and regulate whether we act on an impulse. Here we can choose to order a salad rather than a donut. When we start exercising this type of control, it becomes more natural for the brain to make constructive choices, freeing us up from impulsive thoughts. Then you can focus on more important concepts, such as the direction of your life and career. Focusing on goals and what gives each of us meaning in turn enables the brain to release dopamine to motivate us towards constructive action.

Motivation, in relation to resilience, is the process of developing neural networks of reward that facilitate higher levels of connectivity (the shift from survival to thriving), connection and control. As we progress through life and work, aligning our actions and goals towards an overall sense of purpose, we experience a state of congruence: a highly-rewarding state for the brain. Klaus Grawe says that we are at our happiest and most fulfilled when '...*current perceptions and goals are completely congruent with one another, and the transpiring mental activity is not disturbed by any competing intentions*'.[21]

In sequence of importance, are four key points in this statement: We want clear goals. We want to work towards those goals. We want to see results in line with our goals. Our goals and actions should not clash with other goals.

Achieving this kind of congruence at work is what results in a highly-motivated and engaged workforce. Resilience skills contribute by helping individuals set expectations, challenge beliefs, and align their goals to be compatible with that of the organisation and their own careers. Not only does this allow people to achieve congruence, but it will also help them to stay focused on what is important when facing challenges, so they can find their motivation again.

Everyday resilience means building and maintaining the discipline to keep working towards your goals and a larger sense of purpose, even when things get tough.

---

[21] Grawe, K. (2007). Neuropsychotherapy: How the neurosciences inform effective psychotherapy. Lawrence Erlbaum Associates Publishers.

Self-esteem enhancement

The need for control, connection and motivation all feed into another overall need, which is the need for self-esteem enhancement. To conceptualise this—we can refer to the following:

System 1: The primitive structures of the brain (brainstem, pons, medulla and parts of the cerebrum and motor cortex) as the networks that ensure our survival.

System 2: The limbic structures and networks (thalamus, amygdala, basal ganglia, hypothalamus, pituitary, nucleus accumbens, striatum, hippocampus)—networks to ensure connectivity to the outside environment and activate emotional responses.

System 3: The cortical regions (corpus callosum, parts of the cerebrum, cingulate cortex, parts of the motor cortex and cerebrum and especially the prefrontal regions—left and right)—networks geared towards higher-order functioning, emotional connectivity, empathy and reasoning.

The development of a sense of self and *self-esteem* is closely aligned with the development of a well-integrated prefrontal neural network. Over the years, a huge body of research demonstrated how trauma, distress, and violation of basic needs (like attachment and control) has a significant impact on neural activation. Trauma violates the connectivity between system 2 and system 3 and enhances patterns of survival. The brain becomes wired to default from system 2 (external triggers of distress) to system 1 (patterns of survival/avoidance). This has a significant effect on the development of an integrated sense of self and wellness (high connectivity between system 2 and system 3).

Here we see the neuroscientific underpinnings of what Kahneman refers to as *thinking fast* (system 2 to system 1—patterns of survival) and *thinking slow* (thriving networks—system 2 to system 3).

Self-worth is a key part of this need, which includes whether we believe we are worthy of love, friendship and success. Deeply ingrained within this need is the idea of advancement. Throughout our lives we implicitly strive for advancement. As babies we quickly learn about the world so we can better fulfil our needs and enjoy the world. Then we enter school, dedicating over a decade of our lives to advancement through education, often followed by further education and skills training. Entering the workforce provides a whole new dimension for advancement through duties, responsibilities, skills employed, promotions and salary. We take up hobbies, where we strive to improve skills that we enjoy. We build relationships with colleagues, acquaintances, friends and family. We start our own families. As we grow through life and advance not just in age, but through experience and wisdom, we have a need for our self-esteem to be advanced as well... so we can each confidently say that, yes, I am a worthy person.

Advancement does not happen automatically, nor is it guaranteed. Experiencing stagnation within a position at work grates against this need. A relationship breakdown can strongly affect a person's sense of self-worth. An unexpected loss of employment can be a blow to years of confidence. Being able to protect one's self-esteem against the eventual knocks of life is a key function of resilience.

Protection can come in various forms, one of which is recognising why something went wrong, learning from it and growing through the experience. As per the definition of resilience, the aim is to *advance despite adversity*, prompting us to learn how to grow from the hardships we face, therefore enhancing self-esteem rather than reducing it. This requires understanding our basic needs and how each of us pursues them in a slightly different way.

These days, much of our self-worth comes from the work we do. Our occupations reflect a major choice in what we intend to do with our lives and how we contribute to society. Also, organisations inherently include measures of status through their hierarchical structures. Through position and salary, the organisation clearly indicates how much someone is worth to them. That said, few derive their personal sense of self-worth purely from organisational status, but it definitely contributes. Beyond position and salary, what also contributes within the organisation is how the individual perceives their own contribution to an outcome that is of some societal significance—how their efforts contribute to making the world a better place.

People who work for charities don't often opt for high status or strive to earn top dollar, but rather work for the sense that they are making a positive difference in the world. Most people would like to think that their efforts are useful, that they make a difference, and to be proud of where they work and what they do. These factors powerfully contribute to their sense of self-worth, establishing them as a valuable member of society, as being *desirable*.

Both non- and for-profit organisations who can authentically tap into this desire for self-esteem enhancement can build a deep sense of loyalty and pride within their employees. The way to achieve this comes both from the organisation and from developing resilience skills of the employees themselves, including guiding the basic needs through rational thinking.

Looking holistically at the central theme across all the needs, we notice the essential role of the primitive need—the concept of *safety*. Each of the basic needs have an undercurrent of the safety need. Our need for *connection* with others is in fact grounded in a need for that connection to be safe and not violate our wellness (or in a worst-case scenario—our need to survive). Thriving connections indicate the ability to feel *safe to be vulnerable* with those that we connect with.

The need for *control and orientation* is about a sense of security in knowing which way we are heading, while control itself is deeply rooted in a desire for safety. After all, few things disrupt a sense of safety as much as feeling *out of control*. The need for *motivation* comes from the safety of knowing that we get to do things that we enjoy and can effectively avoid things we experience as painful.

Self-esteem enhancement is an ongoing process of neural activation (connections) that enhances existing thriving memory patterns and continues to develop enhanced networks. This is the essence of neural integration (the flipside of neural deterioration) and wisdom. Resilience then is what builds on a sense of safety, without it being overtly about safety. After all, it's not as effective to generate a sense of safety by just telling ourselves that we are safe. Instead, by building the various skills related to resilience, we strengthen ourselves on various fronts, each aspect contributing a bit more to our sense of safety, in alignment with the fundamental needs.

Guiding the needs

We cannot rid ourselves of any of the basic needs, however our natural approach to meeting each of the basic needs can be modified through rational thinking. Modification is possible because the smart brain can gradually reprogram the impulsive brain. However, neural rewiring does not happen automatically, as the neural patterns within the brain take time and repetition to change. Hebb's principle of 'neurons that fire together, wire together' highlights that these neural patterns need to continually fire together before they will establish stronger links. Since these neural patterns are weak, initially it's easy to revert to old habits. Here, a conscious effort is required to keep thinking and keep acting in a more constructive way.

This practice and repetition is what helps build new neural patterns, making constructive behaviour more natural over time. For example, someone who reacts very negatively when faced with change can start researching what change is coming in their industry, asking about strategic initiatives at work, focussing on what opportunities exist and think how they can use change to achieve their personal goals. This conscious shift in thinking and repetition of thought is what slowly changes the wiring of the impulsive brain until it eventually does not produce a negative emotion when faced with change, but instead may evoke a feeling of determination to make use of the situation.

The key concept is repetition—the brain does not simply rewire overnight. So often organisations send employees to seminars about change and wellbeing, but a few hours of listening to a guru talking and then building a tower of spaghetti and marshmallows does not contain the repetition necessary to rewire the brain. While people generally provide positive feedback for seminars, changing beliefs and building constructive habits takes months to embed in the neural pathways. Even then, there must be ongoing repetition and reinforcement of those ideas during those months.

So, training and development should be ongoing and also be present within the culture of the organisation itself. Research shows us that the brain functions at its best when it is within an 'enriched environment'[22].

An *enriched environment* is one where there are stimulating challenges and the opportunity to learn with relative safety. Within a business, this means being supported to take chances, try new approaches and having the freedom to fail—within reason. This kind of enriched environment has been shown to increase neural complexity and synaptic connection, leading to higher levels of brain activation. It springs from meeting the basic needs of the individual, where they have connection with others, control of what they do and are working towards, and motivation to continue striving for their goals, as connected with organisational goals.

Enriched environments lead to precisely the innovative and disruptive behaviour needed by organisations to gain a competitive advantage in a rapidly-changing digital and automated world.

The lesson here is that sending employees to an innovation retreat or wellbeing seminar for a week is not going to affect meaningful neural and behavioural change. Instead, the everyday work environment itself should be enriched. However, the onus does not fall only on the organisation—individuals also need to have the right mindset to be able to recognise a constructive environment.

Enhanced personal resilience is what provides the mindset to build constructive perceptions and thus succeed both at work and in life. This is because a resilient mindset guides an individual to perceive the world as less threatening, allowing them to meet their basic needs by taking advantage of opportunities that others might miss. It is the combination of an enriched environment and a resilient mindset that can let people achieve their maximum potential within organisations and society in general.

To be able to effectively build resilience and create the right environment, we need to know more precisely what resilience is.

---

[22] Kazlauckas, V., Pagnussat, N., Mioranzza, S., Kalinine, E., Nunes, F., Pettenuzzo, L., ... & Lara, D. R. (2011). Enriched environment effects on behavior, memory and BDNF in low and high exploratory mice. *Physiology & Behavior*, 102(5), 475-480.

3.

Domains of resilience

While we can define resilience as *advancing despite adversity*, achieving this as an ongoing outcome is not a result of just one behaviour or process. Instead, resilience consists of groups of behaviours, skills and beliefs. These groups are called 'domains'.

Understanding these domains allow us to measure resilience for an individual to identify the starting point, highlight areas for focus, and track improvement over time. The better we understand these domains, the more targeted action we can take to directly help individuals and create a more constructive culture.

Starting in 2015, our company has been conducting research into the domains of resilience. We started by looking at various existing models, however there were several shortcomings. Existing models generally do not have clear links to neuroscience and are not applicable to professionals in the workplace. Therefore, resulting insights are not as relevant to organisations, and they are also not as actionable. Worryingly, despite a growing body of research on the role of physical health on the brain and mindset, none of the major resilience models included this as a component of resilience.

These realisations pushed us to build on existing knowledge and construct a new model of resilience, complete with a measurement tool to put it into practice. The measurement tool we developed is called the Predictive 6-Factor Resilience Scale, or PR6 for short, and identified the following domains of resilience (see figure 1):

1. *Vision*, which is about goal setting and a sense of purpose.
2. *Composure*, which is about regulating emotions and managing stress.
3. *Reasoning*, which is about problem-solving and readiness for change.
4. *Tenacity*, which is about perseverance and bouncing back.
5. *Collaboration*, which is about support networks and connecting with others, and
6. *Health*, which is about adequate sleep, nutrition and exercise.

Domains interact with each other and function together to meet the basic needs of the brain. A weakness in one domain can affect others, and conversely, improving one can improve other domains.

The PR6 consolidates decades of prior research and integrates the domains of resilience into their neurobiological foundations. The resultant research paper was published in 2016 in the *International Journal of Neuropsychotherapy*, and included validation of the scale as a psychometric tool by testing it in various workplace scenarios.[23]

In a first for resilience models, our research shows a clear correlation between physiological health and the psychological domains. It also explores the mechanism through which health factors contribute to personal resilience. The combined result is a scale that is highly applicable in the workplace, while providing actionable insights designed to build resilience.

To clarify its purpose, it will help to understand what a resilience scale is not. For example, it is not like an engagement survey, which measures how individuals feel about the organisation. Instead, the PR6 measures how

---

[23] Rossouw, P. J., & Rossouw, J. G. (2016). The Predictive 6-Factor Resilience Scale: Neurobiological Fundamentals and Organisational Application. *International Journal of Neuropsychotherapy*, 4(1), 31-45.

individuals feel about *themselves*. It is also not like a personality survey, where one result isn't necessarily better than another. Instead, the PR6 measures factors that are universally beneficial for people to possess. This makes resilience measurements more useful to an organisation as a tracked index.

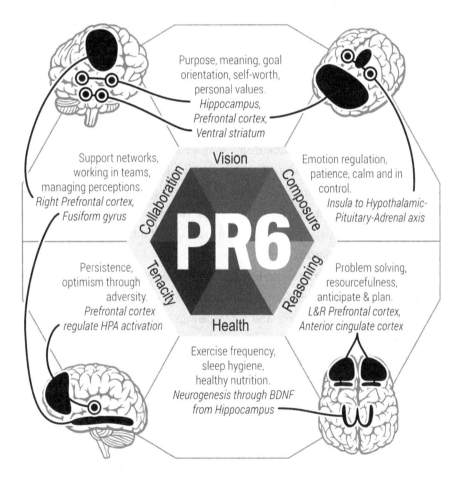

Figure 1 – The PR6 Resilience Model

First, let's explore each of the six domains. Then in the next chapter, we will set out how you can use these domains for your own resilience as an executive, followed by how these domains apply to building a culture of resilience.

Domain 1: Vision

Clarity of purpose, meaning, and goals is arguably the most important component of resilience. After all, we can only advance if we have something to advance towards, which in this case is a purpose, a sense of meaning and goals. This includes: our commitment to pursue our goals, maintaining a hopeful outlook, as well as the vision we have of what we aspire to become. Together, these are summarised as the domain of Vision.

Key neural structures involved in Vision are the prefrontal cortex, the ventral striatum and the hippocampus. The prefrontal cortex is the newest part of the brain from an evolutionary perspective, and is what houses our personality and ability to create very high-level abstractions. What this means is that we can step back from what we see and do, survey our place in the world and decide what it is that we should be doing. This ability is what sets us apart from other animals, as it allows us to pursue more complex goals and delay gratification so that we can achieve greater accomplishments. Assessing the risks and rewards of different options is the job of the ventral striatum.

Working closely with the prefrontal cortex, the ventral striatum helps us to play out ideas as scenarios against our model of the world in order to consider what can go wrong and what can go right. Naturally, the more complete our internal model of the world is, the more accurate our assessment of risks and rewards would be.

Dopamine is the main tool for the ventral striatum to motivate us into action. When we perceive a realistic path towards advancement, be it a promotion, personal profit or emotional gain, the ventral striatum increases dopamine to motivate us into action. Should the reward of an action be high enough and the risk of loss be deemed within personal tolerance, we will want to take that risk. On the other hand, should the risk of loss be deemed too high, dopamine is decreased in order to demotivate action.

Perceptions of reward and loss have an interesting effect on how we are motivated. We see this manifest in two distinct styles, which you have likely witnessed yourself. One style of motivation is known as *approach* motivation. This is when we are motivated into action primarily because we are focused on the potential reward. For example, someone may work hard because they expect that they will be rewarded and possibly promoted. The other style of motivation is that of *avoidance*. This is when we are motivated into action mainly because we are focused on what might be lost. For example, someone working hard because they are worried about getting fired if they don't.

Research into approach and avoidance schemas have indicated that this is a promising predictive indicator of ability to achieve personal goals[24]. The reason being that approach motivation leads to positive risk-taking behaviour, that in turn increases the likelihood of success. Building resilience provides more confidence in being able to manage risks and negative outcomes, allowing people to focus on reward instead. It also allows us to foster an *approach* motivation style.

In this way, resilience sets the foundation for desired risk-taking behaviour, which is precisely what organisations need in a time of rapid change and disruption. We need people to be motivated to consider novel ideas and pursue them, so that we can keep advancing.

Decisions made through the interaction of the prefrontal cortex and the ventral striatum must then be stored within the brain, so that we can remember what we decided and why. Fortunately, our understanding of how memories are formed has vastly improved and we now know more clearly how memories are formed[25]. This is where the hippocampus plays its part. Named after the Greek word for seahorse due to its resemblance, the hippocampus is an older part of the brain and plays an important role in memory consolidation. Damage to the hippocampus will render you unable to store new memories, and is also what is damaged by Alzheimer's Disease.

Fortunately, not all information we experience is stored with equal significance, otherwise our brains would be filled with unrelated information and we'd be unable to recall what's important. To achieve this, the brain uses biases and filters to sort through the overwhelming amount

[24] Jackson, C. J., Hobman, E. V., Jimmieson, N. L., & Martin, R. (2009). Comparing different approach and avoidance models of learning and personality in the prediction of work, university, and leadership outcomes. *British journal of psychology*, 100(2), 283-312.

[25] Preston, A. R., & Eichenbaum, H. (2013). Interplay of hippocampus and prefrontal cortex in memory. *Current Biology*, 23(17), R764-R773.

of sensory data we perceive every day.

The prefrontal cortex seeks to connect incoming information with what it can relate to personal goals. So it assigns meaning to the information, which the hippocampus then consolidates as a memory. This interplay gives context to information, so that we can more easily direct our behaviour towards meeting our goals and basic needs. However, our inherent biases and filters are not necessarily useful. In addition, we have control over what we decide is important to us and what we want to focus on, and by extension what the prefrontal cortex directs the hippocampus to store. Therefore, it is up to us to improve biases that we develop as children, and change them into something more constructive. The way to do this is through the domain of Vision.

Considering our basic needs, Vision is closely associated with our need for control and orientation. While this need speaks to the brain's inherent desire for a purpose and goals to work towards, the domain of Vision is about taking action to define a purpose and set goals. The actual goals we pursue and how we pursue them then determines whether our needs for connection and motivation are met, and ultimately affects our sense of self-esteem. This central role is why Vision is such a crucial component of resilience.

Neglecting this domain can easily lead us to an unfulfilling life of indecision and the pursuit of instant gratification. The effects bleed over to all aspects of our lives and deeply affects how we perceive the world and how we handle those perceptions. Following on from this, it's important for us to take our basic needs into account when we set our goals. This will make the pursuit of our goals more sustainable and fulfilling.

Ultimately, we have a need for our self-esteem to be improved. How we see ourselves and our role within the world is a key part of our sense of self-esteem. Importantly, it's also how we see ourselves in the future that adds to how much we value ourselves. Therefore, our personal vision of who we aim to become is important. We have an innate need to feel that we are worthy of existing, that we are useful to society and that we are desired. It can be tempting to set a vision around obtaining a specific corporate position or earning a certain amount by a certain date, but these targets are far too easily affected by factors out of our control. For example, the desire to become CEO of a certain company can be invalidated should that company fold or be acquired in the meantime.

Another, more resilient approach, is to define a personal vision in terms of *general qualities* that you want to focus on and enhance. For example; pragmatic, wise, trustworthy, influential, and so on. These are qualities that you can pursue and build in various ways, drawing on all your experiences and the hardship you faced along the way.

Your personal vision comes to define you and influences how you treat yourself. In difficult situations and times of adversity, these are the factors that guide your conduct.

Goals are the more concrete targets that sit under your personal vision. This is what you aim to do and achieve that will help you realise your personal vision and help you become who you aim to be. These range from larger, strategic goals spanning years, through to the smaller, tactical goals spanning days, weeks and months.

Whether or not we realise it, we all have goals that we are working towards. When we haven't spent time exploring our goals, they may be mostly subconscious. They might manifest as a desire for achievement, without a clear idea of what actual achievement is desired. The result is a kind of undefined frustration and indecision. The concept of the Vision domain is to consciously explore what your current goals are, put them into context with what you want to achieve, and determine if there are in fact other goals that you should be pursuing and prioritising.

Klaus Grawe pointed out that a critically-important concept is that our goals need to be congruent. This means that our goals shouldn't clash and compete. Instead, we need to find ways to link our goals together so that they support each other. If moving closer to one goal moves us further from another goal, then we experience internal conflict. This often happens when we have not consciously explored our goals and how they connect. The effect is magnified when we haven't prioritised the goals, leading to great difficulty in deciding what needs attention and what takes the back seat.

Times of high stress and adversity is when we can most benefit from having clear goals. Clarity allows us to make difficult decisions faster, even when we are stressed, because we can maintain perspective of what is most important. In this way, the domain of Vision guides our ability to be resilient through influencing all other domains of resilience.

Domain 2: Composure

Regulating emotions and managing stress constructively is what the Composure domain is about. Through our home and work life we will invariably face stressful times and our emotions will fluctuate—that is completely natural. What is important, however, is how we deal with it when it happens.

Emotions are produced by the impulsive brain, based on what we experience and how we instinctively think about the situation. However, as we know now, we can modify this default behaviour through directed use of the smart brain. By resetting our expectations and actively identifying when we have an emotional reaction, we can stay calm and in control when facing difficult situations. Composure, therefore, considers our ability to maintain a state of mental equilibrium so that we can function effectively when we need it most.

Regulation is the key theme within the brain when it comes to the domain of Composure. When considering the brain, regulation refers to how an area of the brain can be up- or downregulated. Respectively, this means that activity in a specific neural structure is increased or decreased. For example, if the area that processes fear is upregulated, then you will become more fearful. Regulation is affected by different factors, such as what you see and hear, what foods or medication you've taken, and internally by your own beliefs and expectations.

A central structure in the domain of Composure is the hypothalamic-pituitary-adrenal axis, or HPA axis for short. Consisting of three parts, the first is the hypothalamus, which connects the brain to the hormonal system, allowing the brain to regulate bodily functions through secreted hormones. The hypothalamus does this through its connection to the pituitary gland, which in turn activates the adrenal glands. These glands control the release of adrenaline and cortisol—the primary stress hormones. When these release, you notice the effects physically, through symptoms such as a racing heart, shallow breathing, sweating, butterflies in the stomach, difficulty speaking, shaking hands, flushed skin and tensed muscles. In short, the effects of the fight-or-flight response.

More importantly, when the HPA axis activates, the smart brain is downregulated, reducing our ability to think clearly. This is because arteries are restricted and cortical blood flow to the smart brain is lowered. Instead, cortical blood flow to the impulsive brain is increased, thus increasing impulsive thinking. The effect is a reduced ability to come up with creative solutions to the challenge at hand and recognise hidden opportunities.

An overactive fear response (through the HPA axis) is particularly problematic in the work environment because stressful times are when we need a highly-functioning, smart brain the most. When there is a crisis or some major challenge, that is when we most need to access our whole brain and its creativity. Instead, if we don't think constructively about stress, the constant activation of the HPA axis will make us more fearful over time. It will drive us to avoid similar experiences, leading to a destructive cycle, i.e. the constant stress at work may result in burnout, depression and other mental health issues.

The crux is that the impulsive brain and HPA axis needs guidance from the smart brain to know when it should be activating in the first place, and the challenge of that is how long it takes the smart brain to make more constructive pathways. In contrast, the impulsive brain can store fear experiences very quickly and make us avoid similar situations. For example, one frightening experience in an elevator can quickly make someone avoid getting into an elevator ever again. From there, the smart brain needs a significant amount of time to constructively process the experience. This is to de-power the emotion resulting from that memory, so that the person can once again get into an elevator without feeling panicked. Without this active intervention, the person may stay fearful of elevators from there onwards, and it may even result in an inability to work in a high-rise building or the like.

In a similar way, if a person at work takes the initiative to come up with a new idea but is subsequently admonished for spending time on frivolous activities, then that single experience can easily create a fear of ever being proactive again. Unless the person has a resilient mindset to be able to isolate that experience and put it into perspective, it's easy to simply say *'never again'*. From there, subsequent managers may have quite a challenge to encourage the individual to come up with and present new ideas.

The Composure domain of resilience has two major components: a *reactive component* and a *proactive component*.

The reactive component refers to what we can do once we recognise in the moment that we are highly stressed. From there, we can use strategies to and thus the stress response. Though even to be able to use calming strategies, we need to proactively work to recognise that stress is not helpful and that we need to come down from that charged mental state.

Therefore, most efforts to improve Composure are proactive, meaning we need to prime the brain to be able to constructively regulate the impulsive brain. *Priming* in this sense means there is a healthy number of neural pathways between the smart brain and the impulsive brain to allow for effective regulation. These pathways form through our thought patterns, beliefs and expectations.

For example, contrast the belief *'nothing will go wrong'* with *'things go wrong, and I'll manage it'*. If these were two project managers, then one is in for a rude shock... as things invariably go wrong. Our project manager might have a naïve belief, but the effect is that this manager's impulsive brain is not prepared for the reality of mistakes and failures. When a challenge arises, the smart brain is downregulated and the impulsive brain is upregulated, as fear takes over. The result is what we've seen many times before—anger, shock, blame, guilt, and a host of other unhelpful emotional responses that don't work towards resolving the situation.

That's not to say that someone with high Composure would be immune to all emotional responses. Instead, they will have the presence of mind to recognise what is happening with themselves and determine the appropriateness of their emotional state versus the situation. Times of profound loss or heartbreak usually warrant an emotional response, and this is necessary to process the event.

With this self-awareness comes a deeper understanding of emotions, such as which emotions provide the most energy to you as an individual.

Can you effectively channel that energy towards something useful? Anger and frustration may not be positive emotions, but they are not negative either. Instead, if you can channel the energy of these emotions toward achieving a goal, then they become 'constructive displeasure', providing energy to help you succeed.

Contrast anger with rage, which is a disruptive emotion. The difference here is that *constructive displeasure* is easier to harness for something useful, whereas disruptive emotions are not. For example, getting angry at dirty dishes might result in you furiously washing them, but going into a rage about the dishes might mean smashing them on the ground. One of these leads to a more constructive result.

Internalising this distinction helps you stay in control when you experience these emotions, so you can use the energy effectively, or alternatively, regain composure to a more constructive state. In this way, the Composure domain feeds into our basic need for control, since maintaining a steady mental state is a way to control ourselves. We gain the presence of mind to exert more control over the situation we're in, through greater use of the smart brain.

Composure is also heavily influenced by our default assessment of events that we experience, known as our 'interpretation bias'. This bias may sway towards positive or negative interpretation, and is particularly relevant when situations are in fact neutral. We've all known people with a negative interpretation bias, where every situation is contorted into a disaster-in-the-making. Tragically, this often leads to self-fulfilling prophecies, where their attitude to the situation creates the very eventuality that they fear.

A negative interpretation bias means that the impulsive brain is strongly wired to detect potential trouble and think about what else can go wrong. So it will keep looping back into itself, creating unhealthy rumination, stress and anxiety. Research shows that the effects of this runs deep, as individuals with a negative interpretation are *six times* more likely to be at risk of depression[26].

Becoming aware of our natural interpretation bias is important for

[26] Kleim, B., Thörn, H. A., & Ehlert, U. (2014). Positive interpretation bias predicts well-being in medical interns. *Frontiers in psychology*, 5.

Composure, as this awareness allows us to take a step back and determine if this bias is appropriate and useful. In other words, is your interpretation bias giving you a constructive experience of life and helping you achieve your goals?

This goes hand-in-hand with being able to accurately identify emotions in the moment, take a step back and assess your state of mind. Referred to as 'emotional granularity', this is not simply the ability to rattle off many different types of emotions, but instead being able to identify one specific emotion that you are feeling in that moment. Studies have shown that being able to accurately identify emotions is related to the ability to effectively regulate disruptive emotions[27]. This is because you are better able to apply the correct strategy to the situation, whereas someone with low emotional granularity has less ability to deal with the emotion.

Composure, therefore, includes an internal awareness of yourself and an ability to articulate your mental state. This allows for a sense of perspective—as the smart brain observes the impulsive brain. From this, follows the opportunity to apply more advanced strategies in order to change mental states, both in relation to the past, and in the moment.

Domain 3: Reasoning

Creative problem-solving, anticipating and planning for scenarios, readiness for change, resourcefulness and innovation are all part of the Reasoning domain.

The major role of Reasoning in resilience is to help us use our whole brain to think our way out of difficult situations. A high Reasoning ability means we do not resort to destructive emotional tactics that the impulsive brain prefers. Instead, we take long-term goals into account and make unusual connections to reach a constructive outcome.

Here we start to see how the domains link together, as Reasoning needs Vision for clarity of purpose and goals to drive decision-making, and it also

[27] Barrett, L. F., Gross, J., Christensen, T. C., & Benvenuto, M. (2001). Knowing what you're feeling and knowing what to do about it: Mapping the relation between emotion differentiation and emotion regulation. *Cognition & Emotion*, 15(6), 713-724.

needs Composure to keep the impulsive brain regulated and under control, so that the smart brain can function at its best. All domains function together in this way to create the overall outcome of 'resilience': the way to advance and achieve our goals despite the adversity we face along the way.

Naturally, the smart brain is the key focus of the Reasoning domain. This neural structure houses our ability to connect different pieces of our understanding of the world to come up with novel and effective solutions to problems. The prefrontal cortex, which sits right at the front of the brain, mainly contains our centre for reasoning and abstract thinking. It's often thought that the left hemisphere of the brain contains the logical component of the brain, but this is not quite the full picture. Instead, the left and right hemispheres of the prefrontal cortex work together to solve problems and be creative.

There is a great deal of ongoing connection between the two hemispheres through the corpus callosum, which is a flat bundle of neural fibres that connect the hemispheres. Through this, Reasoning is not just a domain for 'left-brained' people, but rather a standard concept of using a whole-brain response to deal with life's challenges, so that we can come up with the best solution. The solutions that we do come up with tend to reflect our own internal models of the world, as that is what we refer to by default. Therefore, different people have different ways of solving problems.

This diversity is especially important to organisations, where no one person is likely to have a perfect understanding of the situation, and therefore a diversity of ideas and perspectives are needed. This helps organisations to be innovative and cover all the various eventualities. This way, many ideas can be discussed and weighed until the ideal solution is chosen.

Of course, the brain also has its own system to weigh potential solutions. This happens subconsciously, where the brain uses its existing model of the world to consider potential solutions and determine which option is more likely to achieve the desired goal. As we put these ideas into practice, another area in the brain looks for mistakes so it can optimise future responses.

The area of the brain that performs this function is called the anterior cingulate cortex, or ACC for short, which sits just behind the prefrontal cortex. The ACC notices when your actions didn't achieve the desired result and makes itself available to help you perform better. When you decide to concentrate and put extra effort into a task, the ACC is upregulated and allows you to utilise what the ACC has learned so far.

As you practise this type of concentration, the connection between the prefrontal cortex and the ACC strengthens. You then become better at quickly learning from mistakes and make less mistakes in the future. This type of error-detecting concentration requires conscious effort and is important in the workplace, to minimise errors. A person scoring high in Reasoning therefore has an improved ability to engage the ACC and perform more accurately on a given task.

Alongside the ability to learn from mistakes is the proactive ability to avoid mistakes and plan for eventualities. This tendency to prepare for what may come affects all aspects of our lives, be it losing your wallet, keys or phone, through to loss of employment, family or friends. Just as regularly servicing your car prevents breakdowns, so too does the brain need mental preparation to avoid unhelpful emotional reactions when something goes wrong.

Preparation helps the smart brain regulate the impulsive brain by effectively reassuring yourself that you can manage this situation. The Reasoning domain in this way contributes to Composure through careful deliberation and practising thinking through challenges. At the same time, it's also reliant on Composure techniques to regain control if disruptive emotions do sneak in. However, clarity of Vision is required to be able to know where to steer the outcomes of a crisis and which safeguards to put in place when planning for different scenarios.

Reasoning as a domain cannot function at its best when an individual has no clear goals. These are needed for someone to be decisive, both in the moment of a crisis and in achieving goals in general. For example, a person facing a sudden change at work, such as a restructure, needs these domains to work together to stay calm, process the change, and determine the best way to respond—a way that fits into their larger goals. Resilience here helps to keep the impulsive brain under control, while the smart brain identifies opportunities in the change so the individual can make use of the situation. This enables creativity, so that a way forward can be found that benefits both the individual and the organisation.

Creativity in ideas and innovation is not something we're born with, but is something we practise through linking together concepts in novel ways and by being resourceful. The better we understand the world (and thus building our internal model of the world), the easier it is to link together concepts mentally and think creatively.

The less fearful we are of failure, the more radical the ideas we can consider. People who are willing to mentally combine concepts that are seemingly unrelated have given rise to a great many new technologies and industries. This activity needs the impulsive brain to fully step aside so that the smart brain can reach across all the various neural structures to create and play, much like a child plays with no regard for failure.

Still, one brain can only achieve so much, and as the complexity of the world increases, we need more and different views to continue innovation. Some people think systematically, meaning one step after another. Others think intuitively, skipping over steps to reach the end. Systematic thinking makes less errors, but takes longer, while intuitive thinking is fast, but results in more errors. Good teams embrace this form of diversity to think feasibly radical. This increases the resourcefulness of teams as well as strengthens their ability to identify good ideas and act on them.

Just as resourcefulness is important for teams, so too is it important for individuals, as part of the Reasoning domain. Being resourceful means you have various tools, knowledge, techniques and people available to help you solve problems and achieve goals.

The internet brought with it ease of access, but also an information explosion. The result is that there is an increased need for us to be able to quickly find information needed for a task, but also that we ourselves know more in general. As the world gets more competitive, we now need to have a desire to keep learning about new trends and developments, particularly related to our field and work. However, not only is there now more information available to us than ever, there is also more misinformation available to us.

Here, it is important for us to be able to apply critical thinking to evaluate information and sources, so as to determine accuracy. It's also useful to build a network of people around us who are knowledgeable in relevant fields, helping us to fill in blind spots in our own thinking.

These are all different resources we can draw on when we face challenges in our lives and at work. It helps us to see opportunities during change, value diversity, and provide additional options when planning for eventualities. After all, you wouldn't take out insurance on your car if you didn't know it was an option. Together, these components of the Reasoning domain help you to maintain a sense of stability and this then feeds into the basic need for control.

Not only that, they also help you to identify reasonable pathways to achieve your goals, with the confidence to manage different scenarios, feeding into the basic need for motivation. Ultimately, high Reasoning ability results in a willingness to pursue new challenges and improves resourcefulness and creativity when facing crises.

Domain 4: Tenacity

Optimism through adversity, persistence and bouncing back after disruptive events is what the Tenacity domain is about.

Very few of us get everything right the first time. Instead, the main quality that contributes to success is the willingness to be persistent. Even Einstein said, *'It's not that I'm so smart, it's just that I stay with problems longer'*. Now, Einstein might have been a bit smart as well, but the attitude is crucial. It's something worth paying extra attention to in a time of instant gratification. Our own willingness to remain hopeful despite setbacks and put consistent effort into relationships, friendships, work, investments, projects and hobbies is what will eventually define our success. This is where Tenacity plays a key role in enabling the Vision domain.

Within the brain, the major force at play is the regulation between the smart brain—to persevere with a difficult task—while overcoming emotional desires from the impulsive brain—to give up. Sometimes our desire to succeed is rooted in a fear of failure. While this fear can push us to achieve great things, it's not a very constructive space to be in, since this fear is produced by the impulsive brain, which limits our ability to think creatively. We may also experience a compounding sense of stress over time, adding up to anxiety and burnout.

A side-effect of this fear-based mindset is that eventually we stop taking larger risks that may have a chance of failure. But these risks could be exactly what are needed to overcome major obstacles. We see this behaviour in business as well, where larger businesses innovate less due to a fear of failure, while new smaller businesses focus on failing fast and failing often, enabling rapid innovation and eventual competitive advantage. The behaviour of these different organisations is rooted in their culture and the organisational appetite for failure. Naturally, the culture emerges from similar attitudes of people within the organisation.

An organisation cannot simply tell its people to be more innovative if there is a strong cultural fear of failure. Therefore, if there is a desire to increase innovation within an established organisation, then improving the resilience of its people is necessary. Specifically, helping them constructively approach failure is a critical part, alongside a clear innovation risk appetite. While at a neural level, it's about the smart brain maintaining a long-term perspective so it can regulate impulsive emotions, at an organisational level, strategic managers need to allow risk-taking and reduce negative reactions to failures.

At both these personal and organisational levels, we need to maintain an environment where we focus on goals, take risks to achieve them, and constructively learn from mistakes through lessons. Thus we can increase future potential for success. As a leader, you may start to see how your attitudes to personal failures might affect how you manage innovation in your team.

Motivation determines whether we persistently pursue our goals and innovate along the way. What makes motivation work within the brain is a neurotransmitter called dopamine. Dopamine's main role is to motivate us to take some type of action that may lead to an expected cognitive reward. What's important here is that dopamine doesn't necessarily motivate us towards constructive actions. For example, dopamine can just as well motivate someone to keep working on a project as it can motivate that person to keep abusing alcohol.

The release of dopamine aims to make us take actions that will eventually lead to a 'feel-good' outcome. The problem is that there may be many unhelpful behaviours that also result in these 'feel-good' outcomes. For example, eating unhealthy foods, drinking, smoking, avoiding difficult situations, and procrastinating. Keeping in mind that neurons that fire together, wire together, we understand that the more we repeat some type of action in response to a certain situation, the more we reinforce that as the default behaviour. Essentially, if each time we watch some television before washing dishes, then the brain will reinforce that behaviour. Over time, that behaviour will get so ingrained that we just can't wash dishes without watching some television first. This is because of a strong dopamine release pushing us to switch on our favourite show.

Watching television might not seem like actually doing anything, but when it comes to the brain, doing nothing is still doing something. When you just relax, you might be avoiding the pain of having to do something more challenging, and each time we avoid something, it gets easier to avoid it again in the future. It is through repetition of tasks that we train the brain (and its dopamine) to motivate us towards certain actions. It's therefore up to us to push through... to take constructive actions so that we train our brain effectively. This means not shying away from difficult tasks and challenges, following through, and importantly, being willing to delay gratification.

Through our expectations and beliefs, we cultivate our desires. To keep the brain motivated towards taking constructive action, we need to cultivate a desire for challenge. After all, it is through challenges that we grow and accomplish our greater goals. The main challenge is to remain hopeful that we will succeed through challenges.

Optimism and positivity is often presented as the solution, but there are distinct limits. In fact, research into different types of motivation shows that being overly optimistic drains energy, resulting in less success[28]. As an example, say we have an idealised future that we want to reach, where we

---

[28] Kappes, H. B., & Oettingen, G. (2011). Positive fantasies about idealized futures sap energy. *Journal of Experimental Social Psychology*, 47(4), 719-729.

imagine that everything goes great and we become CEO, or president, or prime minister. The research calls this a 'positive fantasy'. It points out that if we skip over just how excruciatingly difficult and painful the path to that ultimate success will be, then the positive fantasy would not produce the necessary energy to follow through. You see, if we expect to easily succeed in a task, then there is less motivation for us to put additional effort in to ensure success. This low-effort approach reduces the likelihood for success and increases the chance of mistakes and oversights.

This is as true on an individual level as it is for large corporate projects. What we've learned from the research is that a more motivational thought pattern is to have a clear goal, recognise your current position and how far it is from your goal, acknowledge that the journey will be tough and painful, and yet have confidence in your ability to work through it and succeed. This essentially provides a realistic hope for the future—a realistic sense of optimism about achieving success. What follows from this mindset is the willingness to persevere in the face of adversity, so you may ultimately succeed.

What you develop through this mindset is a sense of *realistic optimism*. As compared to pessimism or being overly optimistic, realistic optimism is the best mindset for success. This mindset is enabled by Vision so that you have clear goals you are working towards, by Reasoning, to help determine an effective path forward that overcomes obstacles, and by Composure, so you can overcome impulsive emotions along the way and stay focused.

These factors contribute to a feeling of confidence and thus enable a central concept in the domain of Tenacity, which is to make a conscious decision not to give up.

This decision feeds in to the basic need for motivation, coming from the self-discipline to keep going when things get tough. In fact, recent research indicates that self-discipline and grit is more important than intelligence for goal achievement[29]. This goes against usual expectations, where the drive is often to find the most intelligent people to work for an organisation.

[29] Duckworth, A. L., Peterson, C., Matthews, M. D., & Kelly, D. R. (2007). Grit: perseverance and passion for long-term goals. *Journal of personality and social psychology*, 92(6), 1087.

However, what the research shows is that even where there is intelligence or talent, success more heavily depends on the consistent and focused application of that talent.

Therefore, if we simply aim to hire the smartest people and if they were to give up when things get tough, then they won't be helping the organisation to succeed. To some extent, it is a differentiation between intelligence and wisdom. A highly-intelligent person might be able to do incredibly complex calculations in their head, but that doesn't mean they know which are the right problems to solve in the first place. As well, they might not keep going if something seems too difficult at first glance. Someone with staying power, therefore, can outperform someone with a high IQ.

To avoid burnout, staying power and focus depend on other factors. Simply pushing yourself harder might seem like the logical conclusion of Tenacity, but that in itself does not ensure the long-term viability of persistence. For example, your attitude and beliefs affect how well you handle knocks along the way. This has been observed in a study where around 30,000 people had to focus on a simple question: 'Do you believe that stress is harmful to your health?'[30] Results eventually showed that people who experienced a lot of stress and also believed that stress was bad for their health had a higher risk of early death.

However, those who saw stress as something that strengthens them didn't experience the same negative effects of stress. This is a clear indication of how beliefs affect how well we can tolerate adversity. These beliefs also affect how well we can tolerate our own mistakes along the way and maintain a constructive mindset. If we don't stay constructive about stress and mistakes along the way, then these have a cumulative effect, where they slowly wear us down.

The long-term result is burnout, distress or depression, where we simply do not want to face any more of these challenges; in fact, we'd rather give

[30] Keller, A., Litzelman, K., Wisk, L. E., Maddox, T., Cheng, E. R., Creswell, P. D., & Witt, W. P. (2012). Does the perception that stress affects health matter? The association with health and mortality. *Health Psychology*, 31(5), 677.

up and do something less challenging. Maintaining a constructive mindset is the most crucial component for persistence to remain viable in the long term, as it allows us to effectively process stress and hardship as it comes. This way, we effectively integrate experiences along the way, building on them and growing from them. The result is that we become tenacious, with the ability to persist and ultimately achieve our goals, without this pursuit negatively affecting our health.

Domain 5: Collaboration

Building healthy support networks, connecting with others, adapting to context and managing perceptions is at the heart of our basic human need for connection with others. As the world becomes more complex, we need to be able to more effectively work with others to accomplish meaningful goals. This is especially true in organisations where cohesiveness of the workforce is crucial to building a healthy culture, a culture where people can support each other through turbulent change cycles and innovation. These are the key factors that make up the domain of Collaboration.

Connection with others is so important to us that the brain has developed specific areas to focus on this. Near the bottom of the brain on both sides sit the fusiform gyrus, which is specifically adapted to recognise facial expressions in other humans. It activates when we see the face of another person and produces a stronger reaction when that person is familiar to us. The brain also checks with the amygdala and memory centres to determine if there is any threat from this person. This affects the level of safety you feel around people.

When we do not feel safe, the impulsive brain upregulates the fight-or-flight response to prevent us from being harmed. As the impulsive brain lacks the higher reasoning skills of the smart brain, the response might not be helpful. This is especially relevant in the work environment, where we might feel the threat of losing employment, losing the potential for a promotion, or fear a bad outcome of a project. If our sense of safety takes a dive and the impulsive brain activates, then we effectively lose the ability to think clearly, precisely when we need it the most. These are the times that we need the smart brain to work at its best, so we can come up with novel ideas and solutions to overcome obstacles. Effectively, we need to be able to return ourselves to a sense of safety.

The concept of safety is critical to all our basic needs. It includes the desire for safety around housing and having food to eat. In the developed world, safe housing and plentiful food is mostly taken care of. However, a larger variable remains in the safety we feel around people. Do we feel we can trust those close to us? Can we trust strangers we meet? Can we trust those that we work with?

While we may have nuanced views of specific individuals, our core beliefs about trust have a strong effect on our outlook and interactions with others. For example, if deep down we believe that people can't be trusted, then that will impact how we behave around others. We might share less, be suspicious of motives, and generally try to retreat from people. On the other hand, if we believe everyone can be completely trusted, then we might share too much and let people in that don't have our best interests at heart.

Game theory provides an interesting view of the idea of trust. A series of games were held. In the game, two players must decide how they treat each other. If both cooperate, then they get a reward. If one cheats, the cheater gets an even bigger reward, and the other gets nothing. If both cheat, then there is no reward for either player.

Competitors tried a vast number of strategies to win the series of games, but one extremely simple strategy kept winning—a strategy called *tit-for-tat*. The strategy is to start by cooperating, then do whatever the partner did in the previous round. So, in the first round, player A would cooperate, but if the partner cheats, then player A would cheat in the second round, hence, tit-for-tat. Therefore, when paired with a cooperative partner, all subsequent games would be a harmony of cooperation. And if paired with a serial cheater, the result was a venerable apocalypse. Of all the various complex strategies that were tried, tit-for-tat always came out on top as a reliable winning strategy.

This gives us an interesting perspective, in that if a tit-for-tat player doesn't start off as willing to cooperate, then it would never have found the rewards available through cooperative players. The same concept applies to us—we need to be willing to cooperate and trust people to be able to find opportunities in the first place. If we always avoid trusting, then we will inherently pass up many opportunities along the way without ever realising it.

Naturally, the real world is much more complex than the game tit-for-tat played in, so this is where resilience plays a big role. Through the skills of the resilience domains, we can become better able to predict what might go wrong, plan for those eventualities, understand what we are willing to risk, and have a plan B strategy in place in case something does go wrong. Also important is basic due diligence on people, so we understand them to some degree, and don't blindly trust strangers. When we understand our own vision and goals, we can better put into context the actions and goals of others to determine if they are a positive influence or not.

By following these basic, personal risk management techniques, resilience makes us more confident in our ability to connect with and trust people, as we can manage the impacts of something going wrong. In a way, strategic real-world tit-for-tat embodies 'realistic optimism', as discussed in the Tenacity domain.

This mindset lets us pursue more opportunities through collaboration with others, maximise the ones that work and effectively handle the ones that don't. Collaboration as a domain therefore requires the effective functioning of the other resilience domains, so that we can confidently build secure relationships with people. When we lack resilience, we might be quick to take offense at something that was said, or misinterpret comments or actions in a negative way. Mistrust of others may also make it seem like we don't have a support network, when in fact we do.

Empathy is the key factor here. Having empathy doesn't mean having a bleeding heart for everyone around you, but instead having enough *emotional intelligence* to be able to see situations from their perspective. Empathy is important for family, friends, and certainly colleagues.

Research in the 1980s discovered a new type of neuron that added to our explanation of empathy. These are called 'mirror neurons'. They're named that way since they fire the same way in your brain as they do in the brain of another person when you witness them perform an action or act out an emotion. When we watch a movie and share an emotion with the actors on screen, it's not just our perspective of the story that drives emotion, but also the mirror neurons that help us feel what the actors are portraying. The skill of the actor makes a big difference in being able to feel the emotion themselves well enough to trigger their own mirror neurons, and thus transporting the emotion more effectively to us.

Mirror neurons are largely related to learning by watching, allowing us to know what it feels like to move in a certain way.[31] For example, this adds to our enjoyment of sport, as we can subconsciously feel ourselves doing what the athletes are doing. We feel the joy in victory almost as if we achieved that victory ourselves. Observing role models at work has a similar effect, because seeing how they handle situations, conduct meetings, and perform tasks triggers the same mirror neurons in us. This means we can better understand the mental state and actions of our role models.

Through mirror neurons, research suggests that we not only can feel ourselves doing the same actions, but we can also understand the intention of the person we are observing.[32] The same action literally spreads organisational culture on a subconscious level. If a new employee sees fear on the face of their co-workers when starting their new job, then that person will also feel the same fear. This perpetuates a culture of fear, through the function of mirror neurons, even though the new employee has no factual basis for the sense of fear just yet. Now primed with that bias of fear, any evidence that could support that emotion will be integrated in their mind. This confirms that the feeling is legitimate and that this environment might be dangerous.

Managing emotions through the Composure domain is therefore important so that more constructive emotions are shared through mirror neurons. This seeks to set the foundation of a healthy culture at work.

Lastly, effective collaboration with others depends on our sensitivity to context. As an extreme example, the way we act around friends while having

---

[31] Acharya, S., & Shukla, S. (2012). Mirror neurons: Enigma of the metaphysical modular brain. Journal of Natural Science, *Biology and Medicine*, 3(2), 118.

[32] Gazzola, V., & Keysers, C. (2009). The observation and execution of actions share motor and somatosensory voxels in all tested subjects: single-subject analyses of unsmoothed fMRI data. *Cerebral Cortex*, 19(6), 1239-1255.

a drink on a Friday night is unlikely to be the same way we'd act when presenting to the board of directors. We effectively have different personas that we invoke, given the context of the situation we are in. Being sensitive to these contexts allows us to adapt your style so that we can be most effective in the given situation. This skill relies on other domains of resilience. It relies on Vision, so that we may know which goals fit within a specific context. It relies on Composure, so that we may understand and regulate our own emotions with the situation, as well as understand the emotions of others within the context. On Reasoning, so that we may determine the best way forward, be resourceful, and stay rational within the context. And on Tenacity, so that we may not give up too easily within that context.

All the domains work together to enhance our ability to work with others, just as Collaboration supports us in being able to overcome adversity and achieve more than what we can by ourselves.

Domain 6: Health

Resilience is not simply a mental construct, but also has a physical component. Our own health affects how well we can deal with challenges in our path. Meanwhile, failing health can present the toughest challenge of all.

Good nutrition, quality sleep and exercise are all components of the Health domain.

Our initial inquiries into resilience revealed that physical health was rarely considered to be part of resilience. In fact, none of the major resilience measurement scales included health as a domain of resilience.[33] This is despite mounting evidence that shows how physical health influences mindset and coping abilities in multiple ways.

Throughout our research we showed that health has a strong correlation with resilience, and explored the mechanisms through which this takes place. These include effects on both physiological and neurological levels.

---

[33] Rossouw, P. J., & Rossouw, J. G. The Predictive 6-Factor Resilience Scale: Neurobiological Fundamentals and Organisational Application. *International Journal of Neuropsychotherapy*, 4(1), 31-45.

Some of these factors are not under our control, but many are, so let's explore both levels.

On a physiological level, there is an immediate impact on us through illness and poor health. Where resilience is about effectively dealing with challenges, nothing is quite as challenging and disruptive as falling ill. Even the flu can easily take you out for a few days, halting any progress towards your goals. More serious conditions, such as a major illness or chronic pain, can add a great deal of stress and reduce your ability to cope with other challenges. It may even drive you to avoid taking risks in your life, resulting in missed opportunities to advance.

Lifestyle choices play a major role in how healthy you are. Good nutrition, sleep and exercise affect the immune system, how much energy you have, and your physical fitness. Low fitness levels might easily result in a rising heart rate and rapid breathing. This may be misinterpreted by the brain as an anxious state, increasing activation of the impulsive brain. The quality and quantity of food we eat affects our physical appearance, sometimes resulting in self-esteem problems. On the other hand, feeling physically strong may help you to feel calm and in control.

Life expectancy is also an important factor, affected by your habits. A large study found that people who eat on average seven portions of vegetables per day had a 42% lower chance of dying from all causes.[34] This includes causes such as cancer, cardiovascular diseases, and even accidents. This may sound like an extraordinary claim, however the study included over 65,000 people over 7.7 years. Still, while facts like this make a splash in the media, it doesn't translate so readily into people changing their habits. It's up to us to make an active choice to invest in our own health, and do it early.

We also see major impacts on a neurological level. This is interesting as we don't always think of good health in terms of how it affects the brain. However, recent research reveals that good health has an array of benefits

[34] Oyebode, O., Gordon-Dseagu, V., Walker, A., & Mindell, J. S. (2014). Fruit and vegetable consumption and all-cause, cancer and CVD mortality: analysis of Health Survey for England data. *Journal of epidemiology and community health*, jech-2013.

for the brain and mind. For example, the hippocampus produces a neurochemical called brain-derived neurotrophic factor, or BDNF for short. The role of BDNF is to help existing neurons survive, and also stimulate the growth of new neurons and connections between them.

This is a critical requirement of the brain's ability to learn new skills and adapt to new environments. If BDNF production is low, it can cause a person's thinking to become rigid and they may have difficulty with adapting to changing circumstances. BDNF is therefore a crucial neurochemical for resilience, as it helps us learn and improve our behaviour over time—so we may be more successful in our future pursuits. Beyond this, BDNF has also been shown to have a key role in helping individuals recover from depression,[35] since new, healthy, neural patterns need to develop to underpin a healthy mindset.

What's interesting is that our habits have been shown to affect BDNF production. Exercising four times a week increases BDNF production, even at old age, building a healthy and adapting brain.[36] Eating unhealthy foods, especially foods high in both fat and sugar, like donuts and chocolate, lowers BDNF production.[37]

The case is similar for lack of sleep. Missing out on quality sleep increases cortisol—a stress hormone—and reduces BDNF.[38] The effects accumulate over time, which is why it's important to start as early as possible and consistently live a healthy life. However, research has shown that even at an older age, changing to a healthy lifestyle can still provide benefits.

Sleep is often sacrificed for the sake of being more productive during the day. However, there are many potential negative effects of this. For example,

[35] Castrén, E., & Rantamäki, T. (2010). The role of BDNF and its receptors in depression and antidepressant drug action: Reactivation of developmental plasticity. *Developmental neurobiology*, 70(5), 289-297.

[36] Cotman, C. W., & Berchtold, N. C. (2002). Exercise: a behavioral intervention to enhance brain health and plasticity. *Trends in neurosciences*, 25(6), 295-301.

[37] Molteni, R., Barnard, R. J., Ying, Z., Roberts, C. K., & Gomez-Pinilla, F. (2002). A high-fat, refined sugar diet reduces hippocampal brain-derived neurotrophic factor, neuronal plasticity, and learning. *Neuroscience*, 112(4), 803-814.

[38] Issa, G., Wilson, C., Terry, A. V., & Pillai, A. (2010). An inverse relationship between cortisol and BDNF levels in schizophrenia: data from human postmortem and animal studies. *Neurobiology of disease*, 39(3), 327-333.

lack of sleep has been linked to reduced attention span, loss of coordination, making more mistakes, mood swings, loss of control, and difficulty coping with stress. Each of these affect our ability to be resilient and effectively work towards what is important to us. While it may seem that squeezing out a few more hours of work might be worth it, it might just reduce our effectiveness in the days to come, especially when this happens on an ongoing basis. If, for example, the need to sacrifice sleep is due to an emergency, then we simply need to work past it. But if there's an emergency every night and we enter a state of chronic sleep deprivation, then the effects may severely reduce our effectiveness across all domains of resilience.

Nutrition affects the brain in many ways. We may not realise it, but a lot about nutrition is purely self-medication to alter our mental state. Think about these examples: eating foods high in sugar and fats releases serotonin, a feel-good hormone that can help lift your mood. Caffeine—the most-used psychoactive drug in the world—increases energy, speeds up the brain and improves performance. Alcohol slows down the brain, helping you calm down after a busy day. Between just these three, we can easily fall into an unhealthy cycle of needing coffee to start going, a donut for a late morning mood lift, then another coffee after the sugar crash. Then we need another high-carb snack later, with another coffee to beat the afternoon tiredness, then by the evening we're so wired we feel we need a few drinks to relax and get to sleep... only to wake up groggy and do it all over again.

These cycles we often get into may help us get through each day, but they take a toll on the body and health of the brain. The effects creep in over time. You might feel invincible for a long time and not worry about getting enough sleep, exercise, or eating healthy foods, then one day you find that you're just not feeling as strong and healthy anymore. These effects slowly change the body, until suddenly you feel you need to scramble for health to get back to feeling like yourself.

Ideally, we would recognise the importance of taking care of our health at an earlier point, so that we may enjoy better health and vitality later in life. Failing that, it's never too late to make health a priority.

With that context, there's no doubt that taking care of your health is important. However, that does not necessarily mean that health should be your top priority. Of all the goals we set for ourselves and our purpose in life, maintaining health does not sit well at the top. This is because physiological health in itself does not achieve anything. It simply allows you to do other, more important things. Just like having a computer in itself is not a good thing—it's what you do with it that counts. Our health is there to support us in our pursuit of larger goals, and is therefore in itself not the primary goal. Health issues will certainly take priority when they arise, but the day-to-day maintenance of our health should not take up most our available time and energy (unless perhaps you are a fitness instructor or professional athlete).

Instead, the value of the Health domain is to provide us with the energy, vitality and physical ability to pursue meaningful goals and fulfil our sense of purpose. Good health also enables the other domains of resilience, which in turn are geared towards supporting the Vision domain. This means that Health is a foundational domain, providing a solid base on which to build a resilient mindset.

The resilience effect

Overall, the six domains function together and support each other to better allow you to advance towards your goals and sense of purpose. The domains themselves function in the context of the basic human needs, with the Health domain acting as a foundation for the other domains. The result is an ability to sustain a motivated state, where you can manage life's ups and downs while staying focused on achieving something meaningful. This is the aim of resilience.

Naturally, the majority of the concept of resilience is housed in the brain itself. And fortunately for us, the brain is 'plastic', allowing us to change our neural patterns through our own behaviours and thoughts. Keep in mind the proactive nature of resilience—don't wait until after you've faced difficulty to finally begin working on resilience. The better prepared you are, the more successfully you can manage difficult situations when they inevitably arise.

Through all the complexity of resilience, the most important concept to keep in mind is that resilience aims to build connections within the brain.

This is so it can decrease activation of the impulsive brain and increase activation of the smart brain. At its neuroscientific core, that's what resilience is about.

4.

Building personal resilience

Building a culture of resilience starts with building resilience in yourself. By understanding and growing your own resilience, you gain the perspective and compassion needed to support the resilience of the people around you.

An important nuance here is that you must understand your own resilience. The journey to reach a leadership position requires resilience already, but few who achieve their positions understand the mechanics of their own resilience. They simply know that they are resilient. Using this book's framework, a new understanding of your own resilience will help you to recognise where you can improve. It will also enhance your ability to recognise where others need help. Therefore, only having resilience is not enough—what it means to be a resilient executive is also to understand your own resilience.

Techniques for each of the six domains is expanded on in this chapter, so as to identify ways for you to build and understand your own resilience. What's important to note with each of the domains is that everyone is different. Because of that, some techniques might be more effective than others for you. The key is to identify which techniques work best for you, while also working on and adding new techniques to enhance your resilience.

This work allows you to accurately choose when to use which techniques to keep you on track with your goals. As an executive, this ability is crucial, since higher pressure and time constraints leave less time to calm and centre your mind. For example, having back-to-back meetings, day after day, leaves little time to catch your breath, meaning it's necessary to be able to use resilience skills on-the-fly to stay calm and focused.

This fast-paced environment requires not only to know which resilience skills to use, but also for those skills to be practised enough so you have confidence in your abilities. As an example, many businesses have contingency plans for when something goes wrong, but time and time again we see that businesses are far less likely to use those plans if they have never practised them. Without practise, there is no confidence that the plans will work, and without confidence, the plans are avoided at all costs.

As we see organisations act in this way, so too do humans behave. For us to be able to rely on our coping skills, we need to practise these skills. Practice is that key part of resilience that is usually overlooked—being proactive. After all, we will inevitably face crises of all sizes throughout our lives, so why wait until something happens before you pay attention to your own resilience? We can handle these situations far more effectively when we develop our resilience in advance.

Neural pathways provide the evidence of preparation within the brain. When resilience skills are practised in advance, the connections between the smart brain and the impulsive brain are stronger. This means that the smart brain has a stronger ability to regulate impulsive responses. The formations of these pathways follow the axiom of 'neurons that fire together, wire together', meaning that they have to be activated repeatedly to strengthen. If these pathways are not reinforced through practise, then facing adversity becomes more challenging because you'll need to solve complex problems at a time of high stress. For example, witnessing an accident where someone gets severely injured. In this scenario, if you have never faced this before and don't know first aid or what to do, then the sudden rush of adrenaline from the impulsive brain can easily override more logical responses, causing you to experience shock and retreat, instead of helping the person. Here, the smart brain needs strong enough connection to the impulsive brain to override an emotional response and focus on working out what to do. Naturally, knowing first aid will help you feel more confident in the situation. That confidence comes from these stronger neural pathways and connection within the brain.

Keeping this in mind is important: developing resilience is not an intangible concept—instead, you are physically changing how your brain works. The enhanced neural pathways enable you to activate your whole brain to access the best strategy for the situation so you can achieve your goal. In our accident, the goal is to help the person. Here, even if you don't know first aid, you may direct someone else to call an ambulance, take a deep breath as a fast calming technique, then see what you can do to help the person.

As a leader, you will face many crises in your career. Some crises may be particularly stressful where there is a perception that it can affect your own career. For managing day-to-day work and home life, and the eventual crises, you need to stay clear-headed and keep the right variables in mind. This is how you can keep juggling everything going on without something escalating unnecessarily.

It all comes down to what you aim to achieve—your goals and personal vision. To expand on these in the context of you as a leader, let's start by exploring the most important of the domains of resilience: Vision.

Vision

Purpose, vision and goals guide all the other domains of resilience. This concept is at the heart of goal-directed resilience, and is what sets it apart from nihilistic resilience (where one may appear resilient by not caring about outcomes).

That said, it's interesting that we can make it through our entire lives without having any clear vision or sense of purpose that we are consciously working towards. Without any strategic intent, someone could progress from one opportunity to the next, going with the corporate flow, so to speak. And that someone can actually get quite far this way, achieving goals they may never have dreamed of previously. So, if this is all possible without going through the trouble of defining your own vision and goals, why do it?

The reality is that, yes, there are people who possess an incredibly lucky set of qualities. They just so happen to be capable in the right ways, happen to be around for the right opportunities, happen to know the right people, and happen to be interested in the right things. With this fortunate combination, someone can make it incredibly far without really knowing what their own drivers are, or without having anything in particular that they want to achieve, other than the next step. It would be great to imagine that we are one of those people, but there are several inherent weaknesses of that position.

For one, it's hard to motivate others when you don't know what drives you. Much of leadership revolves around encouraging others to buy into a shared vision. Communicating why others should buy into your vision (or the company's vision) is naturally difficult if you yourself don't know why *you* have bought into it. Another weakness is that it's easy to get off track and not find your way back. If something goes wrong along the way, perhaps an incorrect career choice, then getting back on track is a tough proposition since there's no real understanding of where the track was in the first place. Achieving greater effectiveness as a leader requires a deeper understanding of your own motivation and goals.

Combining this understanding with neuroscience also allows you to construct your own vision and goals to have a greater sense of satisfaction and wellbeing in your pursuit. This is because vision drives so much of our thoughts and actions, that it strongly affects the neural patterns that develop in the brain. Back to the principle of 'neurons that fire together, wire together', it's easy to see how the Vision domain profoundly affects our thinking and therefore how the brain structures itself. Here you may see the inherent weaknesses in those 'lucky' individuals we considered before. By taking a proactive approach to defining and creating our own vision, we learn how to manufacture luck.

Like all the domains of resilience, the Vision domain consists of multiple components. At the top sits your sense of purpose—your vision itself. This drives your own existence, and affects the more granular goals you set for yourself, as well as affecting the implementation of all the other domains of resilience.

Think of your purpose as a metaphorical lake on a mountain. Downstream from the lake are the goals that it feeds. These in turn feed other aspects of your life further downstream, keeping alive the ecosystem of your existence. While we may not have a full awareness of all the little streams down below, we affect them through what we do at the top. Lack of awareness of your own vision is like the lake and its channels being underground. This makes it unclear what is feeding what, resulting in unexpected damage downstream.

On the other hand, taking the time to unearth the source and its channels, allows you as the architect to actively plan and define new pathways to channel the waters—your own energy—towards more constructive outcomes. This is similar in the brain itself—our own path in life is where we have most power to decide, which in turn affects other areas in the brain and how they are wired. It is there, at the top, that we must start, since the depth of the lake (vision) at the top determines how much we can draw from it, and how it feeds the rest of our life.

A resilient approach to vision and purpose

This is meaning-of-life type stuff. More specifically, the meaning of *your* life. Most people make it through their lives without really figuring this out. However, to be an effective leader, you need to have some idea of what *your* life is about.

When it comes to this question, it's important to stay pragmatic and avoid trying to solve age-old philosophical quandaries. You're not attempting to answer *'what is the good life?'*, nor aiming to devise the purpose of all life. Rather than endless philosophising, this is more about deciding what makes sense to you. Of course, you can also call it whatever you like: your vision, your aim, your purpose, your mission, your driver, your duty, your meaning, your raison d'etre. The label doesn't matter. What matters is understanding what you are striving towards. For the remainder of this book, I will refer to it as 'vision', though please substitute whatever term you prefer.

There are some common pitfalls in defining a vision and exploring these will illuminate a more resilient approach. A highly-tempting pitfall is to make the vision too specific. For example, someone might say their vision is to become CEO of ACME corp. For one, this is much more appropriate as a goal, which is downstream from your vision. In addition, a specific vision such as this can be nullified by forces outside your control. For example, ACME might go bankrupt or be acquired, and the CEO position closed. Or perhaps the current CEO will still be there 40 years from now. To be more resilient, your vision should be able to survive changes in the outside world. Therefore, it's necessary to avoid being too specific. Instead, a resilient vision is one that can never be invalidated by external events, and so can always be pursued.

Another pitfall is about a specific word that we really like to use. Consider these vision statements; *'I want to be a great leader'*, *'I want be a good parent'*, *'I want to be a good person'*. See what they have in common? They all refer to *'good'*, which really does not say anything at all. We don't often think about it, but the word *'good'* is a very poor descriptor. If someone says a movie was good, is it because it was funny? Or because it was moving? Or it was fast-paced? Or because it was actually so bad it was good? *'Good'* means different things to different people.

Over time, it can even mean different things to *you,* as your views change. Therefore, asking someone if they thought a movie was *'good'* does not give us any indication that we would like the movie ourselves. Similarly, we tend to use this nebulous word ourselves as a cop-out... such as saying your vision is *'to be a great leader'*. The word *'great'* here is just another way for *'good'* to weasel in. What is a *'great'* leader? Is it one who is very empathetic, or one that is very directive? Is it one whose main concern is shareholder value, or building a great culture? Is it one who single-handedly drives the company, or one who is highly collaborative? The word *'great'* tells us nothing about these questions. Therefore, the vision itself loses power because there is no clarity to pursue goals and drive our decisions. The vision will fall apart and change over time as our own perceptions change, making our decisions erratic and contradictory. Again, this makes us vulnerable and less resilient. Quite simply, avoid the word *'good'* and all its friends, especially when considering your own vision.

'To be happy' is probably one of the most dangerously precarious vision

statements. I've asked many friends and colleagues what their own vision or purpose is. Those who have not really considered the topic tend to come up with this one after about five seconds of deliberation. *'To be happy'* seems like such a natural and innocuous answer, but it is surprisingly quite dangerous because of this simple fact: happiness cannot be pursued directly. It is a side-effect of doing something else.

This is similar to money—you can't get money just by pursuing it directly—you need to do something else to get it. Sure, happiness is 'nice', however, specifying it as your vision is very ambiguous. Quite often we don't intrinsically understand what makes us happy, making it particularly difficult to diagnose what's wrong when we stop being happy.

Another pitfall of this aim is happiness is a very self-focused goal, which can have some nasty side-effects. When we want more of it, we might aim to gain it through methods that are focused on ourselves and have no benefit to anyone else, or even be to the detriment of those around us. After all, if it is our purpose to achieve happiness, then we may well seek to do so in the most efficient way possible. We may even start to behave in ways that produce happiness at the expense of others.

Another effective (and not advised) way of achieving short-term happiness is to take hard drugs like heroin, since it is currently the quickest, most powerful way to produce a euphoric brain state. The effect of heroin is so strong that people quickly desire nothing else, since nothing, not even their wildest fantasies, can compare to the pure happiness that heroin produces. Of course, this is extraordinarily destructive as it has hugely detrimental effects on all other areas of life. Extreme as the example is, it illustrates the point—happiness alone is a precarious vision that can easily become dangerous in certain circumstances. Instead, look deeper into what results in happiness and satisfaction.

The source of happiness might not always be useful. This is a good reason why we should investigate. For example, we may value *results* more than *process*. To understand this concept, let's look at playing the piano. The *process* is the hours learning to play the piano. The *result* is the ability to play a piece. As we progress, perhaps we want to play at a concert. In that case, the *process* of learning and honing takes thousands of hours, while the *result*—playing the concert—maybe lasts for two hours. Here you can see the trouble. If we value *results* more than *process*, then the moment we truly enjoy is only two hours out of thousands. All those years of practice can feel highly frustrating if it is not the part that you enjoy.

Being in the business world often pushes us to think this way, since business is very results focused. The effect is that our results-focused doctrine bleeds over into our personal lives, reducing our ability to enjoy the things we spend most of our time on.

To improve our sense of wellbeing, we need to learn to appreciate the processes that we are engaged in. This applies both at a personal and professional level. Especially given that a great deal of our waking hours go into being at work, where we immerse ourselves in processes. Considering this shift presents a kind of 'existential opportunity', wherein we have the power to choose what makes us happy. We exercise this power by choosing what we value, and shifting focus from results to process. For example, choosing to value the process of learning, the process of improving, the process of doing something well.

Choosing, at a personal level, to value those concepts above results helps to improve your sense of wellbeing, while you can still value results in a business context. That doesn't mean you will be all smiles while reviewing long reports, but you can appreciate what you are working towards and the process of getting there. It is also through process that we produce results, so factoring process into your own vision thereby enables the very means through which you will achieve results. This shift sets you up to persist and endure where others might give up.

Formulaic vision statements are another pitfall that reduces the effectiveness of a vision. These you have likely seen many times, and go something like: '*It's my vision to be an empathetic and inspiring leader that blah blah...*'. These are often generated through brainstorming, where you consider 'passions' and things like that. When a vision is this long, it's unlikely you would ever remember it yourself, and if you can't remember it, then it's unlikely to drive any of your decisions or behaviour. The brain needs a simple concept that can easily be referenced at any time—particularly when making difficult decisions or acting under stress. After all, these are the big moments in life that shape our future.

Lower personal resilience means we are not fully prepared for these moments, resulting in activation of the impulsive brain, reducing critical thinking. The outcome is sub-optimal decisions that do not work towards a larger goal. A complex vision statement is not going to help in stressful situations.

Conversely, a short and clear vision can become so ingrained that the brain can recall it at any time. Plus, this acts as a buffer against activation of the impulsive brain. It provides that moment of clarity, so you can put the situation in perspective to focus on what's important. Ideally, we should keep the vision to one word, maybe three at most.

A clear vision statement like this is not easily generated, but to some extent discovered within yourself. You already have goals, ideals and desires, so a vision statement should connect to those.

In a sense, your vision needs authenticity. Authenticity in this context means a vision that is connected to your past and who you are. While the vision itself is forward-looking, it needs authenticity to be important and meaningful to you. This might come from an event in your past; something that happened to you, something you witnessed, something that made you realise the importance of this vision. Essentially, something that gives meaning to your vision. This could be something like an injustice that you witnessed that was impactful to you. Or something you experienced that felt very empowering. Yet it doesn't need to be one event—it could be something you experienced over time that taught you an important lesson. The important part is that it has some meaning to you, making you willing to stick to your vision even if things get tough. This helps make it an enduring vision.

Broadness adds to the resilience of your vision. Having a broad vision means that it can be applied in any context, and can't easily be invalidated by external forces. Such a vision is one that can stand the test of time and can guide you throughout your life. This makes it a truly resilient vision. With all this context in mind, here are a few examples of resilient vision statements:

'Improve', 'Advance', 'Solve big problems', 'Inspire people', 'Make a difference'

You can see right away how these can be brought into any situation. They are simple enough to stick in your brain and refer to in a difficult situation. They also direct effort in definite directions. These example statements go beyond ourselves—as they involve some benefit to the world within which we exist. This is important because it makes the vision motivating to you, as well as inspirational to others, strengthening your ability to lead others.

Hidden within these example vision statements is a subconscious reappraisal of struggle, suffering, and the pain of enduring adversity. Think of it this way—a vision focusing on happiness is an inherent rejection of this type of suffering. Meanwhile, the majority of processes we are involved in every day involves some element of suffering, be it through difficult circumstances, stress, mistakes, or the like. A vision focusing on advancement or improvement carries with it an inherent appreciation of the necessity of suffering to achieve the vision. The act of improving yourself and your surroundings means a difficult path of trial-and-error, mistakes, learning, and overcoming challenges. This aspiration requires resilience to be able to persist.

So, an acceptance of the necessity of suffering and expectations of such results in a constructive attitude to challenges. Therefore, a resilient vision creates a constructive and realistic mindset that is better suited to achieve the vision itself.

Contrast this with the vision *'To be happy'*, and you can see how that the latter results in a fragile mindset. Such a mindset is not prepared for the eventual shocks of life. Disruptions and challenges do not contribute to happiness, therefore they are experienced as unwelcome events, often resulting in frustration, anger and depression. This further moves one away from the vision of happiness. It is self-defeating, simply because it grates against our natural experience of life as an ongoing struggle for improvement.

Some philosophical systems focus on the complete elimination of suffering (such as bioethical abolitionism), however this may overlook the virtue of suffering that leads to personal and societal advancement. Most would consider studying for a tough exam to be stressful, but the outcome of this suffering is valuable. There will always be events and disruptions to our lives that we need to learn how to grow from.

Let's extend the previous metaphor of *your vision* as the lake on the mountain feeding the rivers down below, keeping the ecosystem of you alive. You will always face storms of adversity. If you are unprepared, those stormwaters will erode the channels and leave you feeling drained. On the other hand, if you build resilience, you can channel the stormwaters back into your vision and to the areas of your life that need it the most, channelling the energy to feeds the ecosystem of your existence. This lets you use adversity as an opportunity to reaffirm your commitment to your vision and fuel your motivation to persist in achieving your ultimate goals. When life is at its hardest, that is when your vision should be most relevant. Through this process, a clear vision produces an incredibly deep sense of resilience.

A clear vision acts as a guide for all other actions in your life. Its existence makes tough decisions easier as you can measure against what has greater potential to contribute to your vision. It also drives personal development by hinting at the personal qualities that you need to achieve your vision. These are the internal attributes that allow you as a person to effect the external change that is your purpose.

Naturally, these attributes vary based on your personal vision. For example, let's say you have your sights set on solving a big technical problem that spans industries which generally don't work together well. In this case, perhaps some of the most important attributes you need is to be *knowledgeable, flexible, diplomatic,* and *persuasive.* Other goals might require you to be *influential, ambitious* and *competitive.* Sometimes the attributes you need for your vision are more personal and less professional, such as being *generous, modest, helpful* or *compassionate.*

What is interesting here is that we have the freedom to consider attributes that are useful, regardless of how socially acceptable they are. Nearly every attribute that is commonly seen as 'negative' can be modified slightly into something constructive. If there are some 'negative' attributes that come naturally to you, then through some purposeful direction they can be modified into great strengths. For example, *stubborn* can become *diligent*. *Cynical* can become *rational*. *Rebellious* can become *innovative*. *Vain* can become *valuing excellence*.

Building from an honest and authentic assessment of yourself is the strongest foundation. Consider an accurate valuation of your current self as a starting point—who are you now is not who you will always be. Instead, it is your vision of who you aim to become that really defines who you are.

With that said, each of us have all attributes to some degree or another. What's important in this concept is the specific attributes that are most conducive to the achievement of your vision. Most likely, who we are by default is not precisely who we need to be to achieve our goals. This is a logical conclusion, considering that none of us are born in our ultimate state. From birth, life is a constant process of learning and advancing. Learning from the lessons of our parents, from school, from the knocks of life, on to tertiary education, through to on-the-job training, and beyond. This means there is always room to improve as individuals.

As our knowledge of the world improves and our confidence builds through our experiences, our personality slightly shifts over time. You might not notice it yourself, but someone who hasn't seen you in ten years might comment on how you are now much more *outgoing* or *focused* than before, for example. This usually happens as an organic process. Although there is particular power in purposefully developing some attributes within yourself, since it's not necessarily the case that we will always improve. Purposeful striving towards a vision reduces the need of relying on chance to become the person you need to be.

Note that this contrasts with the all-too-common platitude 'Be yourself'. While there is generally noble intention when this advice is given, it is rarely helpful and certainly not conducive to personal improvement. Usually when this advice is given, what the recipient actually needs is to be *better* than themselves. At any given moment, we can decide the level of effort we want to put into the activity we are engaged in, and in which way we want to put our effort in. If you are heading into a meeting, you can choose if you want to be more energetic or more calm, more directive or more cooperative, more rational or more emotive. Quite often, we don't realise that we have this choice, but we implicitly make these decisions through the expression of our default personality. So, the real question is simple: are you getting the right results? More specifically, are your existing attributes moving you closer to achieving your vision?

Another way to explore personal development is to consider your vision and ask *'If I was more like this, would I be able to...'*? Answers to these questions will help you identify where there is room for purposeful change—essentially, ways you can specifically improve to become the kind of person who is more likely to achieve your purpose.

Back to the previous point, we all possess all attributes to some small or large extent. What this means is that we are identifying which of our existing attributes need to be enhanced. It is about strategically enhancing what you already have. This concept allows us to take the old platitude of *'Be yourself'*, and upgrade it into *'Become yourself'*. You already have the qualities you need, to some extent, so now expand those qualities into that future conception of yourself. Rather than focus on who you are now, focus on becoming that vision of yourself that will achieve your greater ambitions.

This vision of yourself is not a simple copy of someone else, rather it is still you—it is the *future you* that you are becoming through purposeful development. Let's explore two important aspects to this concept of *becoming yourself.*

First, the idea of becoming yourself intuitively focuses your attention on the future. For example, if your motto is to *'Be yourself'*, then when heading into a meeting you might focus on handling the meeting similarly to how you did in the past. In contrast, a future-oriented focus lets you consider how you can handle this meeting differently. Specifically, what small adjustments you can make in your behaviour to get more useful results. The link here to resilience is clear, because you'd place an inherent focus on continual advancement while using experiences/adversity to strategically grow into a stronger version of yourself, someone better able to roll with the punches.

Additionally, focusing on improving specific attributes is something you can pursue regardless of context. This makes the pursuit itself resilient as it is less likely to be invalidated by external circumstances. For example, moving to a different company would not stop your pursuit, but could instead be an opportunity to accelerate your personal development.

Second, the mechanism that enables becoming yourself lies within the neurobiology of the brain. The brain doesn't change in sudden jumps. Instead, neural pathways build incrementally over time, through practice and repetition. Someone with a short temper doesn't just wake up calm one day. Instead, it takes effort and repetition to practise remaining calm. It's the same with other attributes. Taking a classic example, confidence doesn't come from wishing for it—instead it comes from acting like you are confident. While some might experience this as *pretending*, it is actually *practice*. It is through constantly practising in an effortful and purposeful way that neural structures are built in the brain. That's what makes this practised confidence natural.

Over time, the practised behaviour becomes the default behaviour. There is no such thing as *'Fake it till you make it'*, there is only *practice*. Therefore, *'Become yourself'* takes advantage of the mechanism of neural development—to let your brain build the neural structures of your vision of yourself. This is how you physically become yourself.

To reiterate, it's not simply a mental activity, but instead physical neural structures that you are creating and strengthening. The key concept is to be aware of which attributes would be most useful to achieving your vision, followed by actively practising those attributes every day.

With a vision established that represents your own purpose and the personal attributes you need to achieve it, you can now look towards goals. After all, as a top-down approach to achieving your own definition of success, your vision is the most important part. It guides your goals, as well as your implementation of the domains of resilience.

In business, the company vision and strategy usually receives a great deal of attention. Company strategy drives projects, which must prove value to the strategy. As new input and data is received, the strategy is refined and adjusted. It's interesting that in the business world, we understand that strategy drives tactical goals to achieve success, though in our personal lives we rarely take such a structured approach. Indeed, as individuals, we generally skip the strategy and jump into starting projects. Though as any business leader knows, not having a clear strategy is a sure path to failure.

The evidence of people skipping on the strategy (read 'vision') component is evident—millions of people every day in their 30s, 40s, 50s, 60s, wake up and think *'What am I doing?'*, *'How did I get here?'*, *'Is this all there is?'* It's the classic mid-life crisis—that moment of existential angst that eventually hits us. Usually we manage to find something to quickly distract us from this terrible line of thought. Why? Because it is hard and it is scary to think about the purpose of our own lives.

As with the strategy of a company—it is scary to make a decision. Sure, everyone has ideas of what the company strategy should be, but how many have the guts to commit to a course and stick around as leader when the going gets tougher than projected?

The same fear hits us when considering our own purpose, but unlike a business, there's nothing pushing us to commit to a course. Truth is, we can get through life just fine without ever setting a personal vision. In fact, a great many people do just that. So why bother? What a vision does, quite plainly, is increase the probability of you achieving something great. And that is the true question—do you want to achieve something great?

You will have your own definition of what 'great' means to you, though I would venture to suggest that it be something not simply beneficial to yourself, but also improves the world in some way. This adds deeper meaning and longevity to a vision. This sets nihilistic resilience apart from goal-directed resilience—that desire to achieve something, regardless of how tough it gets. Here we see the parallels, where if you are willing to overcome the mental resistance to defining a vision for yourself, then it will make you a stronger leader. If you're willing to take that leap and commit to a vision, then you secure a personal strategy that can drive your own tactical projects to achieve your vision. These are your goals.

Clarifying goals

Where a vision is long-term and broad enough to be resistant to invalidation, goals are more concrete. In a personal sense, realising our vision relies on the accumulated accomplishment of specific goals along the way. While important in that sense, this deliberate interpretation of your vision has another important purpose.

Functioning together, your vision and goals play an important role in creating a sense of predictability around you as a leader. This is not predictability in a negative sense—instead predictability experienced by your staff as *reliability*. Patterns are the speciality of the brain. As an expert pattern recognition machine, every person's brain looks for predictability to help it make sense of the world. This is a subconscious process of the brain, meaning that people often don't realise how important predictability is for their own fundamental need for control and orientation. Particularly in organisations, this is important.

Your staff, peers, and superiors subconsciously look for predictability as the foundation of an emotion experienced as *trust*. They are able to trust you because they can predict how you would respond in different circumstances. It gives them confidence in approaching you with a difficult situation, and helps them determine what type of advice you might give when faced with more ambiguous situations.

Naturally, they desire a positive type of predictability, where they can rely on you to improve a situation, rather than overcomplicate it. Much of this is about clarity. People desire clarity from their leaders. People bring issues and ambiguous situations to their leaders because they don't have clarity about what to do next.

Your ability to provide clarity comes from your interpretation and understanding of the company strategy and goals, as well as your self-knowledge. Simply, you need a clear understanding of yourself to be able to provide clarity to others. Your personal clarity comes from understanding your own vision and translating that into specific goals. Combine this with an integration of how your own vision and goals fit with the strategy and projects of the organisation you're in, and you have a platform from where you can effectively provide clarity to others. Essentially, they will be able to understand where you are coming from, and come to rely on you to provide clarity when needed.

Clarity starts with yourself. With a vision defined, the next step is to take stock of where you are in your life, and what goals you currently have. These goals can be both on a conscious and subconscious level. Quite often, we accumulate many goals without realising it, and before we know it, we are overstressed and overwhelmed as numerous goals compete against each other for our ever-dwindling free time.

On first thought, we might not even think of them as goals. Instead, they may manifest as needs, duties, obligations, problems, and so on. Whatever they are, they compete for your time and often add to the perception of stress. The first step is to identify these, then prioritise and clarify.

A simple way to start is by looking through the main areas of your life and uncovering goals in each. For now, the aim is only to identify them, and not yet to determine whether they are the *right* goals. Use the question sets below as thinking prompts to uncover goals.

First, think about your family life.

- What's been happening around the house?
- Are you moving house or making big changes?
- Recently had a baby or have small children?
- Is parenthood taking up lots of time?
- Do you have many family gatherings and activities to attend?
- Do you need to look after a sick or elderly family member?
- Are there family problems or tragedies that you need to deal with?
- Are you in a new relationship?
- Do you want a new relationship?
- Do you want out of a relationship?
- Does an existing relationship need some help or attention?
- Are you entering a different phase of your life and need to make some changes?
- Are you preparing for some other big change?

Second, think about work life. Given the amount of time you spend at work, this should be an important one. Note that this exercise is not about listing every project you have going at work. Instead, this is about your personal goals in relation to work. For example, consider these questions:

- Are you working towards a promotion, bonus, or another specific target?
- Are aiming to spend more, or less time at work?
- Are you actively looking to change jobs?
- Are there major changes you are looking to make about your work, or how you work?
- Is your job becoming more demanding, leaving little time for anything else?
- Is stress at work mounting and becoming more difficult to manage?

Third, think about friends, acquaintances and colleagues.

- Do you have friends going through tough times and you are helping them through it?
- Are you actively working on building a larger network of acquaintances and colleagues?
- Do you have people in your life who are having a negative impact on your life, and need to be managed?
- Is it very important to you to often go out with friends?
- Do you plan to go to more social events and outings?
- Or do you want to cut down on social activities?
- Is there a lot of politics between colleagues that you need to deal with?
- Are you planning a big event with friends?

Fourth, think about health, hobbies and side projects.

- Are you focusing on improving your health and fitness?
- Do you have health issues that you need to work on?
- Do you have a hobby or side project that is important to you?
- Is there a project in your personal life that is demanding a lot of your time?
- Do you have something outside of work that is your true passion?
- Is there something you try to spend time on that is very meaningful

to you?

- Do you/are you aiming to play sports at a serious level?
- Are you aiming for personal development, like developing personal resilience, or other ways of improving yourself?
- Do you have a goal of becoming more dependable, or working on another personal attribute?

There are both obvious and hidden goals in all of these. Think through each and note down current goals in each category. Even if it's something that doesn't feel like a goal but it takes up a lot of time, write it down. For example, if you have a child who is serious about sport and you are spending a lot of time helping with training, taking them to games, helping with coaching, and so on, then there is a hidden goal about helping your child succeed in their sport. I highly recommend writing down these on paper or spreadsheet to help with the next step.

Now it's time to make some tough choices—you need to prioritise these goals. Prioritising goals is a fundamentally important task, but is something we are inherently bad at doing. We tend to randomly prioritise goals as different situations come up, resulting in inconsistent actions and internal conflict. These days, there are so many activities that we want to fit in at the same time. Work life, family, friends, hobbies, and everything else, constantly compete with each other and we have to choose what we will give our attention.

When you have not prioritised your goals, it becomes much harder to deal with this conflict, as you have to prioritise *in the moment,* when you are under pressure. When the brain is under this kind of pressure, the impulsive brain takes over and makes less strategic decisions. The outcome is that we make bad decisions about our goals, decisions that don't fully take into account long-term impact.

Instead, prioritising goals ahead of time puts you in a stronger position. When a situation comes up where two goals compete, you will already have decided which one should take priority over the other. Prioritisation enables you to quickly make decisions under pressure and so makes it easier for you to achieve your most important goals.

Once your goals are prioritised, being a goal-driven person becomes extremely useful; tough choices become easier and you become more true to yourself. It becomes clear who you really are and what is important to you. It allows you to make a real commitment to achieve your goals. It realigns your expectations, so that when you make tough choices, you understand your decision and you have a greater appreciation for the outcome.

Here it will help to take a moment to clarify between *goals* and *responsibilities*. To illustrate, think of this phrase: *'Family comes first'*. You have probably heard this a lot, and may even have said it yourself, but what does it actually mean? To explain, let's distinguish between goals and responsibilities. Goals are the big projects we spend most of our time on. Goals need constant time and effort for us to be able to achieve the desired outcome. Responsibilities, on the other hand, are important commitments and obligations that don't necessarily require constant attention, but you would drop everything else if something came up.

So, what does *'family comes first'* mean to you? Does it mean that you aim to spend more waking hours with your family? This makes it a goal. Or does it mean that if a problem came up, family takes priority over everything else? This makes it a responsibility.

To better understand the distinction, let's take another example. Say you have a goal to build a huge outdoor model train set in your backyard. The scale of it means that the biggest chunk of your waking hours go into this goal. However, in the grand scheme if things, it's not the most important thing in the world. In fact, if something came up that needed attention, you could drop the model trains and come back to it later. Therefore, the goal gets more time overall, while the responsibility takes priority when needed.

So, it becomes important to clarify meanings when you think of something like *family comes first*. Is it a case of you being there when they need you, though meanwhile you have other big goals that you spend most of your time on? Or is spending more time with family in itself a major goal? Goals and responsibilities both need to be prioritised together, while understanding their different nature.

Take some time to clarify the nuances of your goals and your responsibilities. Within your list, write down next to each item whether it is more a goal or a responsibility. Clarifying which is which is useful, since it helps you to clearly communicate with your partner, family and friends about what is important to you. This then helps you set expectations with them. Importantly, it allows you to identify and deal with potential conflicts before they arise, especially any misaligned expectations between you and those close to you.

Back to the list; it's now time to prioritise these. This is naturally difficult because we are forced to choose between things without a clear basis for comparison. For now, simply rank them from one to ten, with 'one' being the highest priority. We'll further explore the validity of the priority ranking in the next step.

SMART goals

With your list prioritised, likely containing both goals and responsibilities, it's now time to explore the goals in the list. Just about every manager is aware of what SMART goals are. Naturally, this is a useful technique in a personal sense as well, although here we will look at a slightly different aspect of this technique, as used in business.

SMART is an abbreviation for Specific, Measurable, Attainable, Relevant, and Timeframe. Specific means avoiding vague goals, such as *'Become a good leader'*. Be accurate in your language, such as *'Host strategy update meetings for all staff'*. That's still a bit vague in terms of Measurability, so let's add *'Host daily strategy update meetings for all staff'*. Next is Attainable, meaning aim for something realistic and achievable. Looking at our previous statement, it's probably too ambitious. Let's change it to *'Host fortnightly strategy update meetings for all staff'*. For the moment, we will skip the Relevant step and go straight to Timeframe. When do we aim to do this? Perhaps *'Host fortnightly strategy update meetings for all staff, starting next week'*. This is all quite obvious, though let's get back to 'Relevant'.

Relevance is arguably the most important part of this process, yet it receives the least amount of attention. This is about whether your goals are indeed relevant and congruent with your vision. The question for each prioritised goal is simple—would working on this goal bring you closer to your vision? Usually we don't tend to think of relevance, instead taking on new personal projects and goals simply because we 'felt like it'. For some goals, this might be entirely appropriate, where we give ourselves the space to explore activities that are not directly connected to some vision. However, if you are aiming to achieve something great, then you need clarity and congruence.

In this sense, congruence means that your goals align to, and support, your vision. What's more, goals should also be congruent with each other. Quite often we might not realise when goals are working against each other. As an extreme example, consider someone who wants to run marathons, while also trying to compete in bodybuilding competitions. These two goals are polar opposites, and moving closer to one moves this person away from the other. The result could be frustration, anger, or even depression.

Look through your top goals and see if they are congruent. Do they support your vision? Do the goals support each other? Goals that are congruent with each other have the benefit of multiplying the effort that you put in, since moving closer to one goal might also move you closer to other congruent goals. It is this overarching alignment that enables us to achieve great things, as we then have clarity and congruence.

As you look through your list, are there perhaps some goals that are not congruent with your vision or purpose? Are there perhaps other goals that are low in priority, but more congruent and therefore might need to be reprioritised? Take a moment and consider if you are spending your time on the right things.

While you're looking through these, think back to when we talked about outcome versus process. In business we're usually focused on outcome, but in our personal lives it is mostly the process that is important, more so than the outcome. For example, it's not the outcome of having built that big model train that is all-important, it is about appreciating all the time and effort you are spending on the details and design decisions that make it worthwhile. It's not the achievement of spending more time with family that matters, instead it is the process of being in the moment with them and enjoying your time together.

I like having the SMART acronym printed as smaRt, to highlight the extraordinary importance of relevance and congruence, especially when used in a personal context. But there's another dimension to congruence that you should be suspecting by now. This dimension is about how your high priority goals fit with the fundamental needs of your brain. Remember, your brain has a major need for connection, control and motivation. With that in mind, look back at your high priority goals.

Thinking of Connection, do your goals put you in touch with other people, where you engage in meaningful activities with them? Thinking of Control and Orientation, do your goals enhance your understanding of the world and bring you relevant options you can act on? Thinking of Motivation, do your goals include activities that you enjoy, are meaningful to you, and work towards your vision and what is important to you?

Now look for patterns in your goals. Is there perhaps a dearth of goals with any enjoyable activities in them? Or perhaps there are very few that put you in meaningful contact with other people? Having gaps such as these means that eventually, your brain will feel a void and the pursuit of your vision will feel hollow. Something that should be meaningful will evaporate and you'll be left grasping at air, trying to figure out why you do not feel fulfilled, even though you're having so much success elsewhere.

The needs of the brain are fundamental—we cannot simply ignore them or pretend that we are strong enough to overcome these basic desires. If you need to, revise certain goals to make sure the needs of your brain are addressed. Sometimes this may simply mean adjusting a goal. For example, to add Connection to a fitness goal, instead of running alone, jog with a friend.

It often feels like there is simply too much to do and we can't fit it all in. One strategy to deal with this is to place a higher value on efficiency. That is, aim to make every regular task that you need to do, but might not enjoy that much, work a bit more efficiently than last time. Cutting out unnecessary tasks and doing the essential parts faster can help you achieve much more in less time.

The trick here is to set the process of becoming more efficient as the goal, giving you something to aim for. The effect of this is that you turn a mindless and boring activity into something focused, where you are more mindful of what you are doing. For example, with vacuuming the house, you might start to pay much more attention to how you do it and the results you get as you determine ways to do it more efficiently. Naturally, you can also multitask in these situations, such as listening to an audiobook on headphones while vacuuming. There are so many opportunities to become more efficient once you start looking, helping you achieve more overall.

The other side to this is sacrifice. Be realistic in what does not fit with your overall goals. For example, if you already have a full schedule but would also like to learn the cello and practise mandarin, then perhaps there is something that needs to go. Measure these new items against your goals and always make sure what you include as goals are congruent. The rest can be sacrificed. The trick with sacrifice is to be clear why you are *not* doing something, so you don't regret the decision. Years later, you should always be able to look back and say '*I didn't do that because I was doing this more important thing instead*'. Sure, that more important thing might not work out, but you took a risk, ran with it, and you will learn from the experience and do things better next time. Nowhere in that thought process is there value in regret. You only have this moment and beyond, so use what you've learned in the past to live a better future.

This process of congruent goal clarification and prioritisation forms the basis of a highly-disciplined mindset. As you'd expect, this is not a one-off process either. Instead, year after year, you should revisit your vision and your goals to revise as necessary. As you achieve your initial goals and learn, set new goals and keep advancing. Aim for consistency of thought. That means bringing the same disciplined thinking, goal-setting and prioritisation to both your personal and professional lives.

Calibrating self-assurance

Being a leader requires a substantial amount of self-assurance. In terms of resilience, this self-assurance is what allows you to stay the course when challenges arise. Frequently, people will look to you for guidance in ambiguous circumstances. In these situations, you need trust in your own judgment so as to make a confident determination that in turn inspires confidence in your staff. However, it's not as simple as being the 'decider', since none of us has a perfect understanding of the entire scenario we are facing.

Considering the place of an executive in a large organisation, there could be hundreds of people aware of different aspects of a particular problem. An executive who then decides on an option to address the problem is never going to know all the intricacies that all those people involved are aware of. Disregarding the validity of all this information would indicate overconfidence. However, seeking too much of this information bogs you down in an unnecessary level of detail. Therefore, maintaining a level of self-assurance that is both useful for making accurate decisions and constructive for your own wellbeing takes careful calibration.

Self-assurance feeds into the need of your brain for enhanced self-esteem, alongside the other fundamental needs: control, connection and motivation. However, there are additional factors that affect your self-esteem. These include:

- your values, principles and integrity,
- how committed and decisive you are, and
- your accountability to yourself.

It's easy to see how these aspects can affect your self-perception, which informs your sense of self-worth. These aspects sit very deep within our psyche, and can be very sensitive when they are un-challenged. Constructing an impenetrable wall around us to protect this sensitive interior is no basis for resilience. Instead, we need this inner core to be strong for us to be deeply resilient. This strengthening comes through introspection and challenging yourself, as well as allowing others to challenge you. Constructively processing these challenges is what ultimately builds a solid core. You can do this by having the courage to revise your personal beliefs if new information comes around.

Rigorous self-challenge results in a deep sense of confidence due to two factors. First, it becomes less likely that someone would present some concept that you haven't yet considered. Second, if you are presented with a concept that threatens a deeply-held personal belief, you will be better practised in processing the concept in a constructive way.

The type of beliefs we are talking about here are things like your belief about the fundamental nature of people and the nature of the world. From an executive perspective, it can include the nature of business and the nature of people management. There's a simple way to consider where your mindset is at currently. Think about someone challenging a closely-held belief of yours, like your choice of political party. Can you remain rational, walk through your reasoning for your choice, and be open to consider any counterarguments? Or do you prefer to lash out at the audacity of the other person to dare question your choice? If it's the latter, there's a good chance that some introspection and personal exploration is required to strengthen your core beliefs.

The relevance of this is in how it flows through to your nature as a leader. Your current state will determine if you need to rule through fear, or preferably, lead through rationality. One inspires a healthy culture, and one does just the opposite.

Constructive introspection is how we teach the amygdala in the brain to not unnecessarily activate the fight-or-flight response. Someone questioning our choice of political party is not a threat to our lives, and thus should not increase blood flow to the muscles. Obviously, this would be the wrong physiological response, but it takes conscious effort from us to rewire the brain so we can respond constructively. Engaging in this rewiring helps us to gain more confidence in ourselves and our positions, which in turn improves our sense of self-worth.

Self-questioning also strengthens our own principles and values. This is because we can mentally imagine ourselves in tough situations and think through how we would act, and how we should act. Maintaining a strict sense of morality requires an awareness of your own concept of ethics. Without this awareness, you might only find out what kind of person you are when a challenging scenario arises.

For example, you are made aware of a culture of sexual harassment within your division, though there's no concrete evidence yet. It is a month before bonus determinations, and drawing attention to these allegations might severely impact your bonus, as well as draw media attention to you and your division. Given the lack of clear evidence, you could push it aside for now if you wanted, but you risk it blowing up if evidence comes out in the meantime while you sat on it. Or you could start an investigation immediately and risk your bonus. Do you have a code of ethics that determines what you would do?

Your own personal clarity here determines whether employees would be willing to come to you with problems like these. If they know you would act with integrity, then you can build a more open culture. It comes back to the sense of trust that you build.

Integrity also relates to commitments. In other words, how you hold yourself accountable to what you say and promise. When you say you will do something, how seriously do you take that commitment? Think of a commitment to friends or family. If you say you will do something, would you move heaven and earth to keep that commitment, or is it more a case of *'I might do it if the planets accidentally align'*. When you say you *will* do something (emphasis here on 'will' as an indication of commitment), then you should measure the commitment against your prioritised goals to determine the extent of sacrifices you would make to keep your commitment.

The word 'will' should be saved for those occasions where you are willing to make big sacrifices to keep your word. If that's not the case, use the word 'may' (or similar) instead. This is important both personally and as a leader, since it will determine the level to which people can rely on you. Perceptions of low reliability mean that when you say you 'will' do something, as soon as you leave the room, they'll remark about how 'will' means 'maybe'.

Regarding self-worth, how you keep commitments to yourself is crucially important. If you tell yourself you will do something, then that is a promise you must absolutely keep. In this way, you are confirming your reliability and worth to yourself—that you are worthy to do the things you say you will. However, how do commitments to yourself compare to commitments made to others.

Specific scenarios naturally vary, but as a general rule, always keep your commitments to yourself first. This might seem selfish at first glance, but there are important reasons for this rule. First, if you are constantly sacrificing yourself in favour of others, then you are likely to build up a subconscious resentment towards others, as you 'always do things for them but never for yourself'. This can be personally damaging in the long term. Second, keeping commitments to yourself will practise your ability to keep your promises, allowing you to eventually make commitments to others with more confidence. The outcome is that by helping yourself first, you become better at helping others.

The myth of work-life balance

Thinking about all these commitments and working towards a grand vision, it may be natural to think about the impact on a sense of work-life balance. The idea of a balance between 'work' and 'life' is one that has become pervasive in business language. But, it's also somewhat misleading. Intuitively, work-life balance could be eight hours of work, eight hours of leisure, and eight hours of sleep. That seems quite balanced. This is a very rudimentary view, but often our thinking on this concept is primarily about time—spending too much time at work equals an imbalance.

Perhaps the demands of work and family time should fit into these nice, neat bands of time, so we can have a good balance. However, simply balancing the hours is not suddenly going to give you happiness and a sense of wellness. In fact, someone could have a perfectly 'balanced' life, or be working just one day a week, and still feel depressed. There's no direct relationship here. Instead, feeling that there is an imbalance is more likely about a different deficiency. Given our new knowledge about the brain and its needs, we can clarify this concept and find out what really produces 'work-life balance'.

Quite simply, it's not about the hours. Instead it's about whether you are meeting the basic needs of your brain. Your brain needs *connection* with people and to share meaningful experiences. It needs a sense of *control* through actionable options, orientation (through a valid model of the world), and a clear purpose. It needs *motivation* through engaging in tasks you enjoy. This much you know, but here's the surprising thing—you can get all three elements through work. And if you do get all three through work, then you can work a surprising number of hours without feeling the effects of stress and burnout.

> Frank Lowy, at 84, said: "I work all the time; whatever I do, I do it, and I don't necessarily look at it as work. You could say the Auschwitz project was work, or the Lowy Institute is work, or Westfield is work, or the football is work. It is life."

The presence of all three of these factors lead to self-esteem enhancement, also known as an *enhanced environment*. If you can create an enhanced environment for yourself at work, then you will feel like you have a good balance, even if you work 60 hours a week. In this state, you are working towards something meaningful, connecting with people, and you enjoy the challenge of what you do.

Conversely, it's now easy to see how someone might perceive an imbalance between 'work' and 'life'. If your work leaves you isolated most of the time and you have little connection with others, then that will leave your brain crying out for time away from work. If there's nothing you enjoy about your job, then it's easy to see how that situation won't last. If you feel as if you have no control, perhaps experiencing accountability without authority, then your brain won't put up with that for long either. Deficiencies in our work roles—in relation to the fundamental needs of the brain—is what causes the perception of imbalance. It has nothing to do with hours, but instead with how work meaningfully contributes to our basic needs.

Understanding this is important, as it helps you to diagnose more accurately what is affecting you, and also to diagnose what is affecting others. If someone comes to you saying their *work-life balance is off*, you now have a framework through which you can generate questions to discover the true cause.

It should now seem natural that, should you have something big that you want to achieve, it would require a great investment of time and effort. In these situations, we often feel like we need to disregard the hope of having a 'work-life balance'. However, through understanding the needs of the brain and how they contribute to this, we can still attain a sense of balance, provided we factor these basic needs into the work we are doing. It may simply be a case of making sure you involve more people in your pursuit, so you may share connection. Or perhaps learning to enjoy more aspects of the work you do, helping you to increase motivation. Remaining conscious of these needs allows for sustained high performance.

Composure

Everyone knows a manager or leader who is always in some foul mood, usually to the extent that others in the team avoid interaction. Sometimes this is more nuanced, where a manager is usually in a great mood, until a team member brings bad news—then there is trouble. These are Composure-related problems that impact the culture and performance of a team. In effect, if your team is worried about your reaction should they bring bad news, then they would be more likely to hide things rather than come forward.

This means important risks might not be managed effectively, or poor solutions could be implemented as measures to secretly mitigate potential impact. Here, your ability to maintain your own composure is important—not just for your team, but also for your own wellbeing.

Emotion regulation

Emotional responses have a strong impact on both your ability to think clearly and your physiological health. Emotional responses such as anxiety, fear and rage activate the impulsive brain—through hormones such as adrenaline and cortisol—raising blood pressure and putting stress on your system. This stress can add up over time, producing psychological problems both in and outside of work. For example, chronic stress supresses the immune system, leading to more infections and downtime due to illness. Stress can lead to heart problems and high blood pressure. You might also experience frequent skin problems, like eczema, or chronic back pain due to constant activation of stabilising muscles.

All these effects are due to the body keeping itself in a fight-or-flight state. While the state itself is physical, it comes about due to mental processes. And as we now know, this physical state in turn affects further mental processes. In particular, being in fight-or-flight mode reduces activation of the frontal cortex, where smart thinking takes place, and increases activation of the impulsive brain.

Naturally, this state is not conducive to strategic thinking and remaining goal-oriented. The challenge then falls on us to manage these emotional responses effectively. Emotion management applies to both in-the-moment stress management, as well as proactive adjustment of our responses to situations.

Emotions are generally not something we think about from a thematic perspective. Being able to regain and maintain emotional composure is an important aspect of resilience, so it's useful to take a closer look at the nature of emotions and how we understand them. First, thinking of emotions in a general sense, we should recognise that all emotions are inherently useful. That's not to say all emotions are constructive, but rather that emotions are useful in what they tell us about our underlying beliefs and expectations.

Given that emotions form on the basis of ingrained beliefs and expectations about ourselves and the world, these emotions therefore provide clues for us about what to investigate within ourselves. For example, if you feel anxious in some situations, or get filled with rage when something doesn't go your way, then there is perhaps good cause to look deeper and find out why the emotions come up. Think of this in terms of self-talk—the language you use when thinking to yourself. It should not be a case of *I shouldn't feel that way*, but rather, *why do I feel that way?*

Discovering the origin of emotions will help you decide whether each emotion is useful in the pursuit of your vision. In other words, do the natural consequences of your emotional response bring you closer to your goals? If the answer is 'no', then there is a prompt to change. Important for this is developing your ability to accurately identify your own emotions, known as *emotional granularity*. This strategy has been found to be an effective way to mitigate the effects of disruptive emotions. Emotional granularity is not designed to help you rattle off a long list of emotions, but rather to accurately pick out the one specific emotion that best describes what you are currently feeling.

The effectiveness of this approach comes from an internal ability to distance yourself from an emotion once you have identified it. Once you internally acknowledge the emotion, you have a choice in that moment—continue with the emotion, or alter your response. With the emotion identified, you can step back and consider how the situation is affecting you and if your response is constructive.

This skill is particularly important when facing adversity and challenges through life, as disruptive emotions reduce our ability to act strategically. Naturally, this ability is founded on an emotional vocabulary and framework through which to conduct identification.

As a framework, we can think of emotions existing across two axes. On one axis, emotions range from *pleasure* to *displeasure*, depending on the pleasantness of the emotion. On the other axis, we have *arousal*, ranging from low to high. This is not just for emotions like *love* and *lust*, but instead it's about how charged the emotion is. For example, *boredom* would be a low arousal emotion, while *rage* is a high arousal emotion.

From here, we can distinguish how constructive an emotion is. Let's identify four broad categories of emotions:

- *Constructive emotions* are usually positive in nature and are conducive to wellbeing. However, even though these are positive, they are not always useful. For example, witnessing a great injustice and feeling 'happy' is not going to motivate you to right the wrong.
- *Neutral emotions* in themselves are generally not motivating until they combine with or transition to another emotion. For example, feeling *confused* doesn't motivate you to do something until it perhaps switches over to *frustration*, at which point you are subconsciously pushed to take action.
- *Disruptive emotions* are usually not helpful to resilience and wellbeing, since they activate the Impulsive Brain too strongly and thus reduce your ability to think clearly. These are your prompts to investigate your expectations and beliefs: why are you experiencing this emotion? Is the response useful? When you feel these, it is

important to label them to help shift your mindset.

- *Constructive displeasure emotions* are strong motivators, but require active guidance so that you use them effectively. Here, witnessing an injustice may provoke 'righteous anger', motivating you to take action and set the situation right.

Disruptive emotions are labelled as such because they change cognitive firing patterns. High-arousal disruptive emotions have familiar effects. Cortical blood flow to higher-order cerebral processes reduce, blood flow to the muscles increase, along with heart rate. This causes skin to flush, as well as sweating and a racing breath. It becomes difficult to speak, there's a dryness in the mouth. The whole body is on edge and ready to jump due to all the adrenaline and cortisol pumping in the blood. In short, not a very useful state to be in while at work. Of course, this is not an all-or-nothing state. Larger releases of adrenaline will have more pronounced effects.

In fact, we might frequently be experiencing this state without really noticing, simply because it has become a somewhat 'default' state. In line with the adaptive nature of the brain, we may adapt to stressful conditions to exist in that state. The primary skill to develop is to notice when these symptoms strike. You may not consciously feel afraid or anxious, but subconsciously the emotion is creeping up and activating panic stations in the background. In these cases, you might start to notice that you are sweating, or are taking shallow breaths.

Any of the previously mentioned symptoms can alert you to what your brain is up to. Identifying a symptom gives you a chance to step back, label the emotion, understand what's happening and regain composure. Even if it's just taking a few deep breaths, you now have the awareness to centre yourself.

It's here we need to remember the inherent usefulness of every emotion. While disruptive emotions can cause you to take destructive actions, the emotions themselves are useful in the sense that they highlight an underlying belief or expectation. Experiencing a disruptive emotion is an opportunity to question yourself about why you are experiencing that emotion, and if the reason for experiencing it is valid. This is especially important if the emotion is *not* motivating you to take constructive action to move you closer to your goals. If this is the case, then it becomes necessary to change the underlying belief, so that in the future you don't get upset over something unimportant.

The key here is never to deny an emotion. If you feel an emotion, be honest with yourself that you are feeling it. Then start exploring and asking yourself why you are feeling that emotion. Ask yourself if this event relates to your goals, and if it is worth getting worked up about. Deal with the underlying cause of the emotion.

Beyond disruptive emotions, previously we used the example of washing dishes to distinguish between *disruptive* emotions and *constructive displeasure* emotions. There, the constructive displeasure emotion 'anger' might cause us to wash dishes faster, while the disruptive emotion 'rage' might cause us to smash the dishes. This helps illustrate the difference in usefulness, as one can be channelled strategically, while the other results in a loss of control and is followed by negative effects.

What's important to keep in mind with constructive displeasure emotions is that you still need to guide their application. They are not constructive by default. For example, using anger to motivate people at work might succeed in motivating them in that moment, while in the long run damaging the culture of the organisation. Instead of directing displeasure emotions at people, direct these emotions toward situations. For example, if you are frustrated with something, make it clear that you are frustrated with the situation and not with the people involved. This helps to diffuse tension, reduce impulsive brain activation, and increase strategic problem-solving.

At the same time, the goal is not to constantly feel 'positive' emotions, since these may eventually coalesce into constant relaxation. While that may sound fantastic to you, it is a very low motivational state where you don't take much action to improve yourself, you don't set goals and don't grow. Meanwhile, the environment around you shifts and changes. Soon you find yourself drifting from the pleasure-end of the scale to the displeasure-end, going through 'apathetic' to 'bored' and possibly even through to 'depressed'.

Setting goals creates a sense of incongruence between your current state and where you want to be. This naturally evokes some of the constructive displeasure emotions, such as 'frustration' and 'annoyance'. In this context, these emotions are useful since they motivate you to do something, which in this case is to work towards your goals. As you see results, you shift towards constructive emotions, such as 'determined' and 'excitement'. Then, over time, you may go back to constructive displeasure when you face difficulties along the way.

While this process can seem somewhat painful, overall it is constructive. You are taking the right actions to keep working towards your goals and constantly improving yourself. Having an appreciation for this dance between positivity and constructive displeasure will give you more perspective when you do face difficulty along the way, as you'll know that it is useful and helps you achieve your goals.

Modifying bias

What we've worked on so far provides the foundation for the next part, which include the true mediators of the Composure domain. These include mental skills, such as reappraisal to modify biases, which we will explained.

The concept of *unconscious bias* has gained in popularity in recent years, helping people understand that their own way of seeing the world is not necessarily the *only* way. There are many ways in which each situation can be interpreted, and it's easy to understand once we see how the brain's signals are processed.

In the brain itself, sensory input is routed centrally through a structure called the *thalamus*. Here we find a cluster of nuclei, from where signals from the skin, muscles, internal organs, eyes, ears, and so on converge. The thalamus communicates these signals through to all areas of the brain, including the amygdala and hippocampus, to determine what—out of the vast amount of sensory input—is worthy of our attention. Over many years, these sensory input pathways adjust, based on patterns that are subconsciously recognised.

For example, if as a child you've noticed that a raised eyebrow is usually followed by an outburst of anger, then you may develop a high sensitivity to raised eyebrows. Seeing a raised eyebrow might evoke a subconscious trepidation in you. Meanwhile, your colleague who didn't have that experience has made no such connection, resulting in their brain not really taking note of raised eyebrows. Both of you could be in the same meeting where you noticed a raised eyebrow. You consequently interpret the conversation as being laden with hidden aggression, focusing on the words and body language that support this view, leading to a sense of distrust. In the meantime, your colleague noticed none of these, and thought that the meeting went just fine.

One interpretation isn't necessarily wrong and the other right, but some interpretations are certainly more useful than others. Consider the distinction between these two biases: a bias towards longing for things *to* last, versus a bias toward enjoying things *while* they last. There's a difference here again in valuing the outcome versus valuing the process. Here's another way to say it: *'Don't be sad it's over, appreciate that it existed.'*

This kind of sentiment may seem trite, but resisting the more positive mindset bleeds over into all areas of life, sometimes to devastating effect. Consider the cases of so many people who are traumatised by the loss of parent, partner or child. Many people quite literally never recover from a loss like that, enduring a lifetime of depression, mourning the loss of someone perhaps decades ago. It takes a great deal of courage after a loss like that to keep your mind focused on how glad you are that the relationship existed, rather than how sad you are that it's over.

These biases and mindsets exist as physical neural pathways. The thalamus takes all the sensory input, compares these against neural networks, and then directs your attention to what seems to be most important. The important concept here is that for our own neural networks, it's up to us to determine if we wish to keep these as they are, or consciously put effort into changing them toward what is more useful.

The path to change is aided by having clarity on your goals and always asking yourself *'What in this situation is important to my goals?'* This 'teaches' the thalamic neural pathways what to direct your attention towards, helping you become more objective and effective in the moment.

One of the most effective techniques in the Composure domain is called *reappraisal*. The concept of reappraisal is to take a disruptive emotion and reinterpret it as a positive emotion of a similar intensity.

A great example of this is feeling anxious before giving a public speech. Anxiety is a disruptive emotion that displays physical effects through activating the impulsive brain and the HPA axis—sweating, shaking, butterflies, even arteries constrict, which reduces blood flow to the brain. In a study, individuals were given different strategies to handle anxiety about public speaking. Afterwards, the strategy that showed the best results were those who reappraised their anxiety as felling *excited*.[39] Those who told themselves that what they're feeling and experiencing physically is due to *excitement* were best able to constructively use that energy to enhance their performance and have a better experience overall.

This kind of positive reinterpretation is a highly-useful mental skill that soon becomes second nature through ongoing practice. Eventually it becomes the default way that the impulsive brain thinks, resulting in an ongoing, constructive experience of the world and an inherent ability to maintain our composure in any situation.

Practising reappraisal means challenging how you think in the moment. Naturally, this requires first becoming aware of how you are currently feeling, which is where your skills around labelling emotions come into play. Once you understand your current state of mind, perhaps by noticing physical effects, then you can challenge your thinking through the following prompts:

- Think about what advice you would give someone else in the same situation.
- Think about how the situation might be a good opportunity, or how it will help you grow.

[39] Hofmann, S. G., Heering, S., Sawyer, A. T., & Asnaani, A. (2009). How to handle anxiety: The effects of reappraisal, acceptance, and suppression strategies on anxious arousal. *Behavior research and therapy*, 47(5), 389-394.

- Think about how this can be a good thing in the long run.
- Relabel the disruptive emotion to be a constructive emotion that is on a similar level of arousal. This will feel more authentic, as the feedback from your body will be similar.

In the public speaking example, you can reappraise *anxious* as *excited*. These are on a similar level of arousal, making it more believable, as opposed to trying to relabel *anxious* as *content,* which would not feel right.

You can strengthen this reappraisal by thinking through the points above to build the case for why you are excited. Why is it a good opportunity? Why might it be good in the long term? For example: *'I'm feeling so defeated after that project went wrong'* can be changed to *'I am determined to learn from this experience and make the next project work.'*

The effect of this is interesting, since being *anxious* is an Impulsive Brain emotion, the part which releases stress hormones and constricts arteries. This lowers your ability to think clearly. However, when you reappraise *anxious* as being *excited*, the arteries open up and you get better blood flow to the prefrontal cortex, helping you deal with the situation more effectively. Essentially, it is a proven way to use your mind to control physiological functions.

Be aware that reappraisal sometimes happens unintentionally. Possibly one of the most recognisable forms of reappraisal happens during a breakup, where many people turn their *love* into *hate.* The level of arousal here is still the same between the two emotions, with only the polarity being reversed. Psychologically, it's easier to reverse the polarity of love into hate, than it is to reduce the intensity of love.

Of course, just because things didn't work out, doesn't mean you now must hate each other. It's entirely possible to still love an ex-partner like an old friend. Just because a physical relationship didn't work, doesn't mean that everything else was a waste of time. This comes back to instilling a bias toward appreciating the relationship while it existed, rather than being sad that it's over. It also serves to remind that our emotional world needs constant guidance. You will see important consequences of this control when we explore Composure in the context of building a resilient culture.

The most impressive effect of practising reappraisal is that it starts to change the default emotion that you react with, after regular practice. Situations that might previously have elicited anxiety, fear, or other disruptive emotions might transform into welcome challenges. You might never feel glad that those situations arise, but you might instead feel a sense of excitement and determination to face the test that has been put in your path.

In this way, you consciously guide emotional responses to be constructive, rather than disruptive. This includes reappraising emotions in past events. An example would be looking back at a previous public speaking event that you hosted and declaring that it had been an exciting event with useful outcomes. This past reappraising may include mediating tense meetings, making decisions with high uncertainty, etc...

Choosing to revel in these challenges will result in more constructive emotions surfacing when you face these situations again in the future. This is how reappraisal influences our appraisal of future situations by modifying existing biases.

Embracing stress

Life as a leader involves a great deal of stress. Much of it exists in the form of uncertainty, lack of time and lack of resources. The reality about stress is that it is ultimately useful. Stress relieves us from idleness by pressuring us into action.

What's interesting is that our beliefs about stress itself changes how it impacts us. By examining the beliefs of nearly 30,000 people, researchers found that a belief that stress is harmful for your health resulted in a 43 percent increased risk of premature death.[40] This effect is magnified if you also perceive yourself to have high stress. For example, if you and a friend face the same situation, but you appraised the situation to be more stressful than your friend's appraisal, then you will experience more negative effects than your friend.

---

[40] Keller, A., Litzelman, K., Wisk, L. E., Maddox, T., Cheng, E. R., Creswell, P. D., & Witt, W. P. (2012). Does the perception that stress affects health matter? The association with health and mortality. *Health Psychology*, 31(5), 677.

So, how do these beliefs have such a dramatic impact? Consider a few scenarios.

> *Scenario one—traffic is crawling and cars keep cutting in front of you. Do you feel a seething frustration boiling up as you mercilessly choke the foam in the steering wheel?*
>
> *Scenario two—people turning up late to meetings and catch-ups. As time ticks away, do you consider just how utterly inconsiderate people are, flipping between emotions of shame as you stand alone pretending to look at your phone, through to suppressed rage as you think of all the times this has happened before?*
>
> *Scenario three—people not following through with promises they make. Do you become more and more convinced that people are simply untrustworthy? Are you at the same time thinking that you must be worthless for them to treat you with such disregard?*

These are commonplace occurrences, so it's not hard to imagine how the effects can accumulate over time. Responses like these produce various stress hormones. In the short term, these hormones can be protective, helping to improve immune response, for example. However, when you react this strongly to everyday situations, then the stress response becomes chronic, leading to various negative effects, like high blood pressure and reduced immune response. These add up over time to result in the 43 percent increase in risk.

Meanwhile, you could respond very differently if you choose. In traffic, you can enjoy some music. And besides, showing up a few minutes late is not the end of the world. If people are running late, then keep yourself busy by catching up on some news, or enjoy the sights. It's not like they're purposefully late. If people don't always follow through, then enjoy the challenge of figuring out what else you can do. Perhaps also make a mental note about people who are not very reliable. The point is that there are healthier ways to handle all these scenarios. Not only will it improve your health, but it will also build a more stoic attitude that helps others feel safe.

A key part of managing beliefs around stress is to maintain perspective.

It may be harsh but we only need to read details of the atrocities that happen in wars to realise that in general, what we face in our modern lives is not so bad. For even the worst things that people face in war time, there are those that make it through, so certainly we can find it within ourselves to not get upset when traffic is slow. Bringing it back to your own vision, keeping things in perspective with what you aim to achieve can also help prevent you from being affected by unimportant annoyances. This is because you can quickly determine if something is worthy of your annoyance, and if it is, the focus is then around what you will do about it.

Similarly, taking a holiday is not so much a 'reset' button to re-energise yourself, but rather a way to remind you that life is not just about working. If things don't always go your way, then the world will not stop spinning. Therefore, a holiday is a good reminder to maintain perspective and not get too worried about the small things.

In this vein, it's important to have at your disposal a set of tools to address those times when you feel overly stressed. For short-term stress, the usual tricks such as deep breathing, going for a walk, reaching out to someone, and labelling emotions can work. Reappraising emotions and the situation you are in is a more long-term technique, because it gradually changes your beliefs about stress and stressful situations, to the point where they become welcome challenges. Consider that it's far healthier to wonder what challenges the day might bring, than it is to rely on the thought of your next holiday to get you through the next six months.

What's worth keeping in mind is that it's not up to you to become totally immune to stress. Sometimes the environment itself is toxic. If the environment is legitimately toxic, then the answer might well be to get out. Before jumping ship, of course, it's important to talk to impartial people who can challenge your thinking and interpretation of the situation. Friends, family, and partners will usually take your side and reinforce your conclusions, so they may not be the best avenue to determine if an environment or situation is indeed toxic or dangerous for you. Perhaps you are misinterpreting people's signals or communications. Perhaps others are doing just great in the same situation.

This is important to work out, because if the problem is mainly related to your own beliefs, then you will simply take it along with you wherever you go. Building Composure is therefore a combination of building your own ability to regulate your internal world, as well as factoring in the various scenarios you operate in.

Reasoning

Our capacity for creative and critical thinking is the one thing that effectively sets us apart from being replaced by machines just yet. This ability is not something to take for granted, however, as it's a skill that needs to be practised and enhanced, especially for leaders. Generally, the hardest problems are brought to leaders to solve, where it is their role to factor in aspects of the problem that others might not have considered and take a position.

In leadership teams, we often see high scores in Reasoning when conducting measurement, however, there's also a much higher expectation for high Reasoning abilities in these roles. Pressure mounts because it's expected that you have an ability to remain clear-headed and think critically in even the most difficult situations. Therefore, it becomes more important to hone this ability and explore ways to keep an edge.

Thinking, through adversity

The gatekeeper to critical thinking while facing adversity is the Composure domain. Through our research we observed a strong interaction between these two, where low scores in Composure impacts people's ability to think clearly and solve problems in the heat of the moment. This is a natural outcome, as an upregulated, impulsive brain reduces blood flow to the frontal cortex, where smart thinking happens. With higher intelligence impacted, we can quickly spiral into a slight panic as we realise we are struggling to think clearly, inducing further panic.

Here we have a bi-directional relationship since developing stronger reasoning skills contributes to confidence, which helps you stay calm in a crisis. Much of this confidence comes from being more aware of your own thinking style and having different reasoning strategies given the context.

At a broad level, we can consider two thinking styles—a systematic style and an intuitive style. Systematic thinkers tend to think logically from one step to the next, e.g. 1—2—3—4—5. Intuitive thinkers tend to make intuitive leaps, e.g. 1—3—5. These two styles were identified through research on cognitive reflection. Through a test, researchers explored an ability to suppress fast and error-prone thinking in favour of slower and more accurate thinking. People tended to default to one style or the other through the normal course of their day.

It is not important whether you have one style or the other. Both have advantages and disadvantages. For example, systematic thinking is more accurate, but it is slower. Intuitive thinking is faster but more prone to errors. Therefore, what's more important is recognising your default thinking style. Then you can use this understanding of yourself to manage blind spots and recognise when you should consciously switch style given a specific problem you're facing. For example, if you are a systematic thinker and had a bad day, it might come naturally to you to logically think through every small detail of what went wrong and how bad it was. This can be quite draining, so recognising a tendency like this is important for adjusting your mindset to be more constructive. Understanding your mind this way can help you start to surround yourself with people who tend to spot things you might miss, and disrupt your unhelpful thinking behaviours.

In high-pressure situations, it's natural for there to be some stress that affects your ability to think clearly. On top of this, there is the usual leadership lifestyle, where your head is in 20 places at once, although you're still expected to quickly switch between various concepts and come up with strategy-aligned answers. Considering the brain's tendency to underperform under pressure, we can use some well-tested strategies to get back into a thoughtful mindset.

One strategy is to simplify, also known as 'explain it like I'm five'. Simplifying a conversation makes it easier for your brain to switch from unrelated, complex concepts that you were thinking about, towards the basic blocks of a new concept. On top of this, you can build to more complex concepts again.

When we work at high speed, we need simplification to accelerate concept switching. We see this at even the highest levels, where board members of major organisations need to spend a few days working through hundreds of decisions, usually with limited time for each topic and few breaks. As one topic might be totally unrelated to the next, the need to simplify, give the brain something to hold onto, and then build more complexity on is key to engaging higher-order reasoning centres in the brain.

Embracing your own need for simplicity, to speed up clear thinking, becomes more relevant as you scale an organisation. Higher up, you'll be dealing with a much broader set of concepts, so becoming confident in requesting simplicity from others is important.

Being able to think clearly and strategically under pressure also requires a different kind of simplicity, which is related to purpose and goals. Here we need clarity on our aim to be able to solve a problem. The Vision domain naturally comes into play again, through its role in providing clear goals, goals that we can refer to when we need to make difficult decisions. Confusion grows quickly in a conversation when there is no clarity on purpose, or if there are differing aims among those present. The role of clarity—together with problem-solving—are two aspects at the very heart of resilience.

Through our research we see these aspects come out at the top of what determines overall resilience. Therefore, investing in a conscious exploration of your reasoning skills is a crucial aspect of developing deep resilience. One example of this is developing resourcefulness.

Resourcefulness

MacGyver, from the TV show of the mid-80s, is one of the all-time heroes of resourcefulness. As the joke goes, MacGyver can solve any problem with just a paperclip and chewing gum. The concept of resourcefulness here is that by using what we have in novel ways, we can overcome much bigger problems than what we might think. Often this skill of resourcefulness is suggested to be innate to a person, however, this is still a skill we can learn and enhance.

Putting conscious effort into developing resourcefulness adds to your confidence in having to deal with complex problems since it provides you with more options to exercise. Remember that one of the fundamental needs of the brain is for control, so by improving resourcefulness, you give your brain more options. This in turn generates a feeling of security, leading to confidence.

Resourcefulness can be improved in many ways. One way is to consciously invest in broadening your network of people to include experts in various areas—people you can turn to when faced with particular problems. Another aspect is to organise information more effectively so you can refer to it more easily. As a simple example, if your emails are a big mess of many thousands of emails from many years, then finding that one important email in a time of need may be impossible. Creating small habits to organise the data might end up being very useful in a pinch.

Technology brings with it many new opportunities to be resourceful, though it also makes the same opportunities available to others. To be competitive, we need to learn more about how we can use new developments in areas such as data analytics and machine learning in order to solve problems. Using these tools effectively comes back to our own ability to think creatively and with speed and accuracy.

Investigating your own thinking in itself is useful for resourcefulness. This is because cognitive reflection allows you to recognise faster which leaps of logic might take you to an incorrect conclusion. One way to do this is by investigating different types of formal and informal *logical fallacies*. You can find good lists of these on Wikipedia. These highlight common mistakes in thinking that we might make without even realising it, contributing to bias and blind spots. However, it's one thing to read through these and quite another to be honest with yourself where you might tend to make those mistakes and recognise your own need for change.

Further, you can study more diverse topics surrounding your field. As the amount of information continues to explode, the sheer volume of available knowledge results in greater specialisation, which in itself inhibits discovery. This is because there are fewer generalists with understanding spanning multiple fields that can spot connections that specialists may not.

Specialisation, then, provides an opportunity for you as a leader—a broader knowledge set can help you find these connections. Not to say that you need to be an expert in various fields, but instead know enough to spot areas that may be worth further investigation by specialists.

Unusual connections made in this way is at the heart of resourcefulness. For example, think about the art experts that were struggling to identify forgeries of modern paintings. With art valuations going into millions of dollars, this was becoming an expensive problem. Eventually, someone came up with the idea to look for radiation fallout caused by nuclear bomb testing in the 1950s. This radiation was unique; it could only be found in older paintings, and could not be faked. By combining two seemingly-unrelated items (art and nuclear weapons), an incredibly useful and unique solution was born.

Sure, it is about imagination, but even imagination is about existing ideas and concepts floating in the subconscious being bounced together to see what might fit. And when it does, the combination bubbles up into consciousness. It's difficult for the brain to contemplate something it has no knowledge of—indeed you might have to construct a concept from scratch to mentally use it as a potential solution to a problem. The brain needs access to these various ideas so that it can contemplate them in the subconscious in the first place.

In short, resourcefulness needs observation, knowledge, and preparation. On the topic of preparation, there's a skill enabled by Reasoning that is a key contributor to the proactive side of resilience. This is visualisation.

Visualisation

Here, Visualisation is not about picturing success—quite the opposite. Here we consider 'negative visualisation', which is, in essence, to practise visualising what may go wrong and plan for those eventualities. This may be with something small, such as losing your wallet or phone. Or larger events, such as a major mistake or failure at work, losing your job, or a relationship breakup. To some extent it's easy to think about those events and say, 'I'll get over it', though that doesn't capture the pain and suffering of the event itself.

For example, even just losing a mobile phone is quite a bit more frustrating than we might initially think, so the trick here is to imagine in more detail the effect of the event. In the case of losing your phone, it could mean missing important messages, which impact some projects; running late for meetings since you didn't get reminders; not knowing where to go for a meeting since you don't have your phone to tell you; losing a lot of photos and data because it wasn't backed up, and so on. You might not even have had a password on the phone itself.

Misplacing your phone then means you've not only lost all this valuable information, but someone else now has access to it and knows a great deal about you. They may be reading your emails at that very moment and resetting passwords for your internet banking. This realisation registers in your impulsive brain and given that this scenario was unplanned, produces a strong emotional reaction of panic. This limits your ability to think clearly about what needs to be done next to minimise the potential impact.

Conversely, someone who has considered all of this will have everything backed up and protected, with the main annoyance being the need to get a new phone. This scenario does not warrant a strong emotional reaction— the smart brain stays in control. Going into this detail gives you more clarity on what you will need to deal with, however, rather than just visualising your life going down in flames, it's also about finding out how you can rise from the ashes, so to speak. The critical point about visualisation keeps with the central theme, which is to stay constructive.

Once you have a greater awareness of the emotional and practical impact of an event, then you can consider the following: Can you minimise the impact if it does happen? Is there something you can do to prevent this from happening in the first place? Or otherwise, could you simply accept the outcome?

If you're in the business world, then this might sound familiar. In many ways, this is basic risk management as performed in organisations, except on a personal level. Just as organisations need to effectively manage risks, so do we as people need to manage personal risks. While organisations take risk management very seriously, as individuals most of us are hopeless at applying these same concepts to our own personal lives, with great cost.

Take going to the dentist, for example. If we never consider what might go wrong with our teeth, then we're likely to skip flossing and going to the dentist, eventually resulting in major tooth pain. At that point, we finally go to a dentist and find out we need a root-canal as well as extensive and expensive work in other areas. This results in a disruption to our lives, which may well come at a very unfortunate time. Likely this will not be the only neglected area—so how many other little disasters are waiting in the wings because we never took the time to consider and prepare for them?

Organisations with a good risk management culture are better placed to achieve success. So too does personal risk management set us up for success. Naturally, preparation in this way does not guarantee results, but it does increase the probability of success. Adding up small increases in probability across many areas of your life can result in a much greater overall chance of success. Not just that, this preparation is at the heart of being more proactive and preventative—that crucial dimension of resilience that's so often neglected. Here we can literally prevent crises from occurring in the first place while it also has an important effect on the brain.

Visualisation in this way helps the smart brain stay in control by managing the appearance of unhelpful emotions. Visualising scenarios and taking action to mitigate eventualities builds neural pathways. These pathways improve your confidence to stay calm and in control in a crisis. This is because not only have you probably already considered the scenario, but you also become better at the very act of thinking through a situation in the first place. Simply put, thinking through various crises makes you perform better in crises, even if the scenario is one that you didn't directly plan for.

The brain reacts very strongly to that which it has never considered before. So, if you never really considered that someone might steal your car, then that event might come as quite a big shock. This shock can result in changes in our outlook on people, affect trust and many other areas.

The result is, sudden changes might impact your ability to continually pursue a larger goal. We see this quite often in life when people face larger setbacks. Think about people who lost someone close to them, resulting in a massive personal impact that derails their own aspirations. We see more of the survivors than of those who don't cope. This creates a misperception that we will also survive whatever happens, rather than recognise that we might also be among those who never quite make it back.

Visualisation then brings us to the great tragedies that happen in our lives, such as losing a partner, a parent, or a child. So many I've spoken to have told me that they just couldn't continue if they lost a child, although the harsh reality is that after an event like this happens, you will still wake up the next day and the world will still go on. I will put it to you that it is not wise to avoid thinking about the death or someone close to you. Sometimes there can even be compounding effects, like losing a loved one to suicide. Anyone you know can die or be severely injured at any moment. Today, tomorrow, next week... We all need to acknowledge this simple reality. Visualising a scenario like that should come with pain—there is no preparation you can do to fully avoid the emotion of these tragedies.

Despite this, visualising these events constructively should bring you to important questions. If I lost my partner, parent or child today, what do I wish I had done differently? What do I wish I told them? How would I have liked to spend time differently with them? How would I have reprioritised other areas of my life to make this happen? And from those answers comes the next logical question: why don't I start doing these things right now?

This is the critical part—don't just sit with the pain of the visualisation—instead use that as motivation to live your life in congruence with what is truly important to you. Spend your time and energy with people in a way that, if they did die, rather than being sad they are gone, be happy you had the time together that you did.

Managing 'Declarative Knowledge Overload'

Enhancing Reasoning depends on effective knowledge management. However, difficulty in integrating new knowledge is the natural result of the increasing ease of access to information. Quite simply, we are no longer living in the age of information—we are now living in the age of information overload. With this overload comes nasty side effects that are becoming ever more noticeable. Before we explore those side effects, let's take a step back and consider two forms of knowledge:

Declarative knowledge—This form of knowledge is available to the conscious brain. You can verbalise and contemplate it. This is about knowing 'that'. For example, you may know that to ride a bike means pedalling and keeping your balance by steering.

Procedural knowledge—Knowing what it takes to ride a bike doesn't mean you can actually ride one. This is where procedural knowledge is about knowing 'how'. Here the brain learns how to perform the pedalling and steering motions to keep you upright and riding.

Procedural knowledge is hard to verbalise. Think of trying to explain to someone how to keep their balance on the bike. There's no way for you to just transfer your procedural knowledge to someone else—they can take your pointers, but they will have to practise on their own.

Practice is the key concept here. But how does this happen in the brain? The best way we have to know what a brain structure does is to see what happens when it's damaged. Patient code-named HM in the 1950s had his hippocampus destroyed during brain surgery to cure his epilepsy. While the epilepsy stopped, the hippocampal damage left him unable to form any new declarative memories. Quite simply, you could introduce yourself to HM, and right afterward he would still not know who you were.

The extensive studies of HM added a great deal to our understanding of knowledge transcription. An interesting discovery is that procedural knowledge can form independently of declarative knowledge. That means HM could learn a new motor skill without remembering that he learnt it. For example, HM could spend weeks learning how to knit, and each time he wouldn't know that he can knit, but be surprised to find out he knows how!

Declarative knowledge needs the hippocampus, which handles the initial information storage and is then transcribed to other cortical areas, where it becomes long-term memories.

Procedural knowledge skips the hippocampus, as there are deeper brain structures directly involved with performing the action. For example, the basics of riding a bike sits much deeper in the motor cortex, refined through the cerebellum in the back of the brain.

The frontal cortex, through its executive function, can decide which way to steer and how fast, but doesn't actually know how to maintain balance as you pedal. Declarative knowledge can result in procedural knowledge through knowing what is possible. For example, knowing that it is possible to ride a bike can lead you to practise riding it until you know how.

This concept translates well to the modern world. For example, a manager might learn about a new study on how to manage staff. With the manager now knowing that it is possible to get some outcome, the manager can start practising how to apply that technique. Simple! In theory...

In reality, it is here that we start to see the effects of information overload. Through a digital explosion of information at our fingertips, we now get so much input that our brain can't keep up with turning relevant declarative knowledge into procedural knowledge. And how could it? If it takes months to practise a new technique or skill, how can we keep up, when there are a bunch of new articles and studies coming out every week with more things we absolutely must know?

What we are increasingly experiencing is somewhat like a reverse of HM's case. Instead of HM's hippocampus that cannot retain new knowledge while still forming procedural knowledge, our hippocampi are so overloaded with new information that we form a lot of new declarative knowledge, but very little new procedural knowledge. Simply, we know that many things are possible, but we are not practised in how to achieve it.

While the brain struggles to figure out what new knowledge is worthy of implementation and practice, we stand by, frozen in place. This is the knockout punch of DKO—Declarative Knowledge Overload.

This is the brain's brilliant solution to information overload, because the brain has realised something that many of us haven't: regardless of what we do today, the world will still continue tomorrow. So why should the brain change its ways when it can just do nothing instead? Besides, information to the contrary might come out tomorrow, so it's actually prudent to do nothing...

Rather than practising new skills, we instead build up an ever-growing declarative knowledge database that makes us feel like we know a lot. This is a big challenge with DKO—it can make us feel like we are making progress, when in reality we are not. Constantly learning new things doesn't mean anything if you don't put them into practice.

DKO is about unintegrated and unimplemented declarative knowledge.

Consider some consequences of DKO through information overload:

- **Uncritical investigation reinforces bias**. DKO makes us resistant to critical investigation. Many people think that increased availability of information will increase our collective understanding and compassion for each other. But not all information is equal. There are good ideas, bad ideas, and everything in-between. The amazing thing about information overload is that you can find substantial evidence to 'prove' whatever you want to believe in. Still believe in a flat earth? Well there are big groups out there with lots of flat earth info for you! People naturally look for more of what they believe in, which just reinforces bias. If you don't go out of your way to find out if you might be wrong about something, then you may never improve your world view.

- **A post-truth world.** This term is becoming more prevalent and it represents a key component of DKO: why should we be outraged about something if there are so many alternative views? Who knows what's really the truth anymore? And most likely, something worse will just happen tomorrow. This is why many in politics and even business now skip the facts and focus on saying things that elicit emotion. Emotion can at least still inspire some action and support, even if the information flies in the face of reality. Back to our previous point, as long as the information agrees with an existing bias, then that is as much truth as many need these days.

- **The well-informed who stick to their ways.** Think of the executive or manager who devours all the latest Harvard Business Review articles. Well-read, this person is quick to cite some study in order to look smart or shoot down an idea. Yet for all his knowledge, he still does things the same way as he has for the last 20 years. Often people know exactly what they should be doing, but still don't do it. Many of us fit into this category because it can so often feel like we are doing the right thing by accumulating all this knowledge, except that we are not actually using it.

I see the same effects bleed into wellbeing and resilience training. Many programs shower people with information through seminars, building up declarative knowledge that often doesn't translate into procedural knowledge—or real, lasting change. These programs then measure knowledge afterwards, trumpeting their success, when in reality they have only measured people's ability to remember something said earlier that day.

DKO helps us understand the consequence of information overload. It also highlights a key problem with information overload, which is a lack of putting what we know into practice and thus developing procedural knowledge. Instead, all the best knowledge in the world is reduced to mere trivia that is never acted on. Understanding this mechanism of DKO, we can take action to get back up and fight more effectively. Here are three steps to avoid DKO.

- **Appreciate criticism.** Being open for criticism is one thing, but information overload means we need to have an even higher appreciation for criticism. We need to actively look for criticism in our own ideas and the information we are learning. This will help weed out the bad declarative knowledge so you have a better idea of what to put into practice. For example, if you are learning about a new concept, go to its Wikipedia page and see if there is a criticism section. Read through that and see if you can adequately address those points.

  Also, many people simply agree with whatever they think you believe, so you need to be a little more devious if you want real criticism. For example, if you are considering an idea and talking to a friend or colleague, present an opposing view first. See if they agree with that, then shift to your original idea and see what they say then. If they just agree with whatever you say, then consider that talking to them will mostly reinforce your own biases.

- **Look for themes.** When going through *Harvard Business Review* and all those other articles and papers, don't get lost in the detail. You don't need to become a neuroscientist to apply brain-based management principles, just like you don't need to be a pilot to know a helicopter doesn't belong upside-down in a tree. What's more important than a single study or article is if you can see consistent trends in a concept. This further helps to weed out declarative knowledge with little or no evidence behind it, helping you focus on ideas worthy of your attention.

- **Integrate and apply.** Here you have the opportunity to lead. It is through your own creative combination of different ideas, and putting your integrated idea into practice, that you can set yourself apart as a leader. This happens by taking critically-evaluated themes built on good evidence and following through to develop not just the declarative knowledge, but also the procedural knowledge. This takes courage to do, and you might even find out you were wrong about a thing or two, but the reward is a chance to lead the pack.

As we know from the neuroscience of how the brain changes, it takes time and practice for the brain to change. It's through this practice that declarative knowledge turns into hard-wired procedural knowledge that we can then rely on, even under pressure. The better we embed these skills in ourselves, the better we can then explain them to others and pass on the knowledge. As we'll see, this fits closely with our next Reasoning skill.

Challenging beliefs

Let's consider certainty. Quite often we like to ask people if they are 'certain' of some fact. Perhaps you want to be 'certain' before making a decision. What does this word actually mean? Certainty implies having 100% confidence in the correctness of a fact. In my many years, I've experienced this quite often, where a leader would ask me if I'm *absolutely certain* about some detail. Then I would always think to myself, I'm not even certain about what I had for breakfast, so, no, I'm not really certain. So, naturally I respond with *'absolutely'*, followed by quick pang of anxiety as I think of all the ways I might be wrong.

It is not logically possible for us to be 100% certain of anything. The brain functions through heuristic circuits, where it approximates everything. Memories are never fully accurate. The brain fills in blank spots in our eyesight with approximations of what it thinks we should be seeing. We all have biases through which we filter incoming information on a subconscious level. In fact, you can't even be 100% certain that you are awake right now and reading this book—it might just be a very convincing dream.

Keeping this in mind, it becomes clear that if we ask someone if they are 'certain', what we are really asking for is if they have a *high degree of relative certainty*. This distinction may seem pedantic, but there's an important consequence—anyone can end up being wrong. No matter how totally, absolutely certain they might think they are right, they can still be wrong. Including you. Including every single deeply-held belief that you might have—any of them can be wrong.

This acknowledgement of our own fallibility is important for the brain because it primes us to not interpret challenging information as a threat, but rather an opportunity to revise our beliefs. It also prepares you for the reality that every piece of information that you might be operating under might turn out to be incorrect.

To make this even more evident, we should consider our learning path through life. We start out by knowing nothing, then we learn more through school, we learn more through further education, and we learn more through experience. We are constantly learning more, therefore we can conclude that none of us are born in a perfect state with perfect knowledge. Obviously, this is the case, nevertheless, we still operate as if today our thoughts are 100% correct. This is because we just so hate to be wrong, and even if we are wrong, we hate even more to admit it. Because of this tendency of the brain, each of us hold on to beliefs formed in early childhood—beliefs that still colour our thinking to this very day.

Early childhood beliefs are formed through the eyes of a child, naïve to the true workings of the world. These early beliefs are usually less than ideal. The impact is that your perception of the world is skewed by these shaky beliefs, and if your perception does not line up with the reality of the world, then it reduces the probability of your success. You become less able to find real solutions to problems. Your behaviour doesn't get the right response.

It's difficult to know exactly which beliefs might be in need of revision, so a more effective approach is, quite simply, to explore all of your beliefs.

Though, what does this look like in a practical sense? How does one do this? The simple way to explore your own beliefs is to re-embrace your childhood fascination of the question *'why?'* That simple question allows you to delve into the depths of yourself. Deploy this question at any moment, for example: *'Why did I just do that? Why do I think that is necessary? Why do I feel this way?'* Keep asking the question as you delve deeper, taking care not to be persuaded by non-answers such as *'because that's just how I am'*. Push deeper to find the real answers. Find the evidence for your beliefs, what is it all based on?

For example, jealousy is one of those all-round useless emotions that mainly sows destruction wherever it pops up. Yet many people embrace it as being a fundamental part of themselves. This emotion stems from a far deeper insecurity, that if explored in honesty, can be resolved in favour of more constructive behaviour.

The best part of the question *'why?'* is when you find within yourself a sense of fear, driving you away from wanting to answer yourself. That is when you know you are onto something important! Even if just to yourself, the brain still doesn't want to admit when it is wrong, so you will need to push through to get to the important parts. Part of this is your own mindset. Use some business language and think of it as not finding what is wrong in the brain, but rather finding *opportunities for improvement*. This must be accompanied by the realisation that any belief can be wrong—there is no certainty.

A follow-up question to *'why?'* is, importantly, *'is this belief useful?'* Usefulness here alludes to the achievement of your Vision. Does the belief make it more, or less likely for you to achieve your own goals and purpose? Does the belief lead to constructive action that brings you closer to your aspirations? This line of questioning should start to hone your thinking, largely by allowing yourself to let go of old hang-ups that might be causing more harm than good.

This is especially true when it comes to our core beliefs. These are the beliefs way down deep that many other beliefs sit on top of. In 1991, Seymour Epstein suggested four core beliefs that stem from the basic needs of the brain. The beliefs are about:

- the nature of the world (predictable, or dangerous, or lack of justice, related to control),
- the meaningfulness of the world (the world has meaning, or has no meaning, related to motivation),
- the trustworthiness of people (trustworthy, or not, related to connection),
- and the worthiness of the self (being worthy, or worthless, related to self-esteem).

These core beliefs sit at the base of how we perceive and engage with the world. For example, if you believe that people are inherently not trustworthy, then you can imagine how you might avoid many interactions and opportunities along the way.

Throughout our childhood, and even later in life, traumatic events can impact any of these core beliefs, negatively affecting our perceptions and engagement. Given that there are so many other beliefs and behaviours built on top of these core beliefs, changing a core belief is like standing at the edge of a cliff with a dense fog right in front of you and being asked to jump.

You have no idea what kind of person you'll become when you change a core belief, as all the other beliefs built on that one will crumble and be replaced. You become a new person... one with more accurate and more constructive beliefs who is better able to create or act on opportunities.

Tenacity

Carrying on from Einstein and his tendency to be persistent, we can presume that some people naturally develop this trait. However, as you might expect by now, persistence is like any other skill that we can develop and build. Much of this comes from a conscious decision not to give up on that which is important to us.

This doesn't mean we should stubbornly keep trying to do something that doesn't work. Instead, through critical evaluation of our efforts, we must keep working towards our goals. There are various techniques that go into this ability, many of these being mental techniques that need conscious contemplation to use. Meaning, these are not skills that develop naturally by themselves. We either need guidance from others to help implement these skills, or we need to develop them through the discipline of our own habits.

The neuro-mechanics of persistence

Discipline is an important aspect of tenacity. Discipline is the ability to override your desires to keep doing what you *should* be doing. Sure, there are many things that you *could* do, but you usually know when there are things that you *should* do that you are avoiding. Discipline allows you to keep doing what you *should* be doing, even if you don't feel like it. Discipline needs to be practised, and as you do so, it becomes easier for you to consistently do the right things that help you achieve your goals.

But what is happening in the brain that allows you to be disciplined, or cause you to not be disciplined? This is worth exploring further, as understanding the neural mechanics of how this works might make it more concrete and thus easier to understand the physical results of your mental investment. After all, it's hard to be motivated about building something in a room with the light switched off, since you don't get to see the result of what you are building. Rewiring on the brain can be very much like this, as we don't get to see the brain itself while it's changing. Therefore, it's useful to know a bit more about what's happening.

Our thoughts, beliefs, actions and habits are all encoded by neurons and their connections. We have about 100 billion neurons, and throughout our lives the amount doesn't really change much. What does change more often are the connections between neurons. As the connections change, so do our thoughts and behaviour. Therefore, if we can change the right connections, then we can embed new mental and physical habits that are more conducive to achieving our goals. The way that these connections change is the topic of neuroplasticity. It is quite fascinating, yet important for persistence.

Neuroplasticity is one of those terms frequently bandied about, but how does it actually work? Also, what lessons are there in the mechanics of neuroplasticity? We'll delve a little into the science, as I'm sure you'll find that a little bit of brain knowledge is worthwhile to make sense of how we learn.

One aspect of plasticity is neurogenesis. This is when new neurons are born from stem cells within the brain, which can then form new circuits. Neurogenesis surprisingly only happens in a few areas in the brain. One area is the hippocampus, which needs a lot of new neurons because it encodes new memories. Another potential area is the olfactory bulb, which allows us to sense smells.

Contrast this with the prefrontal cortex. Sitting at the front of your brain, the prefrontal cortex is what performs high level abstraction and 'smart' thinking. Interestingly, the prefrontal cortex is not capable of neurogenesis. Essentially, from an evolutionary standpoint, the brain figured it is as smart as it needs to be, even though there will be many important new smells to identify!

This is a reminder to us of just how wired the brain is towards survival. We need to keep in mind that it takes active effort for us to overcome our survival instincts and rise above our base nature.

Fortunately, the prefrontal cortex can still adapt by altering its synaptic connections. What does this mean? Each neuron connects to the next neuron through synapses. These are tiny extensions that reach out and send signals between neurons. We might think of neurons and their synaptic connections like a simple electrical circuit, where if one neuron fires, the next one fires, and the next, etc. But it's actually quite different.

In fact, one synaptic connection is not strong enough to trigger the firing of the next neuron. Rather, the signal from one synapse is very weak—we need tens to hundreds of synapses to fire close together to trigger the next neuron to fire. What's more, while electricity is what conducts the signal along the neuron, the way the signal jumps to the next neuron is mainly chemical. Through a host of different neurotransmitters that the first neurons release, there are many different effects it can have on the next neuron. For example, some neurotransmitters make it more likely for the next one to fire, and some make it less likely to fire. Some even change how the next neuron operates. This is where we need to look at the fascinating world of neurotransmitter receptors.

For our quick crash course in plasticity, we'll consider the most abundant neurotransmitter—glutamate. This transmitter is mainly excitatory, meaning it usually makes the next neuron more likely to fire. The way it does this is by getting released from the synapse of the first neuron and then binding with receptors at the synapse of the second neuron.

There are many different types of receptors with different functions, so let's look at two that will help you understand plasticity a bit better. In particular, the AMPA and NMDA receptors. These receptors both bind with glutamate. When this binding happens, the AMPA receptor opens up and lets sodium ions in. As the positively-charged sodium ions rush in, the second neuron starts to depolarise. If it depolarises enough, it will trigger a cascade effect, causing the second neuron to fire.

Meanwhile, NMDA has also bound with glutamate, but it has a larger magnesium ion blocking the opening. If the first neuron only fires weakly, then the magnesium ion stays stuck and blocks the NMDA pore. However, if the first neuron fires strongly and in high frequency, then the depolarisation through the AMPA receptors is strong enough to pop the magnesium out like a cork.

With NDMA now open, it lets in more sodium, but also lets in calcium. This is critically important, because the sudden influx of a lot of calcium triggers a process through which the second neuron deposits more AMPA receptors at the synapse. This is important—these AMPA receptors were lying dormant inside the synapse but now they are activated at the cell membrane, meaning that the synapse is now *more sensitive* than before.

The calcium ions also affect other processes inside the cell, leading to gene transcription for the creation of new synapses in a process called synaptogenesis. Sitting around the two synapses are glial cells called astrocytes. All this activity of firing between the synapses cause the astrocytes to get more involved in clean-up, making the connection even stronger. These additional processes are important for long-term strengthening of the synaptic connections.

Here, you can get an idea of your brain physically changing. Through activating specific pathways more frequently, you make these synaptic connections stronger and more likely to fire in the future. Of course, the reverse also works, where ongoing, weak firing causes the second neuron to move active AMPA receptors away from the membrane, making the synaptic connection weaker. This is how you can break habits.

Frequent activation gradually adds more AMPA receptors and modulates other receptors and transmitters. This makes the activated neural pathway more natural. The result is that the effortful behaviour starts to become your new default behaviour. Meanwhile, old habits fade away as AMPA receptors are removed and synapses eventually disconnect.

Importantly, you can't just make all these synaptic connections super-strong in one day—pathway reorganisation takes time and effort.

This is the critical part for tenacity. What we want to strengthen are the neural pathways related to discipline and persistence. Stronger pathways here will make it more natural for us to have these traits, meaning this becomes our new default behaviour. From there, if our default behaviour is to persistently work towards our goals, then we become more likely to achieve them.

So how do we develop these pathways? Well, it's annoyingly simple in concept, which is: if we want to build discipline, we need to act in a disciplined way. For example, if you want to get into the habit of clearing out your email folder each morning, then you need to actually start doing it every morning, and stick to it even if you don't feel like it. Like I said, it's annoyingly simple, because doing things when you don't feel like it, is rather annoying.

Nonetheless, that's what it takes to strengthen these pathways. Every time we follow through with an action when we don't feel like it, we build that pathway, and this makes it more natural for us to just do it in the future. Eventually, it's as if your brain realises that resistance is futile, so it should just do what you *should* be doing.

We all have the ability to force ourselves to do something by consciously overriding other impulses. As we practise this conscious overriding, the right neural pathways strengthen and it becomes a default behaviour. And then we become naturally persistent and disciplined.

Realistic optimism

Previously we talked about realistic optimism as a constructive counterpoint to being overly optimistic. Being in a leadership position requires a larger separation between the scepticism on the realistic side, and the hopefulness on the optimistic side. This means being more sceptical about new ideas and the likelihood of total success, while at the same time being even more hopeful about the potential upside.

The dance between these two mental states is important for motivation. Too much of one may lead you back towards pessimism or to being overly optimistic.

The widening divide forms due to a few factors. On the realism side, you are faced with bigger and more complex projects, with many people espousing the virtues of what they are backing. Invariably, everything turns out more complex than expected, nothing sticks to the timeline, and everything runs over budget. Even the best-planned projects and acquisitions usually turn out to realise less of the expected value. However, this is not to say we should ever lose hope about the potential of big projects.

Hope in this sense gives us an ideal to keep striving towards. An ideal we can measure success against and see when we are not quite there yet, even though remaining hopeful that we can improve all-round. This hopefulness is important in allowing you to keep taking calculated risks—risks that enable you and your organisation to grow faster. Without this sense of optimism, you might avoid opportunities and someone else would take them instead.

Tenacity here plays a key role; a constant effort to work towards realising value that doesn't come forward naturally. Few things are ever quite as easy as we'd like them to be, especially in a corporate setting, where increasing regulatory and compliance constraints can slow progress almost on a daily basis. Even from one day to the next, the same project can become more difficult and complex.

It's easy in such an environment to become cynical, which is where we need to take care in our own mindset. We need both the hopefulness of the possibility of success for motivation, as well as the realistic understanding that it will be tough, so that we don't lose motivation when things get tough.

This mindset can seem contradictory, although Lawrence of Arabia might chime in to say that the trick is not minding the contradiction. More accurately, it's about knowing which perspective to focus on at which time. Aristotle talked of the 'golden mean' as the centre point between the two extremes of a virtue. For example, the virtue of courage at the centre point has at one end, extreme recklessness, while at the other, extreme cowardice. Aristotle talks of striving for this *golden mean* as the path towards a life of meaning and fulfilment. Though the concept is applicable more broadly in modern times.

Let's set our scale with realistic optimism as the golden mean, total pessimism on the one extreme and over-optimism on the other. Hopefulness functions more towards the optimism spectrum, and scepticism works towards pessimism. Now let's say we have someone presenting us with a bold new opportunity—a new piece of software that will solve all our problems. We can detect that this pitch, in all its promise, falls more on the overly optimistic side, so we can deploy some scepticism to bring it back towards the golden mean. The old adage of *'If it sounds too good to be true, it probably is'* would apply here.

Similarly, on the opposite end, where perhaps someone comes with great worry about a project that they are working on, saying the project might be 'doomed to fail'. Well, as this falls on the deeper pessimism side, we can deploy some hopefulness to bring it back to the golden mean of realistic optimism.

It's not all doom and gloom, though neither is it all roses and sunshine. It's more likely just an overcast Tuesday. The challenge for us is to maintain a tempered mindset that is cautious in venturing into the extremes, yet remain steadfastly in a zone that is motivational and constructive in the long term.

Dealing with mistakes

Tenacity requires that we have a healthy relationship with mistakes. This is so that we don't accumulate a pile of mental baggage that we cheerily try to ignore. Eventually, the pile may get so high that it topples over and disrupts our daily lives. Mistakes can also have a more immediate impact on your mental state, and can affect your confidence. Especially if it was a mistake that lead to failure of a large project, or a major missed target.

To understand the effects on your mental state, let's look at a small example—forgetting your credit card PIN. Your PIN is a short number that you use frequently. Likely for years on end, without changing it. Whenever you pay for a bill or withdraw some money, the pin flows right out your fingertips without so much as a thought. This works flawlessly for years, until one day, out of the clear blue sky for no rhyme or reason, just as you reach for the machine to pay, your PIN completely vanishes from your memory. You offered to pay at a restaurant and everyone's looking at you. Instantly, your heart rate rises, you break out in a sweat and dreadful embarrassment sets in. (I'm talking from experience here).

As you try different combinations that absolutely feel right, you keep seeing 'Incorrect PIN' pop up on the machine. The harder you try to remember, the more doubt surrounds each combination you can conjure up. As your fingers move across the numbers, suddenly nothing feels right, but every number feels like it should be right. This doesn't make sense—you used the PIN just yesterday and twice the day before that. Someone else finally offers to pay while you wrestle with the sudden memory blank. All other concerns of your life fall away as every ounce of focus shifts to how you can't remember a simple number you've used hundreds of times in the last few years. Hours later, you're still trying to remember.

Searching for any clue of what it could have been, visualising fingers tapping numeric pads, practising it on your phone to find one that feels right. Then you pick up a keypad, type it in and it seems to come back. It feels right. This is it! 'Incorrect PIN', again. It's gone.

When something that should be so simple and easy suddenly goes wrong, it can quickly grow in your mind—what else is there that can just vanish? How many other memories might already have vanished? What else is just a broken synapse away from mental oblivion? A deep sense of doubt sets in, as this one simple memory just does not come back.

A day or so later, you head off to the bank to set a new PIN since security protocols prohibit them from revealing your old PIN, denying any sense of closure on the sordid saga. While the resolution is relatively easy, the lingering doubt is the hardest to shake. Sure, you can take steps to work around a future occurrence by writing a note somewhere secure to remind you of the PIN.

But how can you prevent memories from just disappearing? Is this bound to happen more often with other memories, or judgments, or mental processes in the future? As jarring as this experience is, it's just a fraction of the emotional impact that a major setback at work or at home can have. That sudden reservation about your own judgement and abilities tends to create doubt around every decision you need to take. Decisions that would have been so easy before suddenly seem dauntingly uncertain.

Often the advice follows that we 'just need time'—time heals all wounds. But, no, time most certainly does not heal all wounds—especially with mental wounds. What time does do, and quite efficiently so, is pass. As it does so, time merely provides us with the opportunity to heal our own wounds. It is then up to us to spend that time wisely to heal effectively. Take, for example, a sports player that tears their ACL— the anterior cruciate ligament in the knee. Through a complicated surgery, the ACL can be reconstructed, and over time the wound heals. However, without extensive and painful rehabilitation therapy, the wound will not heal in a functional way. If no rehabilitation is done, the player would never be able to play again, and would never be able to strive for their sporting goals.

Another threat is how this can affect mindset. The player might become afraid of playing as aggressively in the future out of fear of tearing an ACL again. Therefore, relying on the passage of time alone is not enough. Dealing with the effects of a major mistake or setback requires constructive mental processing and it takes time to heal in a useful way.

Much of this is due to how the brain builds neural connections. Fear-based connections formed through the amygdala happens very quickly. In fact, in research with mice it was acutely observed that a single traumatic event can stop a mouse from participating in an experiment. On the other hand, positive reinforcement requires many repetitions to have an effect of the same strength; sometimes up to 150 repetitions are needed.

This means just one traumatic event has the power to significantly reduce your goal-striving, unless you purposefully and repeatedly process that event in a constructive way. This constructive processing guides your brain to heal and strengthens your mindset. Avoiding this approach can, over time, result in a deeply-ingrained hesitation that affects your confidence.

Repeated constructive processing is what will allow you to once again continue striving for your goals, having learnt valuable lessons from what you have been through.

Getting more practical, let's look at some basic guidelines in staying constructive when managing mistakes. As with resilience in general, you can handle a situation better if you are prepared for it by already knowing what steps to take. This primes your brain with the ability to calm down your fight-or-flight response when you do face a mistake. Acting constructively helps to get a better outcome from the situation. Here are the steps to take:

Be open to admitting that you made a mistake. Stubbornly resisting the idea that you make mistakes is a sure way of holding you back from learning and growing from them. Everyone makes mistakes, even with the best safeguards and processes in place. Recognise that you too can make mistakes.

Acknowledge a mistake. When you have made a mistake, avoid trying to cover it up and be willing to acknowledge that a mistake has been made.

Take ownership of the mistake. If it was a mistake that you made, take ownership of it. This acceptance is a key part of opening yourself up to the possibility of improving. In a work environment, admitting your mistake and immediately focusing on what can be done about it builds trust in your integrity.

Minimise damage. Try to find a way to minimise damage from the mistake. Can you quickly warn someone about it to prevent it from spreading? Do you need to let someone else know about the mistake? Can you fix it yourself quickly? If not, can you offer help to others to help deal with any repercussions?

Learn and grow. Following a mistake, try to find the reason for why it happened. Were you working too fast? Forgot about something? Look for patterns and consider if there is something you can put in place to prevent it from happening again. Can you put a manual check in place, a reminder of something, or get someone else to do a final review? Talk to others about it and see if they have ideas as well, and take their feedback on board.

As you work through mistakes and things that didn't go according to plan, a useful tool is to use constructive self-criticism. This is a way for you to look within yourself at what is and isn't working, and take action to help you move towards your goals. When you get better with constructive self-criticism, you also become better at handling criticism from others.

If your criticisms of yourself leave you feeling saddened and depressed, then you should implement constructive self-criticism. You will know you are doing it right when you feel energised afterwards and want to take action.

Follow these guidelines to use constructive self-criticism:

Don't judge yourself. Don't make broad negative personal judgements like *'I am useless'* or *'I'm so stupid'*. Universal judgements like these serve no purpose other than making you feel even worse about yourself. If you are going to make broad judgements, make them positive, like *'I'm great at [something]'* or *'I'm doing well overall'*.

Be specific. If something didn't go as well as planned, then focus on what specifically went wrong. There is no need to judge yourself for what happened—focus on the specifics of what went wrong, whether you can fix it, and how you can prevent it from happening again. If a report was wrong because it didn't contain some information, then it doesn't mean you are useless. It just means that next time you should double-check that area to make sure it has what it needs. By focusing on the specifics, mistakes become a learning experience that help you improve.

Discard the words 'always' and 'never'. For example, *'I always mess that up'* or *'I never get that right'*. These two words sneak in so easily and they wear down our sense of self-worth. After all, if you always mess up something, then you are making a prediction that you will mess up again next time—even though you might actually succeed. In fact, you are more likely to succeed if you *believe* you can succeed. These two words are far too absolute and we are better off without them. Also, avoid using them in reference to other people as well.

Recognise when external sources share the blame. None of us are immune to the effects of our environment and the people around us. Often you will not be the only one to blame for something that went wrong. Recognise when others are also involved in what happened and hold them accountable as well. Talk to them about what went wrong and together try to find a constructive way to prevent it from happening again.

There is no need to dwell on mistakes past, but there is value in analysing them to prevent reoccurrences.

Working through these steps will help you have more respect for yourself and especially in how you handle mistakes. When you have more respect for yourself, you will notice that others will respect you more as well. Overall, be constructive with yourself.

It's worth noting that I separate a *constructive* mindset as different from a *positive* mindset. The term *constructive mindset* intuitively focuses on goals and purpose—the realisation of your vision. On the other hand, the term *positive mindset* often evokes more a forced positivity, forcing a smile on your face. Being constructive in this sense doesn't mean you need to constantly be smiling and happy. In fact, frustration, scepticism, apprehension, anger, and similar emotions are not conducive to positivity, yet are conducive to helping you achieve your goals when used appropriately. They are therefore part of a constructive mindset.

This leads to a re-evaluation of emotions about what is 'good' and 'bad'. Simply, we don't need to be happy all the time to be able to achieve our goals. We can embrace more of ourselves and use the energy from all these emotions to keep us motivated to persist.

Collaboration

Think back to the metaphor of the lake on a mountain, feeding torrents of water into all the different goals/channels of your life. An extending question here is, where does the water come from? The reality is that we do not live in isolation. Our interaction with and contribution to others and the world around us feed water back into the lake. This is due to the basic need of the brain for secure attachment, allowing us to generate energy from our connection with others. We channel that energy back into other areas of our lives, feeding our ability to pursue goals and add meaning to our goals.

In an organisational context, managing our interaction with others is a conduit for achieving both our personal and organisational goals. Organisations are inherently social, especially given that they literally are groups of people organised to achieve larger goals. Our ability to navigate this environment successfully therefore plays a crucial role in our success within it, particularly when we face big setbacks and adversity. In these situations, it is our support networks that can make a huge difference in how well we cope and recover.

Support networks

The interesting thing about support and support networks is that it is not the actual existence of a support network that counts, but rather the perception of support. People are generally better with managing stressful events when they believe that they have a support network ready to help them if needed.[41]

Alternatively, someone who actually has a big support network ready to help, but doesn't realise all those people are there for them, are less able to manage stressful events. Naturally, it would be ideal to have our perception match the number of people who are there to help us.

Still, this is absolutely a case of where perception creates reality. It is our own perception of the support available to us that adds to our confidence in dealing with adversity. Here we have the option of challenging our own perceptions to realign our beliefs.

We can do this by taking a structured look through different areas of support available to us. The usefulness of this lies in just how rarely we objectively ask about available support. Instead, most of the time we think about how we feel about our perceived support, for example 'no one helps me'. This is a very subjective assessment, and one I've heard quite often from people, even though there are many sources of support available once you start looking. For example:

Friends and acquaintances. In a general sense, these are the people we

---

[41] Wethington, E., & Kessler, R. C. (1986). Perceived support, received support, and adjustment to stressful life events. *Journal of Health and Social behavior*, 78-89.

choose to have around us. Out of the thousands of people we meet through our lives, there are some we choose to spend more time with and retain a connection. Even if a friend might not fully be in a position to understand the kind of support we need, we can take the time to explain and help build a closer connection in the process. Also, while friends and acquaintances may come and go, some level of connection remains. People that you might not be in constant contact with would likely still be willing to support you if you reached out to them. Don't discount people you haven't been in touch with for a while.

Family, including parents, siblings and your extended family. While friends are those you choose to be around you, social norms generally cause family to form a different kind of bond that may last longer than many friendships. An advantage here is that you can take more time to invest in them to explain your situation, with them having the context of your history. Although this can also be a disadvantage, as family often come with decades of baggage that can hinder relationships. So, it is up to us to keep perspective and work within ourselves to let go of any baggage that only serves the purpose of creating a divide between people. If we can do this and maintain some humility, then family relationships can provide a lifetime of valuable support.

Your partner. If you do have a partner, then this is an obvious area of support. Your partner is likely to be the one that best knows what you are going through. Many complicating factors can creep in here, where perhaps we don't want to annoy our partners with all our problems. Perhaps we feel they are too busy with their own problems and we don't want to burden them with ours. Or we feel they just don't understand the environment we work in. Or maybe there is other unresolved tension that needs to be worked through before you can again discuss other topics more openly. A relationship with your partner requires the most investment and resilience of all to be able to survive in these days of ever-increasing divorce rates. As far as goals go, I'd suggest that one of your top goals should be for the success of your relationship with your partner.

Colleagues, peers and superiors. When it comes to challenges at work, others at work generally have the best understanding of the situation, and also might be aware of other angles of the problem. Generally, there are more colleagues available to support us than we realise. It is also up to us to go and ask for help, since rarely do people have enough mind-reading skills to know exactly when and what you need help with.

Executive coaches and psychologists. Most executives these days have a coach available, recognising the need for someone independent from all their existing relationships. These services are useful for sounding out thoughts, feelings and situations that you might not want to broadcast, particularly where there is a risk of it travelling further than intended.

Beyond these, there are many other forms of support available, for example:

Human Resources representatives, company resources. Most larger companies have internal resources available for various situations, as well as HR staff that can help resolve some tricky problems as well.

Support groups and online forums. For specific problems, there are usually groups available to help. An important realisation to make is that whatever you are experiencing, you are not the only one going through it. With over seven billion people on the planet, there are support groups for just about everything.

Pets. A dog or cat or other pet can also be a great source of support, providing a sense of perspective. Many of the problems in our lives are things we bring on ourselves, and if we chose to let it go for a while, we could also be as happy as a Labrador with a tennis ball.

Even with all these sources of support available, it's still common to feel like no one really understands what you're going through. Well, of course, no one really understands... because only you are you. No one else can jump into your brain and 100% experience what you are experiencing. However, it's not necessary for someone to 100% understand what you are experiencing to be able to provide support and perhaps some insight into your situation. What's usually more the case is that we haven't taken the time to fully explain to someone what the situation and its complications are. Should we take the time, we can perhaps bring them up to 60% or 70% understanding, which would be more than enough to have a constructive conversation around the situation.

Just as we need others for support, so too we should keep in mind that we form part of the support network of others. It's easy to get so caught up in everything that you are going through to forget that other people need support as well. Throughout our lives, we all will need different levels of support at different times. When we are part of the support network for others, it's important that we also contribute to their perception that we are available. Building that perception might well mean more to them than providing physical support.

Meanwhile, providing support has been shown in many ways to contribute to our own wellbeing—a cognitive reward for helping others. Providing support adds to a sense of purpose, builds more secure friendships, adds to a sense of gratitude and perspective of where you are in life.

Those friendships and relationships that we invest in have an important impact on our lives. We have a tendency to take in the traits of those we are close to, being influenced in subtle ways through the activities we participate in together, the information we share between each other, world views, philosophical ponderings, connections we make, favours we ask and grant. It's useful to consider what effect our friends have on us, and what effect we have on them. Are these relationships conducive to your goals and likewise can you provide value to your friends by helping them achieve their goals?

These are often the people we turn to when we need help, their attitudes and guidance feeding in as a part of our resilience. Resilience in this sense is not simply an internal construct, but through the Collaboration domain also has support networks as an external component. Relying on your support network is therefore not a sign of low resilience, but instead is an inherent part of resilience itself. Knowing when you need help—and asking for it—is a hallmark of resilience.

Alongside knowing that people are there to support us, a crucial factor is being willing to be supported in the first place. It is tempting to be highly independent both personally and at work. But we all need help from time-to-time and we can accomplish bigger goals, faster, if we are willing to seek and accept help.

This is not just with projects at work, but also when we are struggling personally with emotions, depression, and other conditions. We may not want to show these kinds of vulnerabilities at work, but it's important to acknowledge when we need help and then act on it. There are many avenues available to talk to someone and start working on it.

The pressure to present a positive façade

Being willing to ask for help becomes particularly important at leadership levels. We know that all jobs have some degree of stress to them. Stress comes from the brain's fundamental need for control—simplistically, if we feel we need to complete a task where we don't have an ideal level of control (perhaps with the right speed and accuracy), then we feel stress. Employees at all levels experience stress, though a recent listing of the most stressful jobs listed senior corporate executives as having the seventh most stressful job in the world.[42] This is behind military personnel, firefighters, and airline pilots—mainly occupations that focus on protecting lives.

Rising to the level of an executive tends to display a lot of resilience already, but the challenges only grow from there. A specific challenge for leaders is that there seems to be more pressure to show that you are doing great. That unspoken requirement to present a façade of strength can weigh heavily on executives, often hiding underlying depression and anxiety.

The very journey to become an executive is in itself arduous. Then once there, there's a sense of urgency to show that you are thriving on the additional pressure and responsibility, even if you're struggling.

This is where we often find executives hiding psychological disorders from everyone else—out of fear that it might jeopardise their careers. Ideally, we should be able to openly discuss with those around us what we are going through, so that they can support us. Usually, we'd find that others have similar worries that they struggle with. However, I would not be so naïve to suggest that it is always safe to be this open at an executive level. Some organisations are not yet as enlightened as to handle personal

[42] Business News Daily. (2017). *The 10 Most (and Least) Stressful Jobs.* Retrieved 27 July 2017 from http://www.businessnewsdaily.com/1875-stressful-careers.html

struggles in a fully constructive way.

Sometimes, admitting to major personal struggles can subconsciously erode the trust from others, perhaps in seemingly well-meaning ways. For example, *'Don't give that project to Victoria, she's struggling with X at the moment'*. This type of response is generally not helpful for achieving goals related to work, since you might get cut out of opportunities that you would otherwise have had if other people weren't aware of your own situation.

Given our focus on goal-oriented resilience, we need to find ways to constructively deal with these situations that is still conducive to achieving our goals. This means making a determination on the safety of the environment before you bare your soul to others. If the environment doesn't feel safe enough for that (perhaps you have seen what happened to others who did the same), then the next step is to find peers and other individuals who can be trusted, to open up to. Behind closed doors people may be more open, where you in turn can reciprocate as trust is extended to share more personal matters. Certainly, the answer is *not* to suppress what we are going through.

Sometimes we are so well-trained to suppress our own emotions that we don't even detect that underneath all the busy-ness, we are actually struggling. This kind of stealth-stress can take a toll over time, manifesting in other ways, such as lashing out at people, inability to control eating habits, and so on. Therefore, we can't simply ignore or hide what we are struggling with. It needs to be processed in some way or another. It can be tempting to manage it all by yourself, just as you manage everything else.

However, a far more productive path is to find someone totally removed from the situation, where you can be totally honest without worry that any of it will go back to affect the perception of others. Having an ongoing relationship with an executive coach can be particularly useful, since they can help to detect stealth-stress. They will also become more familiar with your history over time.

Reaching out to a psychologist is something you can do in total privacy, giving you a space to work through complex challenges without worry about anything being made public. The big challenge is to leave your ego at the door for a brief moment. Be willing to admit if, under the positive façade, it's not all roses. This is about being willing to ask for help. If our immediate environment perhaps isn't safe to ask for help, then we should go outside of it.

The answer is never to ignore our struggles, but rather to find a place where we can explore and work through it. While the façade might need to stay in place, being honest with a coach, a psychologist, your partner, and more importantly—being fully honest with yourself—is critical.

Considering context

Assessing the environment and what approach would be appropriate is essentially about understanding context. Context is a function of the orbitofrontal cortex (OFC), which sits just above the eyes. You will notice the action of the OFC when you detect a shift in a social situation. For example, such as when someone says something really awkward in the middle of a conversation and the mood shifts. Everyone's OFCs noticed the faux pas through their knowledge of social norms and appropriateness.

If we're lucky, the OFC develops a comprehensive understanding of various social norms as we grow up. However, for many of us, this is a subject of ongoing education and refinement. Our social style and effectiveness can have a strong impact on our ability to achieve our goals, naturally depending on the type of goal.

For most organisational goals, an ability to motivate people and form meaningful relationships are critical to achieving success. Here we need to be effective within the context. This requires various social skills, which we will explore next.

A central aspect to becoming effective in different contexts is to be able to relate to people and have empathy. This comes from a willingness to put yourself in their position, looking beyond your preferences and considering the preferences of others as likely being different than yours. Then we need to use those conclusions to recognise when a certain style of engaging isn't going to be effective for that person.

The ability to vary our interaction style is a useful skill, though it requires practice and careful observation of the eventual results. For example, getting angry and yelling at people in a meeting might see a high level of agreement right away, but fade away quickly afterwards as people disengage and try to avoid any further interaction.

The perception you create about yourself adds another piece to the social puzzle. Being able to talk with clarity about yourself and your motivation can quickly build trust by helping others understand who you are. Clarity about your own motivation and goals (care of the Vision domain) provides us with the means to be authentic in our communication. Being able to connect your goals to a larger benefit to society also provides the basis for a much more motivational and relatable style.

Developing a sense to know which style to apply requires a level of awareness of the setting and the people that you are with. The brain likes to simplify concepts in order to make faster decisions. One of these simplifications is about how the brain creates perceptions about people. When you see or hear from someone unexpectedly, your mind brings up how that person makes you feel, rather than the factual details of your interactions with that person. As Maya Angelou put it, 'People will forget what you said. People will forget what you did. But people will never forget how you made them feel.'

This is useful to keep in mind, since we can override this within ourselves when it's necessary—such as when we need to work with someone whom we might not get along with all that well. It's also useful to keep in mind how others might perceive us as well, given that their brains are also likely to depend on this heuristic.

Our ability to effectively apply humour to different contexts adds to the perceptions we create. It can lighten the mood in serious situations, which can often be very useful in itself. For example, during a crisis situation when everyone's impulsive brains are on high alert, reducing critical thinking, a well-placed joke can allow people to see that this is not the end of the world. This quick cognitive break reduces blood flow to the impulsive brain and increases smart brain blood flow, helping the group think more effectively and solve problems faster.

Support available at any particular time also depends on context. Being able to recognise what help we can receive, in which situations, is important, though we can influence this through the people in our network. This is curiously demonstrated through what has come to be known as the *Ben Franklin effect*. As Franklin put it, *'He that has once done you a kindness will be more ready to do you another, than he whom you yourself have obliged.'*

In short, someone who has already done a favour for you, is more likely to do more favours for you in the future. This effect seems to be far stronger than doing a favour for that person. The theory goes that the person doing the favour for you rationalises that the reason for doing it is because they like you. This effect was named after Franklin after he described a story about wanting to win over an influential legislator. As the story goes, Franklin heard that this hostile legislator had a rare book in his library. Franklin requested to borrow the book as a favour, which the legislator readily sent over. After a week, Franklin sent the book back, stating his high regard for the big favour. Following that, Franklin recounted how the legislator's attitude changed and he eventually became a great friend.

Interestingly, the effect also works on the opposite end of the spectrum. If we did something wrong to someone or harmed them in some way, we rationalise that away as because they are 'bad' and deserved it. In other words, we come to hate those we harmed.

Knowledge of this effect allows us to get perspective and detect when we might be applying it to someone, when this is happening to us, or even when someone is purposefully trying to apply this on us. As with Franklin, people can deploy this as a specific tactic to win over someone. Understanding this can help us make more strategic decisions when we notice someone is using a similar tactic with us. Though we could rationalise this in many ways— perhaps we say it's dishonest, perhaps it's simply the art of diplomacy. There's no objective truth to be found here.

What is relevant is that our ability to navigate various social contexts is critical for achieving success with complex projects and goals. In an age of increasing digital communication and distance between people, social skills are becoming more valuable. This is because communication is becoming more automated and removed from other humans.

While automation might be necessary to achieve scale with some projects, at a higher level, the ability to be articulate, reason with clarity and motivate action is more important than ever. The brain is still wired for human interaction and greatly values close connection with other humans. As a fundamental need of the brain, the challenge is for us to find ways to still meaningfully connect with others in an increasingly digital age.

Health

Looking after your health is simple. Eat whole foods, cut out sugar, exercise four times a week, get about seven hours of sleep a night, limit/avoid drugs and alcohol. Most of us know what we should and shouldn't do for health, though truly the hard part is sticking to it!

The benefits of looking after your health are not simply about your physical appearance and longevity. Concerning resilience, good health is important in the dire situations that it prevents. For example, preventing constant illnesses, preventing chronic pain, preventing major diseases. Good health helps us steer clear of some of life's major disruptions that we would have to face otherwise.

These disruptions hold us back from achieving our own goals, so in that sense the Health domain contributes through its preventative effect. Similarly, the other domains of resilience contribute to a mindset that enables us to stick to a healthy lifestyle in the first place. Perhaps one's ability to stick to good nutrition and regular exercise is a good measure of resilience in itself.

Finding time for nutrition

Nutrition is only as complicated as we make it. There are some basic rules we can follow, though we just love to make it complicated through all kinds of preferences and eccentricities. One of the toughest components of healthy nutrition is time. The amount of time invested becomes ever harder to justify as we cram more responsibilities into our lives. The subject is complicated further by constant contradictions in the media and companies looking to sell products who make outlandish and inviting claims. To consider the priority of nutrition in our lives, it helps to take a step back and look at why it's important.

Your body has an amazing ability to adapt to what you eat and so it often takes a long time to really start to feel the effects of an unhealthy diet. This is why we can easily make it through our early years eating everything in sight and our bodies just seem to cope. We feel great, we feel invincible, like we don't need to eat healthy to look and feel great. Soon after our 20s end??, problems start to creep in—weight doesn't seem to come off, we get joint pains, headaches, tiredness and more. This is when we start to realise we need to fix something.

By now, the challenge is that we already have some strong habits that are hard to simply drop. We have set routines through which we consume maybe more than what we should. We may have lifestyles that make it hard for us to fit in healthy eating—constant travels and conferences where good food simply isn't available.

The reality is that unhealthy habits accumulate over time. An unhealthy diet might take many years to show the damage it's doing to your body. On the other hand, if you start to eat healthy sooner, you can reap the benefits of longer-lasting health and vitality. Though some might say that a life without chocolate is not a life worth living, however, think of it as investing in a healthy body now and in an improved quality of life in later years. When you hit 70, you can't quickly switch to a healthy diet and expect to undo a lifetime of intestinal abuse. You are not only investing in your body, but also in your brain and your mental health.

Dietary deficiencies can result in cognitive side effects, such as memory problems and mood swings. A diet rich in breads and plant oils can result in an omega-6 overload, resulting in systemic inflammation, which increases the frequency and effect of pain. This inflamed state makes you more susceptible to headaches and other types of pain. A simple lack of B vitamins can result in depression, poor concentration, tiredness, delirium, irritability, and many forms of neural damage. This damage adds up over time and can result in neurological disorders such as Alzheimer's.

When thinking about nutrition, two questions are important. Be honest with yourself when answering these: Is your health at a level that you are happy with? Do you have the body you want?

If you are where you want to be, then you're likely already doing the right things. If not, challenge yourself to be open to make some changes. Though first it's useful to remember to avoid quick fixes. When looking into healthier eating habits, any scheme that promises quick results is likely not going to make a lasting change or might simply do nothing at all. Here are a few examples:

Detoxes. Your body simply does not need 'detoxing'. This is a concept that has been thoroughly debunked and has no scientific basis. Instead, the body is extraordinarily capable of detoxing itself every day and every moment of your life. Besides, your body will be much happier if you make a permanent change, rather than do a quick 'detox' now and then. Any benefit you feel out of a 'detox' is much more likely related to the placebo effect.

Cleanses. Similar to 'detoxes', schemes like a *'two-week juice cleanse'* and other 'cleanses' have no scientific backing that they produce any lasting health benefits. Again, your body is much better off with a permanent change to your diet.

Quick fixes. Any scheme that is focused on fast results through a quick program is something to be avoided. It builds a mindset that health is something that you can focus on now and then, when you feel like it, which is false. Your body needs consistent, healthy nutrition and habits for you to get the benefits of being healthy.

Forget about dieting and instead switch to everyday healthy eating. While a diet is something you do quickly to lose some weight, think of healthy eating as a permanent lifestyle that you do consistently. The trick is to stay consistent. Consistency is absolutely the key to health. If you eat unhealthy all year round, then do a quick *'health kickstart'* come January, only to go back to your usual unhealthy habits shortly afterwards, then you are unlikely to see any noticeable change.

Your health is about what you do consistently. This is why quick fixes are destructive in the long run—they create a mindset where you want something quick and easy and you resist any real, long-term change. This mindset makes it harder and harder over time to make permanent changes, meaning you'll find yourself continually going back to old habits. Often, we spend so much time on trying out shortcuts that just doing it the right way from the start would have been much faster.

If you want to start looking after your health, your body, and your brain, then it is time to put all the shortcuts behind you and focus on lasting change. Shifting your mindset to consistency is important, as it also brings an element of freedom—if you eat healthy most of the time, then one unhealthy meal is not going to destroy your health or make you gain weight.

And surprise, surprise, staying consistent with a healthy diet requires a lot of resilience. This is particularly the case for nutrition, which really comes down to multiple decisions every day of your life. It's a constant effort to stick to healthier options. If you are working at a leadership level, then you are likely often faced with events, travels and conferences, which can make it even harder. Realistically, you don't need to eat healthy foods 100% of the time.

A good start is to know which foods to avoid. Some foods have been shown to produce patterns of addiction in the brain that are similar to some hard drugs. This means that they have a real effect on the brain that makes you crave them. The key is to be conscious of what these foods are so you can eat them only in moderation while maintaining consistent, healthy eating. Beware of the following:

High-GI carbohydrates. Including breads, pasta, sugars, white potatoes, and most baked goods. These are foods that are high on the Glycaemic Index, meaning they are quickly absorbed and spike blood sugar levels, giving you a quick rise in energy usually followed by an energy crash later. These foods are very high in calories, making them easy to overeat. What's problematic is that these foods release a lot of serotonin (feel-good neurotransmitter) in the brain, motivating you to eat more.

Sugar combined with fats. These include ice cream, chips, cookies, doughnuts, and chocolates. Your body has evolved to crave this combination of nutrients because in ancient times they were very scarce. Now these foods are everywhere and the brain still wants them. Unfortunately, these tasty foods are the worst for your brain and your body. They are damaging to brain function and tend to result in fast weight gain. Avoid these as far as you can and try to substitute for sugar-free options where possible.

Four guidelines for a healthy change

Still, healthy nutrition doesn't have to be complicated. Try to incorporate these four simple guidelines to make a lasting change:

Drink more water. Water has no special healing properties on its own, but it is important because of what it replaces. This means cutting back on sugary drinks, including juices and smoothies, which often contain more sugar than carbonated drinks.

Eat more vegetables. Cut back on breads and pasta and replace with vegetables. Both fresh and frozen vegetables are great for health, with seven or more servings per day helping you live longer. One cup, or about 70 grams, is one portion for most vegetables.

Whole foods. As a general rule, processed foods are less healthy than simple, whole foods. It's easy to tell the difference—if it has a list of ingredients, then it's not a whole food. Whole foods usually come from the fresh food isles. Processed foods usually contain unhealthy ingredients and sugars to make them taste better.

Prepare your own meals. Despite trying to make the best choices when eating at restaurants and buying food from cafes, you never really know if the food is as healthy as advertised. Preparing your own meals is a sure way to know you are eating good foods. As you get busier, one way to make healthy nutrition easier is through a pursuit of efficiency. By this I mean cooking faster meals and cooking meals in bulk on the weekend. There are many bulk preparation recipes available and this is also how I have managed to stick to a healthy diet for many years.

Subscription services are also available to deliver prepared, healthy meals to your house, though with these it can be hard to figure out which ones are actually healthy. These are businesses like any other, and people buy more food that tastes good, so many of these companies end up adding extra sugar to meals while still branding it as 'healthy'.

You don't need to do all four of the guidelines at once. In fact, you can start with just one and then add them one after the other over a few weeks or months.

You know you should exercise

Beyond physical fitness, exercise has been shown to increase mental performance and prevent cognitive decline. Along with making you more physically capable, this brain-boosting aspect of exercise makes it an important component of personal resilience and wellbeing. To get a sense of just how important exercise is for your brain and mental wellbeing, have a look at these effects.

In the short term:

- Increases cerebral blood flow. Your brain heavily depends on blood flow to be able to function, so more blood flow helps your brain work better.
- Burns stress hormones, like cortisol and adrenaline, calming Impulsive Brain activation.
- Improves neuroplasticity by boosting hippocampal function.
- Releases endorphins—this can help with treatment and prevention of stress, depression and anxiety.

In the long term:

- Enhances brain plasticity and increases Brain Derived Neurotrophic Factor, which helps to stimulate synaptic connection changes and the process of neurogenesis. This is the production of new neurons that helps your brain grow, improving learning abilities and overall mental performance.
- Protects against cognitive decline as well as declines in complex decision-making skills and memory.
- Contributes to brain size and ongoing growth in the long term.

An important aspect to remember is that exercise is not that important for body weight. Nutrition plays a far greater role in managing body weight, and only training at the level of an Olympian can reduce the effects of a bad diet. Trying to manage body weight through exercise alone is very difficult. Take care of your eating habits first if you want to change your body.

As with nutrition, the important part of exercise is to do it consistently. The effects of exercise accumulate over time to improve your physical and mental health. This means doing an extreme two-week bootcamp every six months is not nearly as effective as consistently doing moderate exercise.

The combination of good nutrition and exercise allows you to control and change your body to reflect the image you want to project about yourself. Again, it would be nice to say that what we look like doesn't matter, although the reality is that your physical appearance communicates a persona. It displays your life choices, what you prioritise, your ability to set goals, have discipline and be persistent. That's not to say you need to look one way or another in particular, but rather to fully embrace the choices that you make—so that you are confident in whatever position you choose to take.

Though I would propose that the health and mental benefits of preventing health disruptions is in itself good motivation to make health a priority.

How much exercise is enough to make a meaningful difference to your brain? To achieve the brain-boosting effects of exercise, you only need to exercise around four times a week for 20 minutes each session, depending on the style of exercise. That's about 2% of your waking hours, which is not much at all.

An efficient type of exercise is High Intensity Interval Training, or HIIT for short. HIIT has become very popular in recent years, and for good reason:

- Workouts are short—around 20 minutes for most sessions
- It's more effective than long, endurance training sessions
- It's better than endurance training at burning fat
- Unlike endurance training, it increases resting metabolic rate for a full 24 hours afterwards

A session of HIIT consists of alternating between *work* and *rest* intervals. These have been shown to work best when the work-to-rest ratio is about 2:1. That means if you are running, you might sprint for 20 seconds, then jog lightly for 10 seconds as rest, before starting over. Doing this for about 20 minutes is a fantastic way to stimulate your body and boost your brain. You can start at a lower level and work your way up. Remember, the most important part is to exercise consistently.

These days there are so many different ways you can exercise that it can seem very confusing. The reality is that there are no specific movements or exercises that you absolutely have to do. Essentially, the best type of exercise is the type that you can keep on doing consistently. If you like running, do that. If you like Pilates, do that. If you like weights, do that. You don't even have to go to a gym. It's your choice if you want to do aerobic exercise, which gets your heart racing, or resistance training, which is more focused on growing muscle mass. Both types have been shown to improve brain health.

If you're new to exercise, start small by simply going for a walk for 10 minutes every day. Gradually build that up into something like running or another exercise that you want to try. If you are unsure how to do exercises, get a personal trainer for a while to show you the basics and get you started. You are also far more likely to succeed if you exercise with someone else, so find a partner or join a group and make a commitment to stay consistent. After all, it is an important part of both your long-term physical and mental health. You know you should do it, so do it.

Wake up feeling rested

Your body and brain has an ongoing requirement for sleep. While your body needs to repair itself and maintain muscles, your brain needs sleep to consolidate memories and maintain neural activity. You can improve the quality of your sleep by investigating and resolving specific factors.

Quality sleep is essential for overall health and especially essential to your brain—just ask anyone who is not getting enough sleep. Not getting enough sleep quickly becomes apparent. You might notice:

- Lack of concentration, reduced attention span
- Loss of coordination
- Increasing pressure to fall asleep
- Negative impacts on perception—being less able to see and hear correctly, resulting in more mistakes
- Inconsistent emotional states and mood swings
- Loss of inhibition and control
- Increased cortisol levels that makes it harder to cope with stress

These are examples of the powerful effect that poor sleep has on your brain and why it is so important to get quality sleep. Sleep helps your brain recover after each day and keep you mentally sharp. When we are sleep-deprived, blood flow to the Smart Brain goes down (meaning we become worse at higher-order thinking) and the Impulsive Brain is much more active than normal (meaning it starts to control our behaviour with impulsive decisions). The end result is that you become less able to deal with difficult circumstances and make good decisions.

It is one thing to know that lack of sleep or poor sleep is bad for you, but another thing entirely to know what causes it, and more importantly, to fix it. Let's look at some causes and what you can do about them:

Too much light. Is there any light making its way into your room at night, such as cracks in the curtains letting light through, or the glow from an alarm clock or other devices? Even if the light source is small, it can seriously reduce the quality of your sleep. This has even been linked to obesity, increased risk of breast cancer and mood disorders. Have a look at your room tonight and see how dark it is and whether you can see any light. If so, eliminate all the light sources. Put in blackout curtains, remove night lights, put phones upside down, or get a decent sleeping mask. You'll be surprised how quickly you notice the difference.

Caffeine. Even if taken six hours before going to bed, coffee and other caffeinated drinks can reduce the quality of sleep by one hour. This means you still get the same amount of sleep, but the quality is reduced, resulting in you feeling less rested the next day. If you are drinking a lot of caffeinated drinks and struggling to get a good night's sleep, it might be time for a change.

Stress and a racing mind. You might be going to bed each night at a good time, but lying awake for hours trying to fall asleep without any luck. Perhaps you're stressing about what happened today, what is going to happen tomorrow, trying to remember this, worrying about that. It is extremely frustrating. Part of managing this comes from setting clear goals and prioritising effectively so that you know what needs to be done and when, all so you can put it out of your mind for now. On a more immediate level, you can try the 4-7-8 Breathing Exercise that has been shown to help for falling asleep. Simply: Breathe in through your nose to the count of four. Hold your breath to the count of seven. Slowly breathe out through your mouth to the count of eight. Repeat until asleep.

Alcohol. Some people use an alcoholic drink as a way to get to sleep each night. While alcohol might help you fall asleep, your overall sleep quality is reduced, as with caffeine, even if the drink was six hours before going to bed. If you regularly drink alcohol before bed, it can add up to sleep deprivation over time, even if you still manage to get a full eight hours of sleep each night.

Too much to do. You might just have a lot of trouble actually going to bed on time in the first place, or staying in bed. Newborn baby? Goodbye sleep! That is a tough situation, but there are often ways to improve the situation. For example, becoming more efficient at doing tasks, better division of tasks in the house, preparing meals in bulk to get some time back in your day. If you start to see that lack of sleep is affecting you, negotiate with your partner or others in the house so you can get more sleep. If you tend to watch TV each night, cut back a bit and prioritise sleep instead. It will make you more relaxed than TV does anyway.

Noise. Too much noise can make it hard to fall asleep and can constantly wake you up during the night, interrupting deep sleep cycles. Find ways to cut down on any noise in the house, like closing the door and shutting down appliances and computers that might be making noise. If all else fails, some earplugs can also do the trick.

Sleep medication. As much as they help you fall asleep, they are not very good for quality sleep. Drugs like benzodiazepines (Valium, Xanax and many others) have been shown to increase sleep duration, but lower sleep quality. They also interfere with hippocampal function, which can prevent new memories from forming. It might be easy just to take one to fall asleep faster, but it's better for your health to find the real issue and fix that instead.

However, how much sleep should we get? Research shows between seven and eight hours of sleep each night is ideal for adults. Dipping below seven hours each night for a few nights in a row can cause significant declines in brain function and cognitive abilities. However, some people can function effectively with lower sleep, so pay attention to your own effectiveness with different levels of sleep.

On top of all the benefits that good sleep has for your brain, sleep is also necessary for muscle repair and healing. This is especially important if you are exercising, as your body needs time to repair itself and build muscle. Many people don't realise it, but your muscles do not grow while you are in the gym—they grow during sleep when your body increases growth hormone and sends protein to the damaged muscles to make them stronger.

5.

Building a culture of resilience

'A gile' is probably one of the most abused business words of the modern age. Agile development, agile business processes, agile workforce, the list goes on. While we might not be using the word in its intended context of software development, the popularity of the term alludes to a concept that is certainly becoming important for business—being able to act with speed and flexibility.

This is the antithesis of the corporate behemoths, though executives of these organisations are often keenly aware of both the power and limitations of size. Hence the preoccupation with agile as something to strive for to be able to compete with small and nimble start-ups aiming to disrupt established industries.

Shifting an established culture to be able to act with speed and a higher degree of innovation and risk-taking takes much more than a memo sent to all staff to 'think outside the box'. At the core of organisational innovation is a sense of safety embedded in the culture, reducing feelings of fear which enables the creativity required for disruptive thinking. In short—innovating from resilience.

Despite this, it's true that some level of innovation can be achieved through desperation, highlighting to staff the very real possibility that the company will go under if it doesn't innovate fast. This type of 'innovation from fear' can produce results, however the collective impulsive brain upregulation results in increased levels of stress and anxiety. Cumulating over time, these increase staff turnover, disengagement, absenteeism and reduced performance. Simply, employees develop patterns of avoidance that slowly leeches energy and resources out of the organisation.

Agility, therefore, needs to combine with *sustainability*. An organisation that aims to get to the cutting edge and also remain there has a more nuanced challenge. To achieve this, the traditional methods of using fear as a prime mover is no longer effective. Sustainability is achieved through resilience. Resilience enables people to thrive through challenges and innovate without taxing mental resources. This is about building a culture of resilience.

Why build resilience in organisations?

By looking at the neuroscience of the human brain, we find that increasing uncertainty presents a particular challenge. It violates one of our basic needs—the need for *control*—resulting in reduction of employee engagement. However, neuroscience also gives clues that can help us rethink how we can prepare our people for this age of disruption.

It's worth remembering that someone's resilience capacity is not a constant throughout life. We can improve our resilience, and our resilience can be worn down. Whether it gets worn down due to the environment and external events or through internal negativity, the fact is, no one is invincible.

As resilience improves, we gain a natural resistance against being worn down, although a toxic environment will eventually get to us. This is worth keeping in mind as the work environment is where many people spend most of their time, meaning it has a key influence on their resilience.

Resilience in a time of accelerating change can be improved by changing what we aim to control. For example, we may no longer aim to control our environment itself, but rather control our interaction with it. Adjusting these perceptions can be achieved at a cultural level, shifting expectations towards a mindset that is intuitively constructive, despite adversity.

The benefit is not just to the organisation, but to individuals themselves. Resilience increases their own sense of safety at a subconscious level, improving relationships, goal achievement, sense of purpose and overall sense of wellness. This translates into greater compassion and empathy at a societal level, highlighting how an organisational drive for resilience can have a profound global impact.

Currently, no one group has taken on the mantle of teaching resilience. It therefore falls to executives, leaders and managers to enable resilience education. Organisations should take on this responsibility, as they are in the best position to do something about it... while also standing to gain the most. Showing that you care about staff wellbeing beyond your own interest will earn loyalty beyond what can be achieved otherwise. Appreciating the benefit of caring is part of the gradual enlightenment of organisations.

The benefit of building resilience into the culture reaches far. Long have we known that genetic factors are passed down to children. In this sense, it was long thought that genetic variation takes many hundreds to thousands of years to happen. Now we know that experiences within your own lifetime can result in changes that are passed down, through epigenetics. One study showed that people with post-traumatic stress disorder passed on specific changes to their children that affect activation of the HPA axis.[43] Effectively it means that in one generation, a high amount of stress can be passed on to children, affecting their lives as well.

Cultivating resilience therefore represents a major long-term opportunity. The positive changes we facilitate now can create epigenetic changes passed on to future generations. Compassion and empathy through resilience and a deep sense of safety thus become hereditable traits.

It starts with you

People look to their leaders for inspiration for their own wellbeing. In this section, as we switch gears to consider the mechanics of building a resilient culture, you may spot some overlaps with what we've covered

---

[43] Perroud, N., Rutembesa, E., Paoloni-Giacobino, A., Mutabaruka, J., Mutesa, L., Stenz, L., ... & Karege, F. (2014). The Tutsi genocide and transgenerational transmission of maternal stress: epigenetics and biology of the HPA axis. *The World Journal of Biological Psychiatry*, 15(4), 334-345.

before. This is because, quite simply, your own behaviour is closely tied to fostering a resilient culture. After all, the resilience skills you are internalising also need to be internalised by employees, allowing the shared mentality to coalesce into the broader culture as deep organisational resilience.

Before you can build a culture of resilience in your organisation, you must first build resilience within yourself. The age-old truism still applies—you must help yourself before you can help others. This task, however, requires more than simply the knowledge of a resilient mindset, but also an awareness of human nature, some cultural neuroscience, and other complicating factors on the horizon. As always, it all starts with Vision.

Vision

Few would care to admit it, but the goals that employees work towards in their careers are often the clearest goals that they have overall. This provides a sense of purpose and belonging that is often lacking outside of work. It is here that Vision, as the most important domain of resilience, provides the largest opportunity for organisations to improve the resilience of their people. When you help people connect their own sense of purpose to what they do at work, then you give them a way to define and achieve their goals. This motivates people.

Through our research, we investigated over 100 questions to help measure the various domains of resilience. We whittled down the questions until only the highest-performing questions that provide the best measurement of resilience remained. Curiously, a few questions gathered at the top as the best predictors of overall resilience. These were the Vision questions.

In fact, you can determine someone's overall resilience through just two Vision questions. These two questions offer close to the same accuracy as asking 50 questions about someone's resilience:

1. Do you struggle to stay motivated?
2. Do you believe in your ability to achieve your goals?

Analysing these questions reveals more about resilience. The first question most highly correlates with resilience, indicating that, most of all, people have a desire for something in their life to motivate them to action. This we have seen already, with the fundamental need of the brain for *motivation*. However, what is surprising is how this is perhaps the most central aspect of resilience. When life is tough and we face many hardships, having something that keeps us motivated helps us overcome the greatest obstacles. This naturally overlaps with Tenacity, as motivation is a key ingredient for persistence.

Motivation at a cultural level is therefore not only important for performance, but also helps employees overcome adversity and thrive, despite the challenges they face. Not that it comes as a surprise that motivation is important in the workplace—indeed this is a concept as old as the Pyramids—however, as we explore further, we'll see that the way in which staff are motivated has a critical long-term impact on themselves and the culture within the organisation.

The second question speaks neatly to another fundamental need of the brain, which is for *control*. Key here is that it is about the individual's perception of being able to reach their goals. Do they believe that they are in an environment within which they can set clear goals and achieve them?

Through the environment at work, control can be facilitated to help people believe in their ability to achieve their goals. One side of the coin is about creating an environment within which individual goals can be realised at work, while the other side is assisting individuals to set goals that are realistic and aligned in ways that are mutually valuable. By doing this, we can access the best of people because they then have a personal stake in their part of the organisation. They'll put their most powerful energy into what they do.

The importance of control is clearly visible through the opposite scenario, where we see disengagement from highly-capable people who no longer believe in their ability to achieve their own goals within the organisation. Perhaps there are too frequent changes that time and again thwart their own efforts. Perhaps their attempts to link what matters to them to the organisation has been rejected or ignored.

Regardless of the cause, a disengaged employee costs an organisation dearly. Disengagement can result in vulnerability, where resilience might drop, and eventually they leave, thoroughly disappointed. Thus they take valuable knowledge with them while the usual rehiring cost kicks in. Remembering these two Vision questions might be useful to you as they provide a quick heuristic to determine someone's overall resilience, and if they might be in need of help.

Similarly, these questions are useful to pose to yourself to see how you are doing. After all, you influence the resilience of those around you.

Lead with vision

Who could feel comfortable when their leader is as directionless as a bumblebee in a tornado? This type of leadership creates a constant apprehension about when the direction will suddenly change again, invalidating any previous efforts and goals. The constant uncertainty eats away at people and leads them to put in less effort. This is due to an expectation that whatever they do will not matter soon enough, or worse, will end up being wrong anyway.

Uncertainty is the key factor at play. The fundamental need of the brain for control is being violated. The brain needs the world to make sense to some degree—to be able to predict with some level of certainty what each new day will bring. The brain is constantly working on an internal model of the world, though if it struggles to understand the mechanics of how an aspect of life works, then uncertainty grows.

Uncertainty isn't necessarily a source of stress for the brain, however. A highly unpredictable character on a television show can be very entertaining. After all, there's no danger to us, so we can enjoy the antics of the character.

However, when uncertainty surrounds someone who controls your ability to buy food and pay rent, then it's not funny anymore. Now uncertainty shakes our basic sense of safety, shifting the brain into survival mode. Blood flow to the HPA axis increases, leading to higher levels of cortisol and related stress hormones. Our ability to be creative and think strategically diminishes, while we become more impulsive and reactive.

Short-term, survival tactics dominate our thinking.

Whether in uncertain times or not, the brain is looking for patterns of prediction. As an expert pattern recognition machine, the brain searches for patterns to predict the behaviour of leaders of the organisation. The consistency with which you lead, including how you treat the people you interact with and your judgements, all contribute.

Leading with high consistency means the brains of those around you can subconsciously recognise patterns of prediction that feed into the need for control. For these patterns to produce a sense of safety at the subconscious level, consistent actions need to make sense and align to broader values. After all, if you are consistently frustrated at the world, then it's not going to produce a sense of safety in employees and colleagues.

Clarity of purpose is what drives consistency in a constructive way. Having this clarity about what you want to achieve allows you to then build a clear connection to the goal of the organisation. Here you can ideally find an authentic connection between your own sense of purpose and how you achieve that through your work at the organisation. Finding this connection is not only motivational for you, but also allows you to clearly communicate to your people what drives you, and how it's relevant to organisational goals.

One challenge here is if your main sense of purpose doesn't at all connect with your work. Perhaps you work purely to earn money so that you can pursue your real sense of purpose outside of work. People pick up on this, and while this motive is not necessarily wrong, it does create a different type of culture. For one, you're probably only going to inspire other people who are also not overly concerned about their careers, while those who feel their work is important might look elsewhere. Those might well be the people the business needs to survive in an age of increasing digital disruption.

Another challenge is in communicating the connection between your purpose and your work. If your own sense of purpose simply seems like a carbon copy of the organisation's vision, then it's not going to energise anyone. If you tell people it's your passion to create the best rubber-coated paperclips, then you're going to have to do some explaining about why that is authentic to you, and is not just you being a corporate parrot.

If people can understand your drivers and it makes sense to them, then subconsciously it produces that crucial sense of safety coming from the brain's need for control—being able to predict the environment. Consciously, this translates as a feeling of confidence in a leader. This allows people to have more trust in you, since their own brain can incorporate a consistent mental model of who you are. According to this model, they can perform strategic planning.

When someone knows what a leader wants to achieve and how this aligns with broader organisational goals, and the person has confidence that their ideas will be met constructively, then we find a mindset that leads to innovation.

On the other hand, if people don't know what your drivers are and perhaps don't feel that you are open to new ideas, then only the bravest of people would be willing to approach you with something that might challenge your preconceptions. While this might uncover who those brave souls are, you won't necessarily get the best ideas, since others with great ideas might stay silent. Beyond that, people may not even invest in coming up with new ideas in the first place.

Your actions must support your words. It's not enough to simply say you want new ideas. For example, if every time someone comes to you with something new and you say, 'This better be good', or 'Not you again', then in future you won't see many new ideas. Not because there aren't any, but rather because you are subconsciously discouraging people.

To sum up, building a culture of resilience starts by having clarity on your own vision. You can then connect that to the organisational goals, so that you can clearly communicate why what you and your people do is important. You can also communicate why it's important to those who benefit from your services. Clarity on these factors provides the building blocks for people to subconsciously understand who you are, feeds their need for control, and brings a sense of safety within which they too can connect, innovate and thrive. Through leading with vision, you can then help individuals align their own goals to that of the organisation.

Aligning the goals of others

A philosophical question now arises about how important work should be to us. It's not necessarily the most important thing, though there are two major things to consider. First, generally people spend the majority of their waking hours at work. Second, as business gets more competitive and more disruptive, there's less leeway for people who are simply interested in punching in and out while not giving it their all. Therefore, it makes sense to help people connect their own goals and sense of purpose to their work. It comes down to this: work isn't everything, but it should be meaningful.

What this means is that if we are going to be spending so much time at work, we should at least find ways to connect our own goals to that of the organisation. This way, what we do is meaningful and motivational to us. In return, this motivation benefits the organisation in ways that build competitive advantage while also providing a better chance for personal advancement. Aligning goals therefore builds a mutually beneficial relationship between the employee and the organisation.

Having clarity on the connection between your own goals and that of the organisation is the first step. From there, you can create an environment within which you can help those around you find ways to connect their own goals to those of the organisation as well. Doing so links into the fundamental needs of the brain. It also helps people gain a sense of *control and orientation*, in that they gain a vehicle for self-fulfilment. Being in an organisation *connects* them with other people around them who share goals. It also provides a sense of *motivation* through doing something meaningful. Therefore, each of the three fundamental needs of the brain are effected, increasing the individual's sense of self-esteem.

When people can create this connection between their personal drivers and the goals of the team and organisation, then we can effectively plain English description here (downregulate the HPA axis) through reduced blood flow to the impulsive brain. Frontal cortex activation would be increased and so people could now use the full capacity of their smart brain to be more creative, take more strategic risks, and innovate in ways that can push both themselves and the organisation forward.

Now, if only it was easy for people to connect their personal goals to that of the organisation. For starters, many people don't have a sense of purpose in the first place. They may not have any clear goals that they are working towards. The very field they are working in may have been something they studied due to pressure rather than desire.

That's not to say there is no hope for someone in this position—quite the contrary. We all start out not having a sense of purpose or a vision for our lives. As infants, we are all born into a world with no sense of purpose other than those that people wish to push onto us. As we age, we might start to question any earlier sense of purpose, or lack thereof. From there, we each need to define our vision for ourselves at some point, and for some it comes sooner than for others.

With all the distractions and entertainment escapes available today, it's easier than ever to avoid having to determine your own sense of purpose. However, within an organisational context, we don't need to turn this into a major philosophical debate. We can keep it practical by focusing on *helping, improving,* or *advancing.* For example, if you are conducting an interview and the candidate says: *'I am passionate about loan settlement administration'*, then I think anyone can quite rightly be sceptical of that statement. Really? Who is actually passionate about that?

Though if the candidate said: *'I want to help people buy their dream home'.* Yes, now we have something real and meaningful. It's simple, it's real, and easier to build an authentic connection to. Perhaps the candidate really valued their own home while growing up, or didn't have one and wants others to have it. In this example, loan settlement administration is a small part, but it's still a key part of the chain that helps real people fulfil their dream. So, an employee can connect to the broader outcome of what they are achieving.

Even very esoteric jobs still build toward something valuable. After all, a job wouldn't exist if it wasn't needed (theoretically, anyway... work with me here). Even if someone took a job mainly because of the need for a salary, they can still retrospectively find some connection to it. This might take some creativity, however, by bringing the connection back to something simple, it can work.

The vast majority of people want to know that what they do is valued and important in some way. They want to help people, making things better, and feel connected to the world that they are in. These things are rooted in the fundamental needs of the brain, which is why bringing it back to something as simple as helping, improving, or advancing works.

The task of creating a connection between an individual's goals and their work is mostly their own responsibility. As an organisation, you cannot force someone to find meaning in their jobs. However, what you can do is to support and facilitate. The first step is to at least not actively stand in the way of people trying to find meaning in their work. This happens more than you might think, often through subconscious behaviour of superiors. For example, when an employee desires to understand the larger impact of their work, only to be told to *just get back to work* because their superior doesn't have time to explain.

Beyond that, as a leader you can construct an environment that encourages clarity of purpose and alignment. One way to enable the resilience imperative is by providing resilience training to staff. Training furnishes them with the mental skills to gain clarity about their own vision, setting them up to find alignment with what they do. Providing additional training to managers and superiors is crucial as well, since it builds a shared language of resilience within the organisation.

With this in place, when an employee goes to their manager with a question about aligning their own goals to the organisation, it will make sense to the manager what the employee is trying to achieve. This shared understanding then creates compassion, enabling them to explore creative ways to align goals together and thus find meaning in their work.

To help guide this alignment, managers might explain how they have found meaning in what they do. They can listen, understand and guide more effectively, drawing from their own experiences and insight about the work environment that the employee might not have. The role here is to support and facilitate connection, though it relies on a shared language and understanding.

All parties at all levels need to be involved in the drive to create a resilient culture for it to be successful. Employees cannot achieve it by themselves and neither can leaders change the culture in isolation. The full workforce needs to be engaged in learning the language of resilience to be able to understand each other's intentions and trust that their efforts to achieve alignment will be welcomed. There's a flexibility that will be needed from both employees and the leadership team, which again, requires resilience.

By doing these things, you are gearing the organisation to become a vehicle for personal purpose realisation. As a reward, the organisation gains resilient employees who are loyal, innovative and have a deep personal investment in what they do.

Composure

Composure touches the heart of that which enables a culture of resilience. And when I say 'heart', I mean the emotional areas of the brain that feels like the heart. This is because our emotions can easily sabotage our ability to think clearly and constructively through the activation of the Impulsive brain. As we've noted previously, this happens through the fight-or-flight response that decreases blood flow to the frontal cortex.

At an individual level, this activation results in a loss of strategic thinking, as short-term survival strategies take hold. However, chronic fight-or-flight activation at scale in an organisation may coalesce into even more serious cultural problems.

The impact of these cultural problems is not readily visible. Instead, the organisation feels the impact over time—an inability to retain key talent, lack of innovation, and slowly losing a competitive edge. When these go unresolved, the impact can lead to the eventual demise of once-great companies.

Dealing with these problems often seems elusive, due to the root cause being so distant from the emergent behaviour. This distance complicates treatment, since organisation-wide initiatives to address the issues may not see results fast enough to know whether the initiatives are working or not. This can result in haphazard course changes as multiple solutions are tried in quick succession, none sticking around long enough to change what's at the heart of the issue.

Exploring Composure from a cultural perspective not only shows us the neurobiological roots of the problem, but also provides a way to address these problematic behaviours. There is benefit in having a mechanistic explanation of what causes the behaviour so that it can be reversed through consistent effort. As we know from how the brain learns (when we discussed the neuro-mechanics of persistence), we need consistency to be able to change neural patterns and rewire effectively. To understand how this works from a cultural perspective, let's explore a harmful, yet common type of leadership.

Innovation and motivation schemas

I mentioned previously the importance of motivation for employees and its role in enabling resilience. However, there's a further aspect to it, which is how this motivation is created. The motivation source activates different areas of the brain, and therefore has different effects over the long term. For example, a sure-fire way to quickly motivate people into action is to use fear via a punishment. People fear a punishment if they don't comply, so they do as they are told. The bigger the potential punishment, the more effective the motivation, for example, threatening that someone will get fired works faster than a lower score on a performance review.

Fear comes from the amygdala detecting that there is danger in the environment, thus alerting the brain to activate survival mechanisms. As the brain switches over, we get rigid compliance—where the requested action isn't questioned but instead, simply followed. The brain focuses on doing the task exactly as requested so as to avoid punishment or pain. What is interesting here is that the brain learns far faster through fear than through pleasure. For example, if a team member brings a new idea to you and you yell at them about it, then likely they will never try that again. Conversely, it takes repeated positive reinforcement to get people to brainstorm in company meetings in order to explore the ideas' potential.

Many leaders fall into fear-based leadership by default, simply because it's easy and they see immediate results. Sometimes we may get frustrated, we don't have the time to explain, and we just want to see fast results. In these cases, fear is such a comfortable and well-worn shoe that we can slip in without us really noticing. It can take the form of veiled threats and passive aggression, sneaking in and slowly poisoning the culture.

There is a concept in psychology known as motivation schemas. These are separated into approach and avoidance schemas. With an *approach motivation* schema, a person is motivated to do well at work due to an expectation of future reward. With an *avoid motivation* schema, a person is motivated to do well at work due to fear of punishment.

Note that both are motivated to do well, so initially we might think them equal. However, one leads to a more constructive outcome than the other. This is because fear-based leadership created these patterns of avoidance. While the intention is similar—do well at work—the brain adapts to fear through closed-loop learning.

Closed-loop learning is when only a small area of the brain is activated in a particular situation. For example, while at work, the brain of someone with an avoidance motivation schema mainly activates the areas related to the required routine. The pattern might be something like: *'Don't get fired—just do the work—so I don't get fired—so just keep working.'* As you can see, this is a very small loop between two concepts.

At a glance, this might seem just fine. However, what's important is that other areas are not activating, such as those that would consider the efficiency of business processes. These are the thoughts that could identify ways to improve the business, to innovate and disrupt. Even worse, someone might have a good idea, but quickly crush it because they know nothing will come of it.

These innovative thoughts come from whole-brain activation—the opposite of closed-loops. Here the pattern might be something like: *'Do the work—this is taking too long—it would be faster if we did this instead.'* In this simplistic view, we can already see divergent thoughts happening in the brain of someone willing to think beyond the status quo and consider ways to improve. These thoughts come from wide-ranging activation through various areas in the brain, such as the prefrontal cortex, the default mode network, and more. These areas need sufficient blood flow and upregulation that cannot happen if the impulsive brain is activated. That is to say, if a person is ruled by fear, then they will struggle to think creatively.

What this means is that fear-based leadership can get you fast results, but it comes at a great cost. This cost is felt in the long term as employees develop patterns of avoidance and closed-loop learning settles into the brain.

On the other hand, building approach motivation schemas, where the impulsive brain is downregulated and the smart brain is upregulated, helps people to think constructively and strategically. This then provides whole-brain activation, which enables a culture of innovation, collaboration and continuous improvement. The challenge is that a healthy culture doesn't happen by default, so we should start by identifying if a fear-based culture exists. Through that, we can find ways to improve and build a culture of resilience.

Symptoms of fear-based leadership

There are many ways in which fear-based leadership affects culture. Sometimes it's subtle, so being able to detect the clues will help you spot it in your organisation, and also recognise when another leader is employing it with their staff. The following are a few tell-tale signs of fear-based leadership.

People do what they're told, but little else. In this environment, there might be high compliance with whatever directives are sent out, but seldom would anyone step outside those narrow confines. Everyone is focused on doing their job and trying to stay out of trouble. Work tasks are rarely questioned, even if it the work seems of little value. New staff often experience this when they see a dubious work task and they ask, *'What's the point of this work?'* The inevitable answer comes back, *'Don't ask—this is just how they want it.'* This indicates that seasoned staff have learned to just do what they're told, probably after having been beaten down themselves when they questioned orders in the past. It's a comfortable place to be, to not question anything, but the fear is evident when someone dares to suggest that the orders be questioned.

Talking about the culture is avoided. As a systemic feature, often middle management are themselves trapped by the culture and rendered powerless, or worse, become complicit in the fear-based culture. From this, it quickly becomes clear to staff that there is little point in discussing the culture. Even though many realise there is a problem with the culture, talking about it only leads to getting punished for pointing out the obvious. After all, management themselves have little cognitive reserves left after dealing with the culture and internal politics themselves. Instead, the rumour mill becomes the preferred source of insight and cultural discussion, creating an undercurrent of toxicity hidden from view of management. A key indicator of this is in a team meeting, where a question is asked about the culture and it is met with an immediate dead silence... each team member's hastily expressionless face disguising sheer panic.

Innovation is a bad word. Nearly every business has made innovation a priority. However, in a fear-based culture, most staff realise that words and actions are two very different things. This happens when the punishment for failure is greater than the rewards for success. Staff quickly notice that there is far too much risk in pursuing any new ideas, having often seen the pain others go through who try something different. This could manifest in new ideas being heavily criticised instead of supported, or with an undue amount of accountability being placed on the person who came up with the idea. As the idea is implemented, a lack of support set it up for failure. Then the eventual failure is blamed on the innovator, affecting their performance reviews, which further discourages anyone else from even trying. More broadly, this could manifest in undue complex approval processes, with managers far-and-wide wanting to be aware, since failure might reflect badly on them in some way. Again, the status quo is much safer, so why risk change? What you might notice in this case is that even though the message is being put out that innovation is a priority, very few ideas are put forward. Not because there are few ideas, but rather because people are too afraid to risk their careers.

Key talent keeps leaving. A strong clue to a fear-based culture is that people keep leaving. Mostly the people that you don't want to leave. These are people who can recognise when the environment is not conducive to them achieving their full potential, so they only stay as long as needed to keep the résumé looking healthy, then jump ship as fast as possible. Perhaps during their stay, their achievements at previous organisations did not reflect their achievements in this organisation, putting into perspective the impact of the culture. As is generally the problem with attrition, the net result is that the best people leave first, while the rest stay, leading to a less-competitive workforce comprised of people not necessarily best suited to push the business forward.

High sensitivity to bad news. We all know organisations where the thought of delivering bad news sends shivers down your spine. This often develops inadvertently—an overloaded senior manager or executive doesn't have time to process any more bad news, so an employee coming over with anything less than positive risks getting their head bitten off. Over time, the result is that bad news gets swept under the rug and problems are kept out of sight until they become too big to hide. The usual corporate strategy here is to hide things long enough until they can move to another role, so that old problems are not their problem. Naturally, this has a big impact on the organisation's ability to effectively manage risk, since you can't manage what you're not aware of. A further impact is that opportunities hidden inside the bad news are not being explored. These can provide insight into how processes and services can be improved to avoid similar issues, and potentially even generate a better product or service.

Engagement scores become deceptive. As much as they are questioned, many organisations still use engagement surveys to measure culture and sentiment within the ranks. Something that often happens in larger organisations is that lower scores on engagement surveys are pushed back on the staff themselves. The thinking being that staff need to take ownership to resolve the causes of lower scores. In a fear-based culture, employees start to understand that answering honestly on the engagement scores simply means they will be punishing themselves. The overall outcome is that they will all be put in a room and forced to discuss why the scores are low, though due to fear, people will not speak about the true causes. Instead, alternate explanations are offered for the scores, leading to actions designed to resolve issues that don't exist. To avoid all this, a mindset develops of *'press five to stay alive'*, with five being the highest score on the engagement survey. This way, people can avoid the pain of dealing with low scores and they can just get on with work and stay out of trouble.

Shifting from fear to resilience

Once a fear-based culture has been identified, the good news is that it can be changed and resolved. The effort involved in achieving cultural change is never trivial, however it is a must for any organisation wishing to maintain a competitive edge as digital disruption expands.

The key is that a fear-based culture developed from the multitude of behaviours affecting the sense of safety of employees. This happens through the violation of the basic needs of the brain, including the basic needs for *control, motivation,* and *connection. Control* is taken away, as they are forced to simply follow orders, and is further affected by ambiguity about future direction. *Motivation* is reduced, as people are not allowed to express themselves creatively and get stuck in routines. *Connection* is discouraged, as people focus on tasks instead of strategic collaboration.

As these needs are impacted, the impulsive brain is upregulated, downregulating the frontal cortex and resulting in the dominance of short-term survival strategies. Here, the survival strategies are focused on making it through the day without losing your job, resulting in the symptoms of a fear-based culture as we explored before. Given the underlying neurological cause of needs violation, it becomes clear that we cannot simply change this culture by addressing the symptoms. For example, when you have a culture like this, you can't stop people gossiping by telling them to stop; or you can't get people to innovate by telling them to think outside the box. The brain is locked into survival patterns due to behaviours perpetuated by management.

Therefore, cultural change needs to be focused on restoring safety through meeting the fundamental needs of the brain. Crucially, restoration of safety through this approach takes time. It's not a task that can be achieved in a few months, since the neural patterns take time to change and need a lot of positive reinforcement for form new pathways. Organisations often go wrong with cultural change by changing paths too quickly when they don't see results fast enough. By understanding what is happening at a neurological level, the chosen path can be followed with more confidence, allowing your leaders to stay the course while allowing neural change to happen.

Let's consider a few ways in which you can start to shift away from a fear-based culture.

Acknowledge the problem. First and foremost, it needs to be acknowledged that there is a cultural problem. Without acceptance of this, change is unlikely to follow because management will continue with their previous behaviour through denial of complicity. This agreement can take place purely at a management level behind closed doors, and need not necessarily be broadcast to the organisation. However, a concerted effort to change the culture should be broadcast, even if only under the banner of continuous improvement.

The importance of this lies in the reality that a fear-based culture stems from fear-based leadership. Due to this, cultural change must be driven through behavioural change at a management level. Generally, if an organisation were to replace all of their line staff without any management behavioural change, then a fear-based culture would re-emerge, due to fear-based leadership that still exists. Ultimately, leadership is responsible for the culture, so acknowledgement of the problem needs to happen at this level to be able to shift the culture. This may also mean becoming aware of subconscious behaviours that leaders were blind to that are contributing to cultural problems.

Support open communication. It is no surprise that a great deal of the culture of an organisation is formed through interpersonal communication. The brain takes input through all its senses to continuously validate its model of the world, while in an organisational environment mainly auditory and visual senses are involved. Therefore, both verbal and non-verbal forms of communication contribute. Developing a sense of safety within staff therefore comes from their brains sensing that the environment is non-threatening. Importantly, it's not enough to simply say that people are safe. The words need to be backed by action and evidence. People who have been working under fear-based leadership will have lost trust in leadership, and that trust needs to be rebuilt over time through consistent words and action.

Consistency is again important, since one transgression back to the old ways can instantly evaporate months of work. For example, an executive with a habit of blowing up when an employee makes a mistake might say that they will never do that again. It all might go well for months, until one day another mistake pushes him over the edge and he blows up again. For witnesses to the event and all those they talk to, the message is clear—

nothing has changed, so watch out.

For management to be able to support open communication, there needs to be clarity on what this is. Open communication is about listening without judgment. It's about listening without interrupting. It's about not questioning feelings, but rather questioning facts. It's about focusing on solutions, instead of problems. This kind of non-judgemental listening needs to start at the executive level when discussing cultural problems. If right away the conversation descends into finger-pointing and survival strategies, then there is much less chance for a meaningful change.

This change in attitude then needs to flow down to all levels, so that employees can experience open communication in an environment where their basic sense of safety isn't threatened. The aim is to enable individuals to be open about challenges, problem-solve with management insight, take strategic risks with support, and collaborate without undue bureaucratic burden.

Control opportunities for retribution. Further to fostering open communication, take care to control/prevent potential passive-aggressive retaliation by management against employees, such as discretionary incentives and performance reviews. Few things are quite as demotivating as putting in a lot of effort throughout the year, only to have it all undone due to one misstep right before performance review time.

Just as employees have a fundamental need for control, so too do managers. Performance reviews and incentives are a key way for managers to maintain a perception of control. These are often used to threaten any poor behaviour or performance. Therefore, they're used to create fear (resulting in an *avoidance motivation* schema), rather than an incentive for high performance (*approach motivation* schema).

As we now know, fear-based motivation results in short-term survival strategies, reducing the likelihood of employees to be creative and take risks. This is particularly evident in roles without clear metrics for success, where eventual ratings are highly subjective.

Turning this into something positive and motivating means proving greater clarity and control to the employees themselves. This includes making clear to management that performance reviews are not a punitive construct, but rather something that an employee has direct control over through their own efforts. Better yet, explore ditching performance reviews, like many other organisations have already. Instead, focus on more frequent discussions about performance—instant feedback where possible. Keep the conversations constructive to focus on growth and improvement; help people see the opportunities of change, rather than the dangers of failure.

Organisational emotion reappraisal. Just as the reappraisal technique is useful at an individual level, so too is it useful at an organisational level. This touches on a different aspect of fear in the culture, being fear about uncertainty that people face. Reappraisal is about taking an emotion, such as anxiety about a big change, and through a bit of emotional alchemy, turning it into a constructive emotion, such as excitement. Many great leaders do this naturally—without even realising the underlying mechanism that they are employing. So, with our understanding that this type of reappraisal has the ability to turn impulsive brain activation into forebrain activation, this technique can now be used more consciously and effectively.

Deploying this at an organisational level has the same requirement as at an individual level. That means, it is not enough to simply say that all the anxiety that people might be feeling about a big organisational change is actually excitement. There needs to be logic and reasoning about *why* people should be excited about it. Uncertainty is often a time of opportunity, but people cannot easily see the opportunities if the impulsive brain is focused on short-term survival, such as potentially losing employment.

Therefore, management at all levels need to buy into the strategy, the opportunities, and be able to communicate this down the line. They must illustrate and back up with conviction that the uncertainty the employees are facing is indeed something to be excited about. A good test for it is your own mindset—if you cannot convince yourself, then you won't convince others.

Develop an awareness of stress in teams. Working on your sensitivity to changes in moods and stress in teams is a useful tool in maintaining a healthy culture. This is less about the day-to-day changes and more about trends lasting weeks or months. Being able to notice when the team is particularly stressed— especially when combined with knowing that there are things going on which are putting them under pressure—can help you to recognise when people need a bit of a break or some encouragement. Acknowledging tough times and reminding people to look after themselves is important in humanising their participation in the organisation.

Thinking back to the myth of work-life balance, what people truly need to stay productive is the fundamental needs of *control, motivation* and *connection.* If you see people particularly stressed, then it's worth exploring these concepts with them. For example, do they have personal goals that they are working towards right now that link back to what they do at work? Do they enjoy the work they are doing right now, or is it meaningful to them? Do they have a support network that they can rely on? Often through these types of questions you'll find more meaningful answers—the reasons behind why someone is stressed. Then you can advise much more helpful action beyond simply suggesting planning a holiday sometime.

All these behaviours combine to generate what we really need in the culture—a subconscious sense of safety—that translates into confident people, willing to take strategic risks that can push the organisation forward. It absolutely starts with yourself, then the other executives, then managers, then everyone else. You cannot change a fear-based culture from the ground up. The problem lies in fear-based leadership that created the culture in the first place.

Fortunately, understanding the simple mechanics of what this does to the brain in terms of regulation between the impulsive and smart areas, it's possible to align everyone in the organisation and shift to new, healthy habits. This enables the culture to change (through neural pathway reorganisation), building on the evidence of a supportive management structure.

Through a concerted effort, the employees gain the confidence to be resilient, creating a resilient organisation that can take risks and be disruptive in the marketplace when it needs to be.

Reasoning

Proactiveness is often the most overlooked component of resilience. Most of the challenges we face in life can be prevented, or at least have the impact mitigated. This preventative capability comes from our willingness to entertain different possibilities and effectively plan for those eventualities. These same preventative principles exist in an organisational context, where we have divisions dedicated to the discipline of Risk Management. As those who work in the field of risk are keenly aware, it's quite difficult for people to be highly conscious of what risks might be involved in their activities. So, often this requires formal techniques to step through in order to uncover risks in business processes and decisions.

This reluctance to consider risk is a natural consequence because we as individuals prefer to avoid the thought of things going wrong. Thinking about impulsive-brain activation, it's easy to see why the brain would try to avoid anything that might produce stress or anxiety. After all, why submit yourself to something you know will be painful? When this fear exists across many people, then we see cultural avoidance of the management of risks. Not that people don't take risks, but rather they avoid acknowledging the risks they take. This is when risk management becomes like pulling teeth— the collective amygdala activation resists any effort to be proactive and mitigate risks.

The Reasoning domain addresses this at the root level by teaching the brain to be constructive in managing risks, and therefore avoid impulsive-brain activation. This means people can calmly consider things going wrong. This in turn leads to greater clarity, creativity to find potential solutions, and ways to effectively manage the potential outcome. Scaling up to a cultural level, this results in a shared propensity to be upfront about risks, allowing faster proactive mitigation.

Reasoning steps beyond risk management, affecting our ability to see opportunities amid change. It also affects how we solve problems and our attitude towards the future. This combination is crucial for the longevity of organisations, as they increasingly rely on radical problem-solving and disruptive innovation. This requires whole-brain activation and the downregulation of impulsive areas of the brain. To achieve this, we need practical ways to foster increased reasoning within an organisation.

Embracing accelerating change

Resilience is interesting in its ability to allow people to thrive in difficult circumstances. A key way in which this is achieved, both individually and culturally, is through redefining what exactly *is* and *is not* a difficult situation. Our perceptions heavily influence our emotional reality, so it's fortunate for us that we can change our perceptions to produce more constructive emotions.

To make sense of this, consider that most people value stability and familiarity. Therefore, if something were to threaten this stability, then people get stressed and anxious. Contrast this to organisations that increasingly need rapid change and disruption to stay in front. Conserving the status quo just a little too long can result in the loss of a competitive advantage, leading to a slow and painful decline. In other words, organisations need to function in a way that's nearly the opposite of what individuals tend to value. No wonder then that mental health issues are increasing across the world.

We need a solution to this paradox of certainty—a way to restore certainty despite increasing uncertainty.

The solution to this paradox lies within our ability to change perceptions. By re-evaluating how we see certainty and of change, we can change the brain's response to these events. That can then allow us to thrive in situations others see as difficult, because we do not see those situations as difficult ourselves. So, how do we achieve this?

Let's consider stability. The default perception might be *'stability is good'*. However, we can expand that to clarify what is important. For an individual, the critical part is likely stability of their income—in other words, you'll have a job a year from now. Beyond that, we can adjust the perception of stability from an organisational growth perspective. For example, *'stability is stagnation, and stagnation is death'*. That might be dramatic, but it's the reality for many organisations that fell from their highs because they didn't keep up. For employees, the message might be *'If a year from now we are still doing things the same way, then something is wrong'*, or more positively, *'A year from now we should be doing things in new ways'*.

This highlights to management and staff that the organisation constantly needs to advance. There is a continual need for new ideas and a drive to improve or radically change processes and products. Devaluing stability creates a desire for change, both at a personal and a cultural level. An individual internalising this mentality might come to think *'If this organisation isn't evolving, then I'm probably in a failing organisation'*. This is, by far, a more change-oriented mindset, as opposed to a mindset where people constantly desire the status quo.

If, on the other hand, the organisation is constantly in flux while people are constantly waiting for things to settle down, then the experience is mentally draining for employees. Too often we hear words like *'We can't do this because there's too much change right now'*, when really, six months from now there will be even more change.

Far more constructive is when individuals expect change—and even *value* change as a necessary part of the continuous evolution of the organisation—therefore matching the reality of continuous change. This collective expectation, combined with consistent support for new ideas, creates a culture of change. With the collective smart brains of people activated during change, people can maintain flexibility of thought to find ways to rapidly incorporate new ideas, even in the middle of change.

We no longer have the luxury of properly finishing large projects anymore. The environment changes fast enough that we need to adapt on-the-fly just to keep pace with market pressures. As individuals, we all need to understand the value in agility by realising that the old value of stability equals a slow demise. As a leader, it falls to you to communicate this revaluation to employees and back it up with action.

People need to see evidence that the organisation will support new ideas. Risks taken by employees should be supported and not unduly punished if they don't work out. This follows on from resolving a fear-based culture and building on the excitement of what change can bring—the shared opportunity in advancing the organisation.

It would be difficult to find someone that is completely happy in their job—there's always something that could be better. Therefore, challenge people to come up with ways to improve the work, the products, or the processes. This challenge—alongside the willingness of the organisation to change—provides a sense of hope for the future, provided it is backed up by evidence that ideas can be realised into action.

A major factor that holds back a change-oriented culture in many organisations is exactly that inability to follow up words with action. That is to say, all the best intentions to build a change-oriented culture can be undone by red tape and roadblocks. This is especially true in large organisations, where change is far easier said than done. Regulatory requirements, increasing constraints around legal, risk, compliance and security, all work against agility. Greater sensitivity to negative social media mentions also makes businesses more risk averse. It certainly is not as simple as just doing away with some of these, since increasing product complexity is what created the comprehensive requirements in the first place.

For many large organisations, the reality is that their processes have become so cumbersome and prohibitive that the only way they can innovate is to acquire start-ups. Yet once a start-up is acquired, its ability to innovate is drastically reduced as it becomes hamstrung by the same cumbersome processes. But at least their work to date can be put into practice.

There is no easy answer for how larger organisations can realistically create cultures of change. Some soul-searching about where the organisation sees itself is needed, since it shouldn't position itself as a high-change culture if that's not backed up by action. Contradictions between words and actions breeds distrust and creates a survival-focused culture. That's the critical component—there needs to be authenticity in the culture for it to develop and thrive at both an individual and collective level. Some ways to achieve this within the organisation include setting up specific structures and resources.

Structures and resources

One way to encourage innovation in large organisations with numerous constraints is to set up separate frameworks for play. These can be separate workplace areas or even entities where ideas can be explored. Guidance would be provided to help develop new ideas and facilitate.

This concept should be aimed at supporting the basic need for safety, allowing people the freedom to explore, the freedom to fail, and guidance to learn from mistakes and keep working towards new solutions. With this in mind, we need to realise that running a 'design studio' or 'lab' such as this needs to be a supportive environment for it to work. If the environment was adversarial, with a lot of pressure not to fail, then it's less likely that it will produce meaningful results.

The very reason why these structures can work is because they have the potential to support whole-brain activation. They do this by giving people an environment within which they are safe to play. With this in place, people can explore ideas freely, maximising whole-brain creativity to better understand the value of ideas. After all, the idea might not be feasible within the organisation, but might be highly valuable as a new entity.

The deployment and realisation of ventures through these structures serve as evidence that the organisation is serious about building a culture that values innovation and change. It's not necessary to have huge successes from these, but to convey its commitment, at the least the organisation should show that it is investing in what comes from these.

Useful—both in these structures as well as more broadly in the organisation—are the resources available to staff. Recalling our discussion about Reasoning earlier, we know that a key part which enables better problem-solving under pressure and creativity is resources. Resourcefulness in this context is not simply an individual responsibility, but can be actively contributed to by the organisation. This may take the form of shared databases, knowledge, analytics and insights. For these to make a difference in people's Reasoning capacity, all employees need to know these resources exist.

Often the teams that create valuable resources don't share them. If we are to explore why this is, it's useful to apply Hanlon's Razor, which states to *'Never attribute to malice that which is adequately explained by ignorance or stupidity'*. Looking from that perspective, teams that don't share usually don't realise how valuable their resources might be to others. Building a sharing culture, where there are fewer boundaries between areas and information, contributes to a culture of openness and trust. High compartmentalisation might be important for top secret projects in the military, but in an organisation information should be shared freely—unless there is a need for strict confidentiality.

Diversity of ideas is another aspect that contributes to the pool of ideas available. Greater diversity of employees provides more perspectives by drawing on their different experiences and views. For this to work, a diverse set of employees need to feel safe with each other and also the culture that they are in. A lack of equality—where one segment is treated differently to another—could result in some of the ideas being silenced.

In this sense, not all types of diversity are desired, for example, you wouldn't want too much diversity in ethical standards, where some are against fraud and others are not. Generally, diversity in competence, where some employees are competent and others are not, are usually also not desired.

Looking within the remaining confines of diversity, we need different types of experience and backgrounds that may contribute to the task at hand. Naturally, these have nothing to do with race, religion and sexuality, which the organisation should be blind to when hiring. For people of different backgrounds to effectively mix, a level of resilience is needed to not feel threatened by others with different perspectives.

Through resilience, people can downregulate the impulsive brain and activate the frontal cortex to better understand the thinking styles of their colleagues. Combined with a greater internal awareness, people can come to develop an appreciation of how others can help cover blind spots.

Considering the role of the Anterior Cingulate Cortex (ACC) to optimise responses over time, continual exposure to challenges and different perspectives eventually result in the brain's model of the world being updated. Essentially, the ACC is trying to find more accurate ways to think, so being challenged will eventually lead to the brain anticipating future challenges more accurately. The result is that people start to clarify their own thoughts to a greater extent prior to presentation, resulting in higher quality ideas. Of course, this does not happen in a room where everyone stays silent or passively agrees with whatever is said. While in a sense, it's more peaceful or safe, passivity is not conducive to helping the organisation or individuals grow.

On the other extreme, too much challenge might get highly adversarial, where the fangs come out and people lose their sense of safety. Again, the impulsive brain is upregulated, smart brain is downregulated, and the quality of thought decreases. The result is stressed people—with the effects flowing through to their personal lives—eventually coming back to impact the organisation.

The aim is to achieve a level of spirited debate, where the safety of employees is maintained. This ensures maximum smart brain activation to enable creativity and novel problem-solving. A useful gauge might be whether there is still some humour in the debate.

It's not always possible to tell within the debate if everyone is comfortable with the level of challenge, so while still learning about each individual's style, it's useful to do a quick debrief afterwards on a one-on-one basis to see how each experienced the session. The goal then is not to acquiesce to people's desires, but rather to help them find ways to value challenge and learn about the perspectives of others... so they can pre-empt where they might be challenged.

This flows through to more stressful situations, where people might be under high pressure and need to think on their feet. Being more comfortable with being challenged on a regular basis will help people stay calm and collected under pressure. For this to happen, the brain needs to build pathways that underscore that there is no danger in being challenged. There is no simple way to build this capability—strengthening these pathways take time and practice. For individuals, it may be necessary to challenge and change their own beliefs—an ability that is closely correlated with resilience overall.

Your role in this is important in order to gauge if the level of debate is being constructive. You can steer the conversation back to a helpful level if it looks to be going too far. Doing this maintains a sense of safety for individuals, while still improving their reasoning skills and thus helping them grow. The benefits of this flow through to their personal lives and relationships, where they can remain calm and de-escalate personal conflict by keeping focus on what is important. And people who are happy at home tend to be more engaged with their work as well.

Tenacity

Staying optimistic and persisting through adversity is as important at a cultural level as it is at a personal level. The research tells us that persistence is more important than intelligence in achieving goals. We can infer from this that persistence is just as critical at a collective level if the organisation wishes to achieve its own goals. Indeed, many of the big success stories in business are about those that stuck to a vision and persisted until they eventually broke through. Therefore, building a culture of persistence is in many ways a necessity for success. It would be hard to find any manager that disagrees with that statement. Still, many inadvertently work against the persistence of their people. Let's explore.

Understand the value of failure

One of the most common ways that organisations stifle persistence is through a fear of failure. Employees are encouraged to try new things, but also to get it right the first time. This desire is easy to understand from an organisational perspective, since failure means a waste of time and resources. It would be so much better if everything could be done right the first time.

In the past, this might have been possible more often, as slower change cycles allowed for more comprehensive planning and due diligence to increase the chance of success. Today, we live in a different environment. Now we no longer have the luxury of comprehensive planning to ensure things go just right. As Amazon's Jeff Bezos said recently, *'Most decisions should probably be made with somewhere around 70 percent of the information you wish you had'*. Essentially, he's saying that if you wait until you have all the information, then you have waited too long. In the meantime, another company will have acted already and left you behind.

The reality of this environment means we need to get more comfortable with failure and mistakes. In this environment, if the organisation is not making mistakes, then it's probably not moving fast enough. The goal now is to act with speed and adjust faster after failure. For this to happen at a cultural level, we need individuals who don't fear failure.

Fear of failure leads to survival thinking patterns, which in turn lead to unhelpful behaviours, such as trying to hide the failure, denying it was a failure, and inability to see opportunities to salvage. It then makes it less likely that people can learn effectively from the failure to turn the next move into a success.

Valuing persistence while fearing failure is a logical contradiction. Persistence is precisely when we overcome repeated failures and obstacles. For an organisation to value persistence, it needs to value failure and learn how to effectively mobilise the lessons from it. This means being willing to openly discuss different failure modes and detail the plan if one of them should become a reality. From there, paths can be explored to re-use work from failed projects to try again, persisting towards the goal.

Here, people may need your guidance as a leader to help them make sense of what went wrong and encourage them to try again. Seeing this from a leadership perspective makes it clear to employees that the organisation truly values persistence and will support them to be tenacious and keep at it.

Considering the mechanics of persistence, it's useful to separate this version of persistence from obsession, though certainly the two can overlap. Persistence here is underscored by a rational connection to a broader purpose that leads to some benefit beyond the individual. In other words, there is some level of ethical judgement involved to persist towards a worthwhile goal.

Obsession can be quite the contrary, where there is often a lack of logic in the pursuit, and the end goal itself may be more self-serving. When obsession exists at a leadership level, it is often quite visible to the team, and affects their perception of their leaders. At a cultural level, obsession might exist when there is a great deal of focus on metrics that are not well thought through. These could be metrics that reward for a specific type of performance, leading people to find ways to bend or even break rules in order to improve their metrics. In large organisations, we often see this type of focus result in fraudulent behaviour, producing damage to customers and the company itself.

As we work towards a culture that values persistence, we need to keep in mind the potential impact of how we incentivise it. Monetary incentive schemes are often not as effective at personal motivation and can lead to a reduction in ethical standards. While also being expensive for an organisation, monetary incentives have side effects, such as pitting employees against each other, which creates an adversarial culture. Finding other ways to incentivise persistence can be more effective and efficient for the organisation. For example, team-based incentives tend to result in greater motivation and connection between people, leading to a more constructive culture, where people are supportive and there is greater diversity in ideas.

Incentives themselves can be more focused on non-monetary rewards, such as recognition, awards, or spending time with executives for mentoring. If the incentives are about motivating innovation, then the idea itself could be funded as a reward. Here the incentive doesn't go directly to the individuals, but rather provides the people with more to play with and see their own ideas come to life. Persistence itself could be rewarded, such as giving recognition for the best recovery from failure, or highlighting examples of where a failed project was re-purposed or salvaged effectively. Repurposed failures result in high value to the organisation regardless.

The goal here is not to provide a safe space for incompetence. After all, the idea of pursuing innovation with speed is to be able to produce results more quickly than before. This means learning faster, adjusting faster, and constantly growing through the experience. Individuals progressing through this should be growing their own professional skills as a result.

Importantly, resilience allows an individual to see this process as a welcome challenge, while a less resilient person might see it as adversity that produces undue stress. Therefore, resilience allows a person to interpret the same situation in a more constructive way, which actually reduces stress and avoids mental harm.

This is the reality of the world we live in now, and these challenges we face will only become more acute in the future. As individuals, we all need to work on our resilience to be able to embrace this environment so we can thrive in it. Our aim is not based on a delusion, but on a realistic appraisal of our own skills to manage challenges and persist towards success.

Cultural optimism

Reflecting on what we discussed before about realistic optimism at an individual level, this is precisely what we need at a cultural level—a shared, realistic sense of hope for the future. This perception is critical for Tenacity since it gives people hope that their efforts are contributing in a meaningful way to worthwhile goal. It motivates people to work through all the ups and downs and keep going—the essence of persistence.

At a group level, optimism can easily start to spiral. This is often the case when we see hype about a new project or technology. People get swept along and even those who are usually realistic can let go of their normal sensibilities.

Research firm Gartner developed an interesting view on the cycle of hype, showing it progressing through five stages. The first stage is a trigger, kicking off the process. From there, endless possibilities for the new technology is considered, with everyone marvelling at how it will solve all their problems. As these expectations rise, we eventually arrive at the fever-pitched top, called the 'peak of inflated expectations'. After this peak, we start to see implementation of the technology not live up to expectations, along with repeated failures for early adopters. Then we fall down to the 'trough of disillusionment'.

Investment goes to those that survive the fallout of the disillusionment. Those that stick around eventually gain more success at a more realistic level, climbing up the 'slope of enlightenment'. Eventually, the emerging success of the remaining players results in mainstream adoption and we reach the final stage: the 'plateau of productivity'.

This cycle is interesting because by taking a step back, you can easily see this with most new projects in organisations. People might start off highly excited, then get very disillusioned when their expectations aren't met, then eventually feel a bit more positive when they finally work through the bulk of the problems. Knowing this, you can provide guidance to temper the extremes, cautioning when expectations seem unrealistic, and offering encouragement when the project runs into trouble.

Creating a shared sense of realistic optimism is aimed at tempering this cycle from within. The concept is for individuals to have a basic assumption that there will be many challenges along the way, but through persistence they can achieve a worthwhile outcome. With this view deeply ingrained in the group, there might be less tendency to overhype the possibilities, and similarly, less disillusionment if tough times come around because these will have been expected.

Maintaining motivation is the aim here. While people are highly-motivated during the height of the hype, the overhype results in a major decrease in motivation, when we fall towards disillusionment. If the fall is very far, then people might not want to have anything more to do with it. The key component here is the neurotransmitter, dopamine.

At the 'early hype' phase, we are focused on possibilities and we know that others are excited about it as well. Realising this, it's a safe assumption that talking to other people about the project would be a positive conversation. Being the pattern recognition machine that it is, the brain uses this prediction of positivity to motivate further collaboration by releasing dopamine. This dopamine motivates us to keep working on the project because it's fun and positive.

When the hype fails to live up to expectations, then the brain predicts that future collaboration will be pessimistic and overall less 'fun', so dopamine is reduced and we notice a distinct drop in motivation. Here we can see how subconscious expectations—and perceptions about the group—lead to differences in motivation for the individual, which in turn again affects the group motivation. Sometimes it takes just one person to be stubbornly optimistic about what can still be achieved to eventually get others back on board.

Whatever the case, it is useful from a leadership perspective to determine where motivation levels are, provide the right type of feedback to moderate overhype, and keep people motivated in times of disillusionment.

Other aspects also contribute to the overall sense of optimism. These need to come from multiple sources, with evidence to back it up, for it to have a meaningful impact on the business culture. At the top level, there needs to be a vision of what the organisation wants to achieve that represents something of value to the broader society. Individuals need to be able to see how their own goals can fit in with organisational goals. People need to see that their efforts make some meaningful contribution to the organisational goals. They need to see that management supports ideas and provide guidance and backup along the way. People need to be able to see themselves grow over time in the organisation and have a realistic connection to their own development.

All of these aspects combine to help people see that, even if things aren't perfect now, they can work towards a better future—and the organisation won't resist their efforts along the way. This mentality is about expecting that there will be challenges and adversity along the way. It's about not having an overly optimistic view about the future, where everything works perfectly the first time. We all know this almost never happens.

Setting this expectation creates a buffer in the brain, where setbacks are no longer interpreted as a threat, and therefore don't activate the amygdala and fear response. This allows dopamine to release more easily, which means people stay motivated, even during adversity.

Overall, your influence plays an important role in maintaining optimism in the culture. Being aware of behaviours within yourself will also help you notice how other managers behave around their own staff, helping you more accurately determine what kind of effect they might have on their people.

Knowing which behaviours result in a greater activation of the impulsive brain in others will help you discover what is negatively affecting the culture. What might be working against people's ability to be persistent? Through this knowledge, you can then take practical steps towards alignment of messaging across management. Importantly, you can support the right initiative to develop a culture where people are not afraid to test out new ideas and thrive on the challenge.

Collaboration

Our connection with each other is one of the most critical areas affecting the culture of an organisation. In playing a major role in our ability to meaningfully connect with other people on a daily basis, organisations allow one of the fundamental needs of the brain. In fact, if it was not for jobs, many people simply wouldn't be exposed to regular interaction with others.

Even though the brain has its fundamental needs to feel fulfilled, we are still not highly aware that we need these things. For example, it's like potassium. We may not realise that we need potassium, but if we have too little of it, we feel weak and tired, get cramps, and feel depressed and confused. None of these symptoms make it obvious to us that we have a potassium deficiency, yet it is the cause regardless.

In a similar way, many people don't realise the fundamental need of the brain for connection. If there's something wrong with their level of connection at work, then it too can result in many symptoms that individuals might not necessarily be able to diagnose themselves, just like a lack of potassium. Here it's useful to realise that our main source of connection tends to come from the work environment. Our willingness to engage in connection with others, have meaningful relationships, support others and be supported all add to the domain of Collaboration.

At a cultural level, it is therefore important to take into account this fundamental need and recognise its contribution to the success of the culture, even though others might not realise its full importance. This leads to some interesting considerations, given recent trends towards flexible working.

Technological isolation

It's no secret that increasing usage of social networks has resulted in a greater illusion of connection while people are now more isolated than ever. The trend continues in the workplace, where there's a desire for remote working, both from people who enjoy the flexibility and from organisations who stand to save on real estate costs. What is important about our ability to meaningfully connect with other people is that the brain has evolved to value face-to-face connection. It's not hard to understand this evolution, given the lack of mobile phones in ancient times. For 99.9% of human evolution, all communication was effectively face-to-face. Even longer, considering where we evolved from.

The relevance of this is that the brain has developed specific areas in itself for non-verbal communication. Facial expressions, for example, play a huge role, through activation of the fusiform gyrus, and also mirror neurons, which help convey the emotions and mental state of others. Mirror neurons also help us to more effectively understand the goals of others, conveying these at a subconscious level, in addition to conscious verbal communication. Convergence of the different modes of communication is what leads to having a sense of trust in others. Meaning, if we don't activate these different areas of the brain, then it is hard for people to form meaningful connections.

Working remotely is where this becomes highly relevant. Someone who's rarely in the office has much less meaningful connection, since they simply cannot activate those areas of the brain effectively over distance. Cutting out face-to-face connection with colleagues means less opportunity to build trust and form lasting and compassionate connections. The result is a lower perception of support, and it has other impacts as well. For example, promotions in the ranks and high-profile projects are often given to those who are trusted by management. If someone has had less opportunity than others to develop that trust, then they tend to get left out of opportunities, regardless of level of competence.

Lack of connection in this way leads to feelings of being left out and so can contribute to anxiety and depression. This might even lead to them withdrawing even more, compounding the problem. Like an undiagnosed potassium deficiency, people in this position often don't fully realise what is wrong.

The march of technology and our desire to make the most of tech doesn't take into account what the brain needs to feel fulfilled. Technological isolation can have important impacts on people without them even realising what is the cause. This is why it is important to provide people with resilience training that helps them understand their own basic needs and what might be behind their feelings.

As an organisation, this is important to take into account. Having staff working remotely or from home on a regular basis is a catalyst for the need to create opportunities for meaningful connection. This might mean to regularly fly staff in, have team meetings on days where everyone can attend, and most importantly, finding time for face-to-face conversation. To date, there is still no technology that effectively replicates talking to someone right in front of you. Until that happens, we need to keep in mind that working remotely means a negative impact on a fundamental need of the brain. So, we should at least pay additional attention to the wellbeing of staff working in this arrangement.

Infusing collaboration into the culture

Cultivating connection between people has a lot of benefits. The increased sense of camaraderie between employees feeds into their need for safe and secure *connection* with others. It allows people to feel that they have others they can trust, meaning they don't constantly have to watch their back when they're at work. This safety comes from a downregulated impulsive brain, which in turn allows for whole-brain activation and greater creativity, innovation and sharing of ideas.

Some large organisations suffer from major cultural issues due to low general collaboration. In these, we tend to see behaviours where people see knowledge as power, or more specifically, their own knowledge is their own power. Therefore, they avoid sharing at all costs. This type of adversarial behaviour is rooted in survival thinking, focusing on their own advantage rather than that of the organisation and others around them.

This type of culture is generally created by how the company is run in terms of incentives for specific behaviour. In fact, if this type of survival culture lasts a long time, then these behaviours become highly ingrained in the management structure as people who had to go through it get promoted. They then perpetuate the adversarial culture from a viewpoint of *'I had to go through it, so you will as well.'*

Here we can see many toxic elements take hold in the culture, the kind which might end up in the news. Still, this type of culture might be preferable for some people, who are indeed mainly focused on their own personal advancement in spite of the cost to others or the organisation itself. Certainly, there are many highly-capable people who have this mindset, though it is up to the organisation's leaders to determine the type of company that it wants to be.

Sustainability is a key consideration here, in that an adversarial culture is not sustainable. It means a high employee turnover rate, resulting in a constant loss of knowledge. This happens as individuals refuse to share what they know unless there is benefit to them. The organisation then depends on constantly attracting new talent to fill in the gaps. The net result is that the business doesn't benefit overall while individuals keep extracting value for themselves.

Building resilience into the culture through a collaborative spirit has more potential to be sustainable. This allows people to meaningfully connect with each other, openly share ideas and knowledge, and build lasting support networks that provide a true sense of safety. This creates a sense of cohesion that is quickly visible to new recruits, in turn allowing faster integration and faster contribution. In a time where speed is essential, this ability to absorb new ideas faster through cultural cohesion becomes highly valuable.

To achieve this type of collaborative culture, it needs to be supported at all levels. One way to foster this is by putting formal structures and events in place to encourage collaboration. This can include setting up a mentorship program, where everyone by default is assigned a mentor.

With a program like this, it's important to keep the nature of the relationship in mind to create a complete sense of safety. For example, setting up someone with their direct manager, or their manager's manager as their mentor, is not a safe relationship. This is because the management line above the employee have a conflict of interest with what might be best for the employee. After all, it might be in the employee's interest to move to another area of the organisation, though this advice is unlikely to come from someone who is employing them in their division.

A mentorship program needs to put safeguards in place to ensure that the relationship is free from such unintended conflicts, allowing an open relationship where the employee doesn't constantly need to worry about what they say. This can highlight problems earlier, showing where new opportunities lie for the organisation to improve.

Focusing on team recognition instead of individual recognition also helps to shift towards a culture of collaboration rather than individual glory. This provides evidence to individuals that collaboration is truly valued and that they need to work together to get recognition. Through this, there should be constant encouragement for people to invest in relationships and build support networks, which might be a bit more difficult than it seems. In fact, many managers don't feel they have enough trust in their staff to let team members go out and build their own relationships, preferring instead to maintain those relationships themselves.

As with knowledge, there's a level of personal power to be gained by not sharing relationships. Sharing in this sense is again reduced when managers feel there might be danger to themselves if something goes wrong and they weren't involved directly.

First, there needs to be a sense of safety for the managers themselves in their own position. They are far less likely to encourage employees to build relationships elsewhere if they as managers are feeling threatened. They would therefore be more likely to want to handle tasks directly, delegating less to employees. This behaviour often leads to managers who feel overwhelmed and stressed, with a perception of not enough support available to them.

Causes of this type of scenario are far and varied, with no simple answer available. In these cases, it's helpful for managers to discuss with their own higher-ups what is making them less prone to delegate more important tasks. Though for this conversation to happen, there needs to be a sense of safety in knowing that a frank and open discussion is not going to result in some overt or covert action against them. A lot of this has to do with the perceptions that people have of their leaders.

Leadership, crises and perceptions

It's often during a crisis that we discover who we really are underneath the persona we choose to present. The reason for this is that a persona presented by choice requires a conscious energy to remain active. That is to say, if we choose to put on a positive façade while underneath we're feeling frustrated, then the façade can quickly come down when presented with a crisis.

This is because a crisis situation upregulates the amygdala and impulsive areas of the brain, which in turn downregulates the frontal cortex, the part in charge of maintaining the façade. The frontal cortex is constantly exercising restraint to hold back inner frustration. Therefore, if the blood flow to the frontal cortex is reduced, then the brain effectively loses its ability to maintain that restraint.

The size of the disparity between the façade and the suppressed mental state is important, since a greater disparity requires greater restraint and can more easily appear when the impulsive brain activates. This is where you might see someone who was fine a moment ago simply 'snap', flying into a fit of rage. This disparity can take many forms, such as someone who is feeling somewhat depressed but trying to stay upbeat becoming withdrawn when facing a crisis.

Considering this situation first, resilience provides two benefits. One benefit is that higher resilience reduces impulsive brain activation, allowing us to remain in control and maintain a particular façade. The next benefit, more importantly, is reducing the need for a façade by improving our underlying mental state. After all, it's far more ideal to not require the mental effort of maintaining a façade... if who we are underneath matches who we want to be in public. If currently we have a disparity, then it's up to us to work on the causes of the disparity and practise developing a mindset that resolves the difference.

Leading during a crisis, therefore, communicates a lot about who you are. People see how you react under those circumstances and make that part of their internal model of the world. In other words, they learn whether or not they should be scared of you in a crisis. This often happens when people see a leader lash out during a crisis—perhaps taking out frustration and anger on others that are nearby. Some leaders are quick to lay blame and point fingers, often before the problem is even resolved. Some leaders become indecisive as the wealth of information and pressure of a crisis overloads the brain. Whatever the reaction, people learn from it and they use it as a heuristic to predict your behaviour.

The brain is always looking for patterns, and the patterns it recognises during a crisis carry particular weight. This is because it's an emotionally-charged situation. You can spend a year being nice to your staff, but one crisis where you end up yelling at them is enough to destroy trust and create a fear in the culture.

This is simply how the brain works—organisms that can quickly adapt quickly to dangerous situations are the ones that survive the longest.

Therefore, the brain has developed the ability to very quickly form strong memories when faced with situations it experiences as dangerous.

The structure of the brain itself shows how this works. Within the brain, the hippocampus is the area that is responsible for memory formation. Without the hippocampus, we cannot create any new memories. The amygdala is the area that detects danger and activates the HPA axis and the impulsive brain. What's important is the amygdala sits directly in front of the hippocampus, resulting in a strong connection between the two. This connection allows the amygdala to almost instantly form a very strong memory when it activates.

In fact, this is exactly how traumatic memories form, the kind that keep people awake at night and result in panic attacks. It takes just one traumatic experience for this memory to take hold, and can take many years of therapy to undo what the amygdala does in a single moment.

Keeping this in mind is important because it should push you to temper your reactions. If you can show people that in a crisis you are still calm, then you provide a sense of predictability. It is this that the brain highly values. This way, you can show them that it is safe to communicate openly and that you will support them throughout.

If people don't have this perception, then they might inadvertently (or even purposefully) hide bad news from you during a crisis because they are worried about how you might react. Where I have seen this happen previously, people avoided going to a leader they fear, trying instead to fix it themselves, until eventually the problem becomes so big that they cannot hide it anymore. At that point, the news goes up to the leaders in a much worse state, with less that can be done to mitigate the problem.

Much of the damage during a crisis can be prevented if people feel like they can trust their leaders. It allows for faster and more open communication, leading to more trust in delegation and resolution. Following this, people will gain confidence in you as a leader. It also improves their perception of you outside of a crisis (which is most of the time). This confidence comes from a subconscious level, where they perceive a sense of safety around you, knowing that they don't have to fear your reaction should things go wrong. After all, there's always the possibility that they may need to come to you with a crisis, and their sense of safety would allow this.

Health

Coming to the final domain of resilience, health has recently been the focus of many organisations. There has been a collective realisation that health has a correlation with mental wellbeing and performance in the workplace. What is important to clarify is that good nutrition and exercise is not simply about appearance. Instead, together with quality sleep, these provide the basis for a healthy brain. For resilience, a healthy brain is one that is well nourished and rested, with higher levels of BDNF, enabling individuals to quickly learn and adapt.

Adaption at a cultural level allows the people in the organisation to better keep pace with change and disruption in business practices. Simply, competition will only increase, so we need people who can thrive in that environment. Organisations now have the incentive to promote health interventions so that we can create this type of workforce. The benefits go to competitive advantage, but also beyond... to the personal lives of people and society as a whole.

One challenge with health in the workplace comes from technological advances. In particular, the ability to readily measure many aspects of health has proven to be problematic.

Prevent data overload

We now have more tools than ever to measure health. We have wearable devices that can track steps, heart rate, sleep cycles, and more, along with apps to track every aspect of our nutrition and exercise. Each adds to a growing collection of data. This data enables analysis and reporting, through an endless array of fancy charts and reports. It is here that we start to run into trouble—we have so much reporting and analytics available on health that it distracts us from more important aspects.

Resilience is a construct that consists of six domains. Of the six domains, we know that Vision is the most important, providing guidance to the implementation of all the other domains. However, Vision and the other domains are generally not as easy to measure as the Health domain. Health's ease of measure then becomes a problem because in many organisations, Health receives attention at the expense of other domains.

For organisations, it's far easier to implement something that is easily measurable so that progress can be tracked along the way. Where organisations have not had the ability to determine the status of the other domains, more and more health-focused companies have come in with promises of measurable results and analytics.

This wouldn't have been a problem, if it wasn't for the crucial role of the other domains to help people stick to a healthy lifestyle in the first place. Lacking the proper functioning of the other five domains of resilience, a person simply won't have the mindset to stay consistent with their health. Consider that you need goals for your health (Vision), you need to stay in control and not give in to emotional eating (Composure), you need to research and find the right solutions (Reasoning), you need to be persistent and stick to it day-to-day (Tenacity), and you need to manage social pressures and integrate health into your relationships (Collaboration). Miss any one of these and you are unlikely to achieve any lasting results.

Within the organisation, simply providing access to health-based resources does not help people generate the resilient mindset needed to stick to a healthy lifestyle. A holistic wellness program is thus needed to achieve a meaningful change.

Health benefits from the other five domains, and in turn those domains benefit from improved physical health. This virtuous circle of interaction between the domains is what can be achieved through an integrated program.

Through our work we have shown that these domains can effectively be measured, providing the basis for a holistic approach. This approach allows the organisation to see where the primary deficiencies are, addressing the areas that will have the most impact for cultural improvement. The aim here is to not get distracted by the wealth of health data available. Just because we could use it, doesn't mean we should.

If we as the organisation promote products that focus on health data, the risk is that individuals themselves also get distracted by the belief that health is the most important aspect of their wellbeing, when it simply is not.

Health as a domain must be seen in context and must be promoted alongside the improvement of the other domains of resilience. Only then can we achieve long-term change that benefits both individuals and the organisation as a whole.

Healthy living as a cultural norm

Assuming we have a shared focus on all the domains, we can now look more specifically at how to incorporate a healthy lifestyle into the workplace. Most large organisations who promote health also inadvertently sabotage their own efforts by actively working against the efforts of staff to be healthy. Consider promoting healthy nutrition, only to serve up sweets and fast foods at every staff gathering. Work functions overflow with foods high in simple carbohydrates and sugar, while alcohol might be the drink of choice, with an expectation to join in and be part of the group.

Alcohol in particular promotes many other unhealthy behaviours, such as further unhealthy eating, poor quality sleep, risky behaviour, and more. Yet alcohol consumption is often ingrained in the culture and treated as 'a must' to fit in. This consistently works against other healthy habits being promoted by the organisation. If alcohol is an inherent part of every work function, then the message is *'Despite what we say, this is what it's really about'.*

Incongruences such as these are common, because the people who promote wellbeing in the organisation are usually totally separate from the people who organise events. While one is focused on helping people be healthy, the other is trying to make people happy. These are two very separate goals.

Consider that for many dieters, one day of unhealthy eating results in them writing off the rest of the week, vowing to eat healthy again from next Monday instead. Therefore, passing around chocolates or cake often has a much larger effect than simply that one occasion. People are adept at finding ways to rationalise unhealthy behaviour, so any interference easily disrupts the consistency needed to maintain a healthy lifestyle.

And yet, the organisation can help to make it easier for people to be consistent. For catered events, offer healthy alternatives at a 50/50 ratio—to emphasise that health is a priority. Save alcohol for the big events, rather than every Friday night. Provide sit/stand desks and discounted gym memberships. Encourage walk-and-talk meetings rather than sitting down all the time. The options are endless—more than what can be summarised here.

The key point is to make sure that the organisation isn't contradicting its own push for healthy living, and therefore undermining its own efforts. At a leadership level it must be decided to facilitate health and be consistent in its messaging. There could even be incentives for healthy behaviours, though there are some caveats around these.

Promotion and incentives

Given the positives of improving health in the workplace, many options are emerging to incentivise participation. Incentives might be in the form of recognition in the workplace, such as an award for the most steps over a period of time using a fitness tracker. This could involve a team challenge, where groups compete with others for an award. Awards could be in the form of a team lunch, a donation to charity, time off, or the like.

Some companies have started to offer pure financial incentives to encourage participation. One company is offering a per hour reward for sleep that is tracked through an app, an additional reward for each km jogged or cycled, and another reward per fitness class attended. This allows people to increase their own salary by about $2,000 per year if they fully comply with all the requirements.

On the face of it, this may seem like a positive step, however there are complications. Primarily, incentives are mainly used by people already living healthy lifestyles. Now they simply get rewarded for the things they were doing already. Incentives often only provide temporary motivation as well, so people who are in-between super healthy and super unhealthy only change behaviour while the incentive is available. For example, a team-based exercise challenge may get them moving for one month, but as soon as the challenge ends, then it's back to their old lifestyle.

Meanwhile, the people who can benefit the most from a healthy lifestyle get alienated by incentives because they probably would not take it up in the first place. The small benefit of incentives usually does not make up for how much they dislike exercise and healthy foods. Incentives and challenges can then inadvertently shine a spotlight on their non-participation. For these individuals, it's more about the mindset that would enable them to incorporate a healthy lifestyle that is missing. This needs to be addressed before incentives will have any meaningful effect.

To this extent, what is helpful for an organisation is an analysis of which component of the employee population takes up which health initiatives. Often this analysis has revealed that the main consumers of promoted content and activities are those that need it the least. This requires quality data on the subject, starting with measurement to determine where individuals sit with their own health across different aspects. From there, data is available on take-up of available content and initiatives. There are also conflict-of-interest concerns for individuals if this data is accessible to the organisation, so this analysis often needs to be conducted externally.

Each organisation is different, owing to industry and cultural peculiarities. Because of this, different initiatives and content will reach individuals in varying levels of impact. Therefore, it's better to conduct ongoing analyses of take-up across the spectrum of people. This is so that initiatives can be refined to drive uptake in individuals in more need of help.

Here we can start to see how data can be used more constructively— going from the overwhelming and distracting data that health applications can provide, through to integrating various data sets—to determine what is actually making the right kind of difference.

6.

Making a data-driven difference

U nderstanding where to start with building a culture of resilience requires insight. Such insight is usually hidden from view, since resilience is a personal concept. There may be factors in play at home that are affecting a person, while their manager is none the wiser. Someone may be struggling and no one at the workplace would know. The only external visible element may be more frequent sick days and a decline in performance.

In large organisations, this is particularly relevant, since there is a large divide between those who make decisions about the culture, and those who live the culture. When executives try to change culture without sufficient insight, there often results a perception among employees that leaders are 'out of touch'.

Traditional employee measurement tools don't help either. Tools to gauge employee engagement measure how employees feel about the company, but they provide no insight into how employees feel about *themselves*.

Research increasingly shows that neglected wellbeing negatively impacts workers and the organisation. One study showed that people with high-stress jobs spend 26 percent more on healthcare costs,[44] resulting in higher levels of absenteeism and disruption at work. Another research paper showed that individual wellbeing is a greater determinant in performance, over and above job and work attitudes.[45] Our own research supports this, showing that resilience has a strong influence on job satisfaction.

The implication is important—if resilience influences job satisfaction, and resilience is a personal concept, then it means that factors outside the work environment affect how a person feels about work. *Projection* is a simple way to think about it—someone who is experiencing difficulties at home might project those frustrations on the organisation. Through no direct fault of the organisation, there may be lower performance, less engagement and higher absenteeism.

However, the organisation does play an indirect role. Under the resilience imperative, the organisation can provide training and resources to improve the resilience and wellbeing of individuals, helping them manage their lives outside of work. This in turn affects their satisfaction with work.

We can now understand this clearly through how resilience reformulates what people see as adversity. This opens them up to embrace challenges and helps them to manage their lives proactively. It comes back to enhancing a feeling of safety.

Providing this training provides benefits to the individual, the organisation, and society as a whole. Not only is it beneficial, it is necessary given the rapidly-changing environment we are heading into. This is also why simply focusing on health alone is not enough—we need holistic resilience-building to be able to thrive during rapid change.

Organisations are in an advantageous position that can't be overstated. Resilience training provides such a strong win-win-win (individual, organisational, societal) proposition, that it simply cannot be ignored as a management strategy. Importantly, the method of intervention, benefits

---

[44] Azagba, S., & Sharaf, M. F. (2011). Psychosocial working conditions and the utilization of health care services. BMC Public Health, 11(1), 642.

[45] Robertson, I. T., Jansen Birch, A., & Cooper, C. L. (2012). Job and work attitudes, engagement and employee performance: Where does psychological well-being fit in?. Leadership & Organisation Development Journal, 33(3), 224-232.

and return can be measured. Each of the domains of resilience can be measured at an individual level and aggregated to quantify the approach and results. This lays the foundation for evidence-based resilience programs.

From intuition to data-based decisions

Evidence-based people management is rising in popularity. Much of this is due to an increased ability to access and analyse data. It's ultimately from data that we get our evidence to support key decisions. That said, Human Resources is usually seen as a 'soft skills' industry. This means evidence frequently takes a back seat while intuitions rule the day. Though this may be appropriate for one-on-one interpersonal interactions, setting Human Resources policies and evaluating success is where we can most benefit from using evidence.

Many larger organisations are investing in people analytics teams to better understand their workforce. Currently, a lot of people analytics effort is put into headcount, hiring and retention timeframes, remuneration, and HR spending questions. Requests for these types of analyses usually come from business managers and executives, and are mainly basic operational reporting. This results in less time available for more in-depth review and analysis.

Where evidence-based management is particularly important is when a business is considering implementing a staff wellbeing program, as these are often selected due to intuition rather than evidence. When evaluating the effectiveness of implementing a wellbeing program, we often hear phrases like *'We used these people before'*, *'I like the presenter'*, *'People said they enjoyed this'*, etc. Relying mostly on intuition often results in the wrong kind of program being selected, rather than a program that meets specific individual and business needs. It also limits your ability to clearly identify what to invest in, and how much to invest in wellbeing.

There is often also no follow-up on the effectiveness of the program. Where follow-up has been completed, it's usually limited to exit interviews or feedback that simply shows how much people enjoyed the course. Enjoyment, of course, does not mean that any real or lasting change has been effected that translates into actual personal and business benefit.

As we move towards evidence-based HR, we need to bring evidence about wellbeing programs into the picture. To maximise success, there are five points to consider when implementing wellbeing programs:

- What evidence is backing up the program itself?
- Is it based on credible research?
- Is it focused on long-term development, or on temporary motivation that doesn't last a week after the seminar?
- Is it structured to achieve real results, or is it a quick seminar that will never have the same change potential as a gradual, interactive course?
- Particularly relevant to programs offering wellbeing measurement—has the measurement questionnaire been validated as a psychometric scale?

If there's no evidence of its validity, then the measurement system may yield results that in themselves are not valid, leading the business to make incorrect decisions. Critical evaluation and looking for evidence is crucial in order to select a program that has both the credibility and capacity to achieve results.

Determining the success of a wellbeing program is becoming increasingly important, particularly as leaders are becoming more interested in the topic of wellbeing. There's a desire to see numbers and measure progress along the way. To be able to show numbers, we naturally need to conduct measurement.

The key here is to look for measurement that will be useful and consistent. Consistency is particularly important, since changing data collection methods over time will mean that data is not comparable. Inconsistent data prevents you from identifying trends, or other time-based analysis, which is a key part of determining program success. For example, a good program would measure people at the start, then on a regular basis afterwards. This way, the organisation gains a clear view of the effectiveness of the program over time, as well as timely identification of trends.

Usefulness of measurement is determined by what is measured. Consider that if participant satisfaction is mainly measured, then the results are unlikely to highlight actual improvement. Similarly, testing participant knowledge of the course material is also unlikely to indicate improvement.

Instead, wellbeing measurement needs to focus on psychological domains that are informative to both the participant and the organisation. Data that informs action lays the foundation for true evidence-based HR.

Armed with useful and consistent wellbeing data, the next step is to combine it with existing data sets within the organisation. This is how we can get a realistic view of whether wellbeing programs are actually improving the lives of employees. After all, this is not simply about improving the bottom line, but making a meaningful improvement to the lives of everyone in the organisation.

Avenues for analysis include correlating wellbeing data to determine effects on the following.

Retention, one of the largest costs that can be avoided by building resilience. Estimates of the cost of turnover range from US$25,000 to $50,000 for a single employee. Preventing just a few people from leaving can quickly cover the cost of a resilience program. A personal problem can cause someone to hop between jobs, taking the same problem from one place to another. Helping people identify and take care of such personal challenges can help each manage their current job more effectively, making them less likely to leave. In our measurements, we often see people with very low resilience scores are the first to leave, providing a predictor of staff turnover. Fortunately, timely intervention can improve retention.

Absenteeism, a useful measure, particularly alongside categories such as annual leave, carers leave, stress leave, and so forth. Reviewing the impact of various wellbeing programs (by participation) can provide an intriguing insight into what is really making a difference. Insight such as this provides the basis for optimising wellbeing investment, though it depends on a single measurement that can be applied across the organisation to serve as a measurement standard.

Presenteeism, an increasing cost for business. Presenteeism is when someone shows up for work while sick, resulting in lower productivity than usual. The rise of remote working capabilities is making this more common, since people can 'work from home' instead of calling in sick. While employees may see this as doing the organisation a favour, it makes it harder to track trends because absenteeism rates incorrectly seem to fall. The main challenge is in finding ways to measure presenteeism—this is easier for transactional work. Once measurement is in place, data can be compared against different aspects of wellbeing to find a pathway for change.

Performance. Many organisations are starting to move away from performance measurements, though even so, most still end up ranking employees in another indirect way, such as by bonus allocation. While regular catch-ups and other techniques may become more common, the business still needs to know who is doing better relative to others. It would seem that performance measures will remain with us in one form or another, and while it does so, we can use that to compare against resilience to see which specific domain of resilience contributes more to performance. Not all organisations are the same; differences in culture, industry and so on means different approaches need to be taken to enhance resilience and performance. This is where deeper correlation analysis is useful.

Engagement: measuring how the employee feels about the organisation. There's a lot of research behind engagement, though we need to be mindful of how the mindset of the employee affects their engagement. Building resilience helps employees embed an approach motivation schema, making it easier for people to be engaged and find satisfaction in their jobs. In particular, the Vision domain has the strongest connection to engagement, highlighting once again it is about helping people find meaning in their work. Engagement scores are often held by a third party, however aggregated results can still be compared to find meaningful insights.

Contract vs permanent employees. As more people move to contract or at-will roles, there is a reduction in security and sense of safety. This reduction increases impulsive brain activation, resulting in less creativity and innovation. Measuring the impact of increasing the number of contractors is important to determine the broader impact to the organisation. Often, organisations simply turn a blind eye to contract workers, taking the view that *'They're not really our people'*. This mentality leads organisations to not offer any wellbeing benefits or other perks reserved for permanent employees. An 'us' and 'them' divide then develops, and the pool of ideas and collaboration diminishes. Much more productive is to include contract workers in wellbeing measurement initiatives so as to determine what opportunities exist, and then find ways to work with that to improve the culture collectively.

Part time vs full time employees. Another dimension is whether employees or contractors work on a part time or full time basis. Here it's worth looking into the effect of different working modes, including flexible working arrangements. If it seems that a certain type of arrangement has a particularly strong effect on wellness, then it's something worth exploring. These working modes may be promoted or discouraged based on the effect, with ongoing monitoring enabled to see how overall levels of wellbeing improve.

Differences in staff levels. We often see in our measurements that staff at higher levels score higher in resilience, while lower-level staff score lower. Sometimes this is related to Collaboration and not having a sufficient support network internally. Other times it's related to Vision and having difficulty relating to the goals of the team or organisation. Every organisation is different, therefore, measuring and understanding challenges across staff levels leads to the critical insights needed for enhancing support structures.

Time in tenure, also overall time in the organisation. The trajectory of employees once they enter the organisation is important—do people grow over time, or does the organisation chew them up and spit them out? An initial insight into this can be obtained through a snapshot, correlating time-with-the-organisation with resilience scores. This is also relevant for specific job types—are there particular roles that are detrimental to wellbeing? If so, what is it about those roles that cause this decline? These are all insights that help to optimise the business and build a positive and healthy culture.

Through this, an individual's perception of themselves is something that must stay confidential to the individual. For an organisation, there are far too many conflicts of interest in having access to this information directly.

People may be unfairly treated, left out of opportunities or inadvertently discriminated against if this information was openly available. This can open avenues to legal action, so it must be effectively managed.

Further, when employees know their data isn't private, then they are far more likely to artificially inflate their scores out of fear of some type of punishment. Again, we see fear-based behaviour sneak in and reduce outcomes. Having an external party facilitate this service helps to save costs (avoiding the need to develop specialised content internally), and also protects against legal action.

As the benefits of wellbeing programs are established through hard evidence, interest from the business's board and leaders will grow. They will focus more on the finer nuances of the programs themselves and how the data can help them better understand their people. Quality evidence about the effectiveness of wellbeing programs is the goal. This is what will help drive informed investment in building a healthy workplace with a strong culture and people who find meaning and purpose in their work.

A practical path forward

Measurement is critical to successfully build staff wellbeing within organisations. It clarifies the starting point, identifies priorities, and informs goals for action. Ongoing measurement is what tracks progress and creates a data set for benefits tracking. These are all critical factors for the success of a wellbeing program.

But if measurement is so critical, why do so few organisations deploy robust measurement alongside wellbeing initiatives? Here are some of the most common reasons why measurement is often left out:

- **Survey fatigue**—Current wellbeing measurement tools tend to use long questionnaires, some with 102 questions! Most larger organisations already regularly use surveys for other aspects of the business, so another long survey results in low participation rates as people simply do not have time.
- **Lack of insight**—There are surprisingly few validated measurement tools that are directly suited to adult professionals.

Instead, the focus is usually children, mental health patients, elderly, or veterans. This results in insights that are not designed to be useful in a corporate environment and often don't lead to meaningful action.

- **Lack of validation**—Given the difficulty of finding a measurement tool that suits the corporate environment, many businesses resort to developing their own surveys or use surveys that have not been scientifically validated. This produces unreliable insights that may misdirect effort, leading to a waste of time and money.

Before looking at ways to address these challenges, there is a larger question to consider—what is actually useful to measure? Many measurements may seem useful at the outset, but later lead to fruitless conclusions. This includes measuring how much someone enjoyed a wellbeing initiative, or measuring how happy they are.

Those quick surveys handed out at the end of a seminar invariably result in positive ratings. People dislike confrontation, so those who didn't enjoy it usually just don't fill in a survey, while the rest usually give a 'high' or 'very high' enjoyment rating, out of politeness. The result? High ratings overall and sponsors going around talking about how *everyone loved it*. But these transient measurements do not provide any insight into whether the event actually led to any real change or long-term improvement. There's no benefits realisation.

Meanwhile, focusing on aspects such as happiness, satisfaction or positivity brings another challenge—these are the outcomes of wellbeing that we want to achieve, but they don't give direct insight into what should be done if scores come in low. The measurements may be interesting, but they're not useful. They don't direct effort meaningfully.

What is needed instead is measurement that looks into the causal elements that lead to improvement in wellbeing. In other words, measuring what is useful to the person and the organisation. Deeply-held attitudes, beliefs and behaviours are the factors that enable wellbeing. These factors can be changed, learned and enhanced, and in fact are the construct of personal resilience. By measuring these resilience factors, we can find insights that are useful. This is because measurement tends to direct efforts to build improvable skills, that in turn lead to greater wellbeing.

Resilience is often mistaken simply as the ability to bounce back, but it is actually so much more. There are two key themes that are not immediately evident from the usual resilience definitions. The first is that resilience is not just reactive, but crucially is also proactive, meaning managing risk in advance, learning from the experience of others, and actively preventing personal disruptions. Second, resilience is not just about coming back to where you were before, but instead using each setback as an opportunity to advance towards a larger goal and purpose.

The result of this more complete concept of resilience is a set of factors that are fundamental to achieve wellbeing. These are the factors that need to be measured within organisations to be able to meaningfully help people to increase their own wellbeing.

These were the challenges and questions that drove us to develop a new resilience measurement scale. After more than a year of design and scientific validation, we developed the Predictive 6 Factor Resilience Scale. The PR6 is designed with the following in mind:

- **Based on neuroscience**. First and foremost, the PR6 is built on an exploration of how resilience functions at a neurobiological level. Measurement identifies an individual's current state across each of the six domains of resilience. Exploring the neuroscience of these resilience domains provides insight into more effective ways to enhance resilience, and in effect, wellbeing.

- **Ongoing measurement.** Critical for quantifying benefits over time, the PR6 is designed to be used for regular measurement. This provides a centralised platform to compare other measures against and find the best ways to continue building a culture of resilience.

- **Fast to use.** The questionnaire takes little time, with only 16 questions—around 3 minutes to complete. This makes it easy for anyone to fit into their day, enabling high participation and more complete insights for the organisation.

- **Predictive.** The PR6 also includes a forward-looking component by measuring psychological approach and avoidance motivation schemas—which are predictive of future resilience and goal achievement.

The 2016 study on use of the PR6 and subsequent publication of a research paper confirmed the PR6 as a valid psychometric scale. It has since been adopted by many psychologists and businesses as an insightful way to measure and improve resilience. Following that, in November 2017 we published additional research, showing more accurately how the different domains of resilience contributes to job satisfaction and engagement.

Our original research has inspired many around the world to conduct further research into the various domains of resilience and how they relate to different factors, such as stress, trauma, self-compassion, and more. Many universities come to us to use the PR6 in their research as it's the only psychometric tool they could find that includes health factors as a key component of resilience—it takes a holistic approach.

Regardless of which measurement platform you use, we would advise you to follow the same guidelines above. These help you put in place a program that can be analysed and tracked so that it can be improved over time. Results can be quantified and you can effectively see precisely where attention is needed and what kind of attention.

With the data available, you can perform more advanced analytics to see what types of content connects with which people. For example, are your biggest consumers of wellbeing content the people who already score highest? Do the people who score lowest miss out because they're not in a mindset to participate? These are important questions to investigate. Data provides the way forward, toward practical decisions that can be measured for success.

This is your imperative

Twenty years from now, resilience will be a crucial skill to survive and thrive as the speed of innovation dissolves the traditional boundaries of safety. Now is the time to plant the seeds of resilience. Now is the time for all of us to do our part for global resilience—to provide training and enhance the culture of organisations.

If you are in any type of leadership position—as an executive, a manager, in politics, among your peers, as a parent, even among friends—then you have a responsibility to help build resilience in people. You have the power to make a meaningful difference, a difference that can last a lifetime, and flow on and magnify over time.

I would suggest for you to take action—spread the concept of resilience. In particular, here are five rules of resilience to incorporate into your own resilience strategy.

1. **Lead by example.** Most critically, it starts with you and your own embodiment of resilience. Your example sets the stage for others to follow. People look up to their leaders to see if their actions follow their words. If wellbeing is simply given lip service, then no change will follow. You need to show how you are participating, let others see you are serious about it and that you live your words. Show people an example of resilience through your own ability to prepare for and manage situations effectively. Lead across each of the six domains of resilience.

2. **Be mindful of the brain.** Taking a neuroscience-based approach provides insight into the effects of different management styles and techniques. This insight helps leaders shift aware from fear-based management towards more constructive methods that enable both the people and the organisation to thrive. A further benefit is that, over time, our understanding of the brain improves, thereby bringing new insights and techniques that can be employed to increase resilience and wellbeing. It's not about becoming a neuroscientist. Instead, focus on the actionable components—in other words, practical neuroscience.

3. **Build meaning and purpose.** We have seen the importance of the Vision domain as our guiding light. It is the key to improving job satisfaction, along with many other areas of our lives. The concept of meaning and purpose, of having clear goals to work towards, is of critical importance from many perspectives. These concepts guide how we implement all the other domains of resilience, and drive what we spend energy on in our lives. So much time and effort is spent on things that don't really matter, when we don't know what's important. For you as a leader,

you play a role in helping people find a sense of meaning in what they do. Purpose transcends happiness, as it defines what it is that makes people happy in the first place.

4. Measure culture and track results. Measure your efforts, track benefits and cut out inefficiencies. Focus on what really works and keep going. Keep in mind that the brain doesn't change overnight. It takes a while to build new, healthy, neural pathways, so ongoing measurement is needed to keep an eye on trends and ensure there are real benefits to individuals and the organisation. The danger is always that wellbeing programs are the first to be cut when times are tough. But when there is a clear business case about its benefits at a quantified level, then leaders would be more likely to stay the course.

5. Let your data be your guide. Get scientific about building resilience and wellbeing. Bring together all the different data sources and find where the true influencing factors are. Every organisation is different, so simply relying on research done externally is not going to uncover what really works for your people. Start walking the path of data discovery, break down information silos and combine data sets to find insights specifically relevant to you. This is where the hidden potential of people can be uncovered, bringing efficiencies that extend competitive advantage. It also makes you readier for rapid change and innovation. Insight from data builds resilience at scale.

Heed the needs of the brain. Live the domains of resilience. Follow the rules of resilience. The resilience imperative falls on you—so join in and help us build a resilient civilization.

Appendix A – 2017 Research

Predictive 6 Factor Resilience Scale – Domains of Resilience and Their Role as Enablers of Job Satisfaction

Rossouw, J.G., Rossouw, P.J., Paynter, C., Ward, A., Khnana, P. (2017).Predictive 6 Factor Resilience Scale –Domains of Resilience and Their Role as Enablers of Job Satisfaction. *International Journal of Neuropsychotherapy*, 2(1), 25-40. doi: 10.12744/ijnpt.2017.1.0025-0040

Jurie G. Rossouw, Pieter J. Rossouw, Christine Paynter, Anne Ward, Peter Khnana

ABSTRACT

Continuing from previous research on the Predictive 6 Factor Resilience Scale (PR6), this study provides further domain-level validation in addition to investigation of resilience as an enabler of job satisfaction.

Methods: A multi-stage testing format was employed using a group of primarily professional adults (n=617). Domain-level scales were developed through ratings from the research panel. Validation data was collected through an online measurement device. Multiple versions of the scales were tested for internal consistency, with scales retained, modified or rejected based on resulting scores. From this, domain-level scales were finalised, an extended 50-item resilience scale (PR6-50) was developed, and the 16-item PR6 was revised. Analysis was conducted against the Brief Index of Affective Job Satisfaction (BIAJS) and demographic data.

Results: Scales for each domain were validated with good internal consistency (>0.70). The PR6-50 showed high internal consistency (0.9372), while the revised 16-item PR6 showed improved internal consistency (0.8398). Resilience results showed a correlation of 0.536 (P value <0.001) with BIAJS, while the Vision domain showed the highest correlation at 0.607 (P value <0.001).

Conclusion: The result strengthens the internal consistency and domain validity of the PR6, as well as establishing an extended version (PR6-50) for further resilience research and clinical purposes. The relationship of resilience to job satisfaction, in particular the Vision domain, provides additional pathways for exploration to improve employee engagement and performance in organisations.

Automation advances now stretch beyond manufacturing and agriculture, and increasingly into service jobs traditionally considered as secure careers. A study by Oxford university estimates that 47% of jobs may be automated in the next two decades (Frey & Osborne, 2017). The impact of automation on developing countries may be up to 85% (Frey et al, 2016). Faster technological advances bring with it increased uncertainty about one's own future. Increasing personal resilience provides psychological skills and techniques to manage uncertainty and adapt faster to a changing environment. Understanding resilience at a deeper level for each domain (Rutter, 1985; Olsson et al, 2003) and their relevant relationships provides more effective ways for organisations to train and develop resilience capacity in people, as resilience can be improved throughout life (Herrman et al, 2011). This illustrates the growing importance of resilience as a critical life skill for a time of rapid change.

The Predictive 6 Factor Resilience Scale (PR6) published in 2016 described the overall validation of the scale as a resilience psychometric (Rossouw & Rossouw, 2016). Domains were identified through their neurobiological foundations building on work from Davidson on the emotional styles of the brain (Davidson & Begley, 2012). Theoretical foundations were explored in relation to other major resilience scales (Windle et al, 2011) to construct a meta-model of resilience. Research identified that physiological health hygiene factors also contribute to the resilience construct. These include nutrition, exercise, and sleep hygiene factors. Approach and avoidance motivational factors were shown to have a positive correlation and impact on internal consistency, adding a predictive component through prediction of future goal achievement (Jackson et al, 2009).

Primary objectives of this study are as follows: 1. Conduct further domain-level validation of the PR6 model, constructing separate domain scales alongside a Momentum scale. 2. Compile an extended version of the PR6 for future research projects. 3. If relevant, revise the 16-item PR6 to increase overall and domain-level consistency. 4. Correlate resilience to job satisfaction to determine relevant relationships.

In addition, areas for further investigation were identified in the previous research paper which will be revisited. These include gender differences where females scored higher in Health, while males scores slightly higher in Tenacity and Reasoning. Differences in resilience scores over age groupings could not be validated due to insufficient data in the original research. Expectations were for resilience to stabilise with additional data, and therefore will be revisited. Sleep hygiene indicated lower correlation with resilience. Consequently, this research expands sleep into component factors to investigate relative importance. One Collaboration item related to working with others also indicated lower correlation with overall resilience, leading to further investigation.

METHOD

Research design

To achieve the research objectives, individual domains were built out as separate scales to measure each component of resilience. Item generation was conducted with the named panel of researchers in accordance to the thematic concept and theoretical foundation of each resilience domain. Items were combined alongside research references and justification. All original items of the PR6 were included as a standard measure. Excluding demographic and job satisfaction items, 101 items were developed.

Item development was approached from the perspective of domains as representatives of the neurobiological constructs. Each domain therefore presents a thematic construct for practical intervention. Interaction between the domains is expected, however their continued separation is valuable for further treatment development. Each domain is investigated separately relating to its theoretical foundations, allowing further granularity for enhancing resilience overall.

A review round commenced where the research panel cross-examined all of the 101 items. Each reviewer ranked items on a confidence level of their contribution to the domain. Through multiple review rounds, items were discussed and revised until ratings were finalised. Resulting ratings were aggregated for each item to produce an overall confidence score.

Confidence scores were used to produce two extended test scales which also included the original PR6 items for comparison. The first was a High Confidence (HC) scale constructed from the items with the highest scores, maintaining a balance of positive and negative scored items. Each domain, including Momentum was allocated six items, except for the Health domain which was allocated 11 items to further investigate health hygiene (particularly sleep) factors. A second Wildcard (WC) scale was constructed by swapping the two lowest-scoring items from the HC scales with the next two items below that. The aim of the WC scale was to test a wider range of items without extending the overall test scale sizes beyond practical limitations for organizational application.

The HC and WC versions of the domain-level scales were then tested for validity. Scores were compiled and a progression determination was made based on relative scores. Where needed, modifications to the scales were applied until sufficient internal consistency was achieved. This included the addition of items for low consistency domains to conduct a deeper search as needed. For these domains, item omission analysis was conducted to establish acceptable internal consistency scores.

Following the multi-stage testing format, the domain-level scales were established and the combination of the domains were tested as an extended version of the PR6 (TESTPR6). Internal consistency was tested alongside demographic and other dimensions. Domain-level relationships were tested, including correlations to the original PR6 (OPR6) to determine potential adjustments. The extended domain-level scales were then analysed for highest internal correlation, taking the top two items (balance of positive and negative items, except for Health) and were proposed as revised items for the 16 item PR6 where they represent an improvement on previous values.

The Brief Index of Affective Job Satisfaction (BIAJS) developed by Thompson and Phua (2012) was chosen as a measure to correlate with resilience factors. This BIAJS was chosen due to its comprehensive validation and reliability as a job satisfaction measurement. Our interest is in determining a potential relationship between resilience and job satisfaction, as well as determining which domain of resilience is a stronger enabler of job satisfaction.

Positive Impression Management was also tested through the inclusion of items to potentially control for this effect. Of interest is Crowne and Marlowe's (1960) social desirability scale and its intent to measure the desire of a person to be presented in a positive light. This effect may result in individuals artificially inflating scores on the resilience scale due to social desirability. A mitigating factor within this study is that confidentiality is assured for each participant, reducing the need to inflate scores that others will not see. We include items for consistency measurement related to alcohol use to potentially measure differences and inconsistencies in scoring. Analysis may reveal further exclusion criteria to refine results. We note that Crowne later criticized the use of his original scale to 'decontaminate' study samples (Crowne, 1991), as well as criticism from others (Odendaal, 2015). We also note that Positive Impression Management is generally not a feature of resilience psychometrics, potentially relating to difficulty in attaining meaningful insights. Data analysis is conducted with this in consideration.

Resilience and the basic needs

Adding to the foundation of the resilience domains, we propose connections to the four basic needs identified by Epstein. He suggested that there is no single basic need for psychological functioning, but instead that there are four basic needs of relative equivalence (Epstein, 2003). The four basic needs provide further explanatory power to the diversity of the resilience domains, indicating inputs into one or more of the basic needs. Domains contribute to the needs through positive affect, while ineffective functioning of a domain can produce negative affect to the relevant need. An individual's skill in implementing the relevant resilience domain therefore determines their ability to contribute positive affect to the basic needs.

Maximisation of pleasure and minimization of pain is the first basic need. It draws on the work of Dollard and Miller (1950), and also Freud (1909) at an earlier stage. Through the individual's experience of predominantly pleasure or pain, a basic belief is fuelled about whether or not the world is a malevolent or benign place. A belief that the world is benign adds to optimism, while the opposite may produce pessimistic attitudes. We summarise this need for pleasure and the avoidance of pain as the need for *Motivation*.

Control and orientation is a need for a sense of stability and predictability related to the world in which we exist. This includes concepts such as controllability and justice existing in the world, indicating a sense of meaningfulness. As Epstein (2003) viewed this need, the opposite is a sense of "unpredictability, uncontrollability, and lack of justice" (pg14). This builds on the work of Rogers (1951), and gives rise to a belief of relative meaningfulness or meaninglessness of one's life. We summarise this as the need for *Control*.

Relatedness is the need for stable and secure relationships with others with whom we can form meaningful connections. Epstein (2003) references work from Bowlby (2008) as a basis for this need through his founding concept of attachment theory. A basic belief regarding whether people are trustworthy and loving vs untrustworthy and rejecting develops based on relatedness experiences through life. We summarise this concept as the need for *Connection*.

Self-enhancement is the need to improve the status of the self. Work from Kohut (1971) and Allport (1961) contribute to the concept of personal growth and improvement. Related beliefs cover whether the self is viewed as competent, worthy, moral and strong, vs incompetent, unworthy, immoral and weak. We summarise this as the need for *Self-esteem*. Relationships to resilience is considered.

Resilience and Neuropeptide Y

Neuropeptide Y (NPY) has been implicated previously as being inversely related to the stress response (Zhou et al, 2008). Subjects with major depressive disorder (MDD) have also been shown to have less NPY, and that a genetic variation or lower NPY expression predisposes to MDD (Mickey et al, 2011). This has led to conclusions that NPY upregulation has an anxiolytic effect, lowering the stress response when released at higher levels (Morgan, 2002). Research on special forces military personnel during enemy capture and interrogation training revealed that NPY has a protective effect against dissociation (Morgan et al, 2000).

Differences found between special forces and non-special forces personnel indicate that additional training results in greater release of NPY, suggesting training provides additional resilience effects through NPY upregulation. Recent research provided additional support, showing that chronic stress leads to epigenetic dysregulation of NPY receptors (Lomazzo et al, 2017). Epigenetics provide a mechanism for fast, generational changes in genetic encoding. In relation to resilience, these changes may either provide the next generation with stronger resistance against stress, or instead predispose them to psychological diseases due to the experiences and actions of the current generation.

Generational changes have already been witnessed through a study on transgenerational transmission of post-traumatic stress disorder following the Tutsi genocide (Perroud et al, 2014). Inherited alterations were witnessed within the HPA axis, as well as lower cortisol levels than those who have not been exposed to the genocide. Cortisol and NPY release during stress are positively correlated, where NPY provides a reduced stress response. Epigenetic changes in NPY receptors and related neurobiology may contribute to generational changes in stress management. We hypothesise that resilience domains acting on NPY may encourage epigenetic changes that improve stress response. These epigenetic changes provide a mechanistic pathway to build resilience on a generational level, resulting in a measure of stress-inoculation for future generations.

Domains of resilience

Details of the resilience domains and their neurological correlates are set out in the previous research. For the sake of clarity, a short overview is provided for each domain. Proposed relation of the resilience domains to the basic needs are explored.

Vision (VIS) refers to having a sense of purpose, clear goals, and the behaviour of goal-striving. Skills related to this domain includes an ability to define and clarify goals worth striving for, prioritise between goals, develop congruence between goals, self-motivate, and a belief in an ability to achieve goals. VIS is suggested to contribute to all the basic needs. Goals define a sense of purpose and direction in life, contributing to the orientation component of Control. One's sense of purpose and goals also define whether there is engagement in pleasurable activities (need for Motivation), and also if there is engagement with others on a psychosocial level (Connection). Collectively, these support the outcome of Self-esteem enhancement and a sense of self-efficacy, suggested by Bandura (1988) to be a key component of social cognitive theory. This central nature of VIS crossing all basic needs leads to the hypothesis of VIS as potentially the most important domain of resilience. Neural correlates include the prefrontal cortex (PFC) as the centre for long-term planning and executive functioning. The ventral striatum plays a role in risk/reward cognition and reinforcement (Davidson, 2012), facilitating decisions between various goals as options available for pursuit. Hippocampal/PFC interaction play a role in higher-order meaning assignment to memories (Preston & Eichenbaum, 2013).

Composure (COM) concerns emotion awareness, emotion regulation and stress management. Skills related to this domain include emotional granularity, emotional reappraisal, self-calming through breathing and related techniques. As an emotional domain, COM factors into the need for Motivation through striving for pleasure and the avoidance of pain. The earliest identification of this was by Walter Bradford Cannon in 1929, noting that pain and suffering in this context activates the HPA axis, leading to a loss of emotional composure. The COM domain then refers to the ability of someone to regain and retain a sense of composure. HPA activation may also lead to a loss of personal control, or a reduction in Control as a basic need may lead to reduced composure. Conversely, being able to maintain a sense of composure contributes to Control within the experienced situation. Related neural structures include the insula as an interpreter and processor of audio-visual signal integration, as well as interoceptive capabilities that enable cognitive emotional regulation techniques (Critchley et al, 2004). The insula has pathways to limbic structures such as the amygdala, enabling potential regulation of the HPA axis to achieve physical and mental composure.

Reasoning (RES) relates to problem-solving, resourcefulness and being ready for change. Skills related to RES includes cognitive abilities such as planning for adverse situations to mitigate outcomes in advance, challenging and changing beliefs through introspective questioning, and building one's own ability to be resourceful. This domain closely relates to the need for Control, striving to devise options available to act on to achieve goals, and also through planning to produce better solutions to problems to attain control over outcomes. This relates closely to one's internal map of the world and understanding of potential outcomes through cause-effect relationships. Neural structures include the enablers of logical thought such as Wernicke's and Broca's areas in their role to interpret and produce symbols and language for rational thought. PCF connection to the anterior cingulate cortex (ACC) in its role to screen for errors and optimise responses assist in rational learning and improvement (Peterson, 2014). Preparatory exercises and planning for adverse situations such as those practiced by the military align with RES skills. These have been shown to increase NPY release, providing an improved stress response and promoting resilience (Morgan et al, 2000).

Tenacity (TEN) relates to hardiness and perseverance. Skills include beliefs concerning optimism for the future and being persistent in the face of adversity. Research by Duckworth et al (2007) has indicated that the capacity to persist has a higher correlation to goal achievement than intelligence. In this sense, TEN relies on the need for Control via orientation to know what to persist towards, while also contributing to Control through one's conscious ability to continue along the chosen path. This conscious decision not to give up may align internal reward systems towards chosen objectives, feeding into how the need for Motivation as pleasure aligns to achievement and pain to failure, or giving up. Perceptual changes effected by a conscious appraisal of stress in this context may reduce mortality, as indicated in research by Keller et al in 2012. Neural structures include the ability of the PFC to downregulate HPA activation to overcome adversity and sustain goal-directed activity. Dopaminergic neurons emerging from the ventral tegmentum play a key role in motivation required for persistence despite adversity and challenge.

Collaboration (COL) includes secure attachment, relationships, and maintaining social perceptions. Skills include one's social skills, ability to build support networks, awareness of social context and willingness to ask for help. COL relates most strongly to the need for Connection, combining the importance of support received and provided, and awareness of social context and perceptions. The functioning of this domain is therefore enabled through the basic belief that people are trustworthy and loving, therefore support is available when needed and it is worthwhile to support others in turn. Neural structures include the right PFC which has been implicated in the process of secure attachment (Schore, 2000). In particular, the orbito-medial PFC serves a crucial role in sensitivity to context, detecting social cues and changes in the environment (Schoenbaum & Takahashi, 2011). These may function in concert with the fusiform gyrus, responsible for interpreting visual signals to identify faces and related associations to identified individuals. Produced results include deeper understanding of what support is appropriate from whom given the situation, where higher skills here aid in producing appropriate behaviour when facing challenges.

Health (HLT) includes physical hygiene factors such as quality sleep, healthy nutrition, and regular exercise, as well as perceptions regarding one's own health. Primary skills include the ability to research and understand which healthy habits to follow, the motivation to implement the habits, and the persistence to maintain these habits in the long term. HLT outputs to the need for Self-esteem enhancement, providing internal validation XXthat the self is worth looking after and to be enhanced through physical means, not just emotional. Key neural relationships within the HLT components related to the regulation of BDNF as an enabler of neuroplasticity, enhancing neurogenesis in the hippocampus, as well as increasing NDMA expression and AMPA release and expression during synaptic connection strengthening. Exercise is also shown to increase NPY, potentially further enhancing the stress response and aiding in resilience (Lewis et al, 1993; Morris et al, 1986; Lundberg et al, 1985).

Momentum

Momentum (MTM) is a forward-looking measure, standing in contrast with the resilience domains that represent a point-in-time measurement. MTM measures approach and avoidance motivational schemas which have been indicated as a potential predictor of goal achievement (Jackson et al, 2009). The measure investigates individual attitudes toward future opportunities, appraisal of new challenges, problem-solving approach, as well as avoidance attitudes such as procrastination tendencies.

MTM in the previous research showed a high correlation with the resilience construct. We expand the items in the current research to develop a specific approach/avoidance scale for further research and predictive analysis.

Study sample

Participants for the study were recruited through workshops (primarily education and healthcare workers) and through an online survey using social media platforms (broader diversity of participants). Though the PR6 is currently used by students, eligibility for the research was set at 18 years or over. Incomplete surveys were removed from the study sample.

The overall study sample (n=671) was screened, with entries removed which were incomplete (n=46), under 18 years were removed (n=6), and a duplicate entry was removed (n=2). The remainder (n=617, 73% female) entered into data analysis. Median age was 43 (StDev 10.98). Demographic data was incomplete for some entries (n=7). Of the used sample, n=93 was entered into HC, n=98 was entered into WC, while the remaining n=426 proceeded on to TESTPR6.

RESULTS

Comprehensive analysis using the OPR6 as a standard component of all samples collected indicated data normality of the population (n=617). Negatively scored items were reversed, then domain scores were calculated through the mean, averaging all domain means together to create the overall resilience scores. Scoring between 0 (lowest resilience) and 1 (highest resilience), the mean for the sample was 0.65215 (StDev 0.569) at a 95% CI ranging from 0.6409 and 0.6634. Internal consistency for the OPR6 was validated at an alpha of 0.8004. No significant differences were found between male and female populations. Age grouping reveals a statistically significant increase in resilience scores as age increases (Table 1, Fig 1 and Fig 3).

The BIAJS showed high internal consistency with an alpha of 0.9107 (n=617). Mean was 0.7404 (StDev 0.8383).

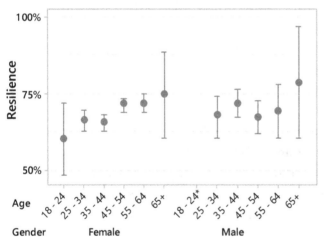

FIG 1: Interval plot – Resilience by age group and gender
*Insufficient data to plot

HC & WC validation

Validation of domains within HC and WC were conducted to determine which domains to discard, progress or modify (Fig 2). HC sample (n=93) achieved an overall alpha of 0.9305, compared to the WC sample (n=98) which achieved an alpha of 0.9202. HC VIS alpha was 0.8096 (vs WC VIS alpha = 0.6765) which was kept and modified due to one low performing item. HC COM alpha was 0.6856 (vs WC COM alpha = 0.6860) which was kept and modified with the addition of two items to investigate further. HC RES alpha was 0.7071 (vs WC RES alpha = 0.7837) which was discarded in favour of the WC model. HC TEN alpha was 0.7506 (vs WC TEN alpha = 0.7091) and was modified with a high performing item from the WC model. HC COL alpha was 0.4610 (vs WC COL alpha = 0.6347) which was discarded in favour of modifying the WC COL model with four additional items. HC HLT alpha was 0.8078 (vs WC HLT alpha = 0.8701) which was discarded in favour of the WC HTL model which was kept intact. HC MTM alpha was 0.6406 (vs WC MTM alpha = 0.6235) which was retained and modified with four additional items. Items added underwent panel scrutiny to determine consistency with theoretical underpinnings.

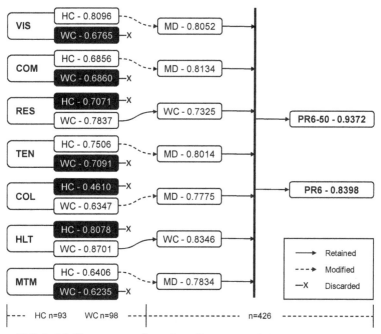

FIG 2: Multi-stage testing of resilience models.

TABLE 2: PR6-50 Item analysis

Item ID	Type	Alpha if omitted	Item ID	Type	Alpha if omitted
PR6-50 Cronbach's alpha = 0.9372			**COL (alpha = 0.7775)**		
VIS (alpha = 0.8052)			49	Reverse	0.6986
8	Positive	0.7606	50	Reverse	0.7159
21	Reverse	0.7611	44	Positive	0.7391
39	Reverse	0.7635	3	Positive	0.7584
15	Positive	0.7717	37	Reverse	0.7625
31	Positive	0.7817	43	Positive	0.7789
2	Reverse	0.8087	**HLT (alpha = 0.8346)**		
COM (alpha = 0.8134)			13	Positive	0.8056
19	Positive	0.7615	20	Positive	0.8074
22	Reverse	0.7772	14	Positive	0.8077
47	Positive	0.7866	18	Positive	0.8119
4	Positive	0.7889	11	Positive	0.8139
35	Reverse	0.7927	30	Positive	0.8151
32	Reverse	0.7961	41	Positive	0.8174
RES (alpha = 0.7325)			28	Reverse	0.8329
25	Positive	0.6629	24	Positive	0.8333
5	Positive	0.687	12	Positive	0.8444
9	Reverse	0.69	**MTM (alpha = 0.7834)**		
36	Reverse	0.6999	23	Positive	0.7512
42	Positive	0.7112	48	Reverse	0.7569
29	Reverse	0.7183	46	Positive	0.7579
TEN (alpha = 0.8014)			40	Positive	0.7593
33	Reverse	0.7641	6	Reverse	0.7619
38	Reverse	0.7655	17	Reverse	0.7648
7	Reverse	0.7665	10	Positive	0.7672
26	Positive	0.7696	34	Reverse	0.7724
1	Positive	0.7706	27	Positive	0.7742
16	Positive	0.7882	45	Reverse	0.7811

TESTPR6 validation and refinement

Following modification, the second round of testing (n=426) was conducted on the composite TESTPR6 created from the retained and modified domains. Domains were targeted to finalise to six items each (three positive and three negative scored items), except for HLT which was targeted for ten items. MTM was also targeted to finalise to six items.

TESTPR6 domains alphas are as follows, targeting > 0.7. VIS alpha was acceptable at 0.8052. COM, after item omission to reach six items was 0.8134. RES alpha was 0.7325. TEN was 0.8014. COL at ten items prior to item omission analysis was 0.8261. Pure omission analysis aiming for highest alpha ended at 0.8284, though resulted in a narrower definition of COL with

TABLE 1: Summary of Age Grouping by BIAJS and PR6-50 scores

Age Group	N	PR6-50			BIAJS		
		Mean	SE Mean	StDev	Mean	SE Mean	StDev
Female							
18 - 24	9	0.604	0.0511	0.1533	0.7153	0.0552	0.1657
25 - 34	58	0.6614	0.0171	0.1306	0.7134	0.0305	0.2321
35 - 44	91	0.6563	0.0135	0.1292	0.7115	0.0224	0.2134
45 - 54	96	0.7135	0.012	0.1178	0.7747	0.0196	0.1918
55 - 64	52	0.7197	0.0159	0.1148	0.7825	0.0259	0.1871
65+	7	0.7486	0.057	0.1507	0.7946	0.0664	0.1757
Male							
18 - 24	3	0.348	0.157	0.272	0.542	0.182	0.315
25 - 34	17	0.6783	0.0322	0.1328	0.6324	0.0536	0.2208
35 - 44	41	0.7201	0.021	0.1343	0.747	0.027	0.1728
45 - 54	25	0.6733	0.025	0.1251	0.6725	0.0548	0.2738
55 - 64	20	0.6935	0.0407	0.182	0.7656	0.0415	0.1857
65+	6	0.7859	0.071	0.1739	0.813	0.116	0.285

highly similar items. The authors believe that a broader definition of COL to be more valuable in measurement and treatment, therefore undertook an item omission analysis focusing on broadness rather than pure alpha optimisation, reflecting views of other authors noting unnecessarily high alpha (Tavakol & Dennick, 2011; Sijtsma, 2009; Neuendorf, 2011). A broadness path for COL resulted in a final alpha of 0.7775. HLT alpha after one item omission resulted in a ten-item alpha of 0.8346. MTM alpha during omission analysis decreased significantly with each item removal, therefore a decision was made to retain the MTM scale to ten items resulting in an alpha of 0.7834. With these results, the domain and MTM scales were viewed as finalised and ready to contribute to the new extended scale.

Combining all the domain scales and MTM provided a final extended version of the PR6 with 50 items (six each for VIS, COM, RES, TEN, COL, and ten each for HLT and MTM). This version achieved a final alpha of

0.9372 with a mean of 0.6874 (SE 0.0264, StDev 0.5449), 95% CI 0.6744 to 0.7004 (n=426). This new extended 50 item scale is named as the PR6-50. See table 2 for the remaining item omission statistics.

Analysis for PR6 revision

Domain-level representation within the 16-item PR6 can now be revisited to determine if different items provide higher correlation with the domains than the domain related items in the OPR6. To make this determination, we examined the OPR6 domain representative items as correlated against the new domain-level scales developed, then investigated different item combinations from the new domain scales to find more highly correlated item combinations. Where higher correlated item combinations exist, these are replaced to revise the PR6. Item combinations are kept to one positively and one negatively scored item, except for HLT which retains four items as before to represent the various factors included in it.

The combination of one original item and one new item for VIS was noted to achieve a slightly higher correlation (0.891) compared to the OPR6 items (0.861). For COM, two new items produced a higher correlation (0.884) compared to the OPR6 items (0.658). An original and new item combination for RES showed a slightly higher correlation (0.850) than the OPR6 items (0.8633). TEN correlation also improved slightly (0.860) through two new items compared to the OPR6 items (0.853). COL correlation improved through a new two-item combination (0.874) compared to OPR6 items (0.609). HLT correlation improved slightly (0.930) through replacement of one item compared to the OPR6 four items (0.925). MTM correlation improved slightly through the use of two new items (0.786) compared to OPR6 items (0.781).

Revised item combinations were then used to establish an overall revised 16-item PR6. Correlation of the original 16-item OPR6 to the PR6-50 is 0.945, while the revised 16-item PR6 correlates to the PR6-50 at 0.960, representing a small increase in overall accuracy. The new PR6 provides an alpha of 0.8398 (mean = 0.6695, SE = 0.0294, StDev = 0.6066, median = 0.6785).

Demographic analysis

Demographic data collected included age, gender, location, and occupation. Gender data revealed no significant differences. Female mean was 0.6858 (StDev = 0.5126, 95% CI 0.6716 to 0.7001), while male mean was 0.6921 (StDev = 0.6307, 95% CI 0.6626 to 0.7216). 73% of participants were in Australia, with participation from various countries as the remainder. No statistically significant differences were found between Australian participants and other participants.

Occupation data indicates potential trends, such as lower scores in Education professionals (n = 147, mean = 0.6715, StDev = 0.5208, 95% CI 0.65002 to 0.6927), compared to Healthcare workers (n = 69, mean = 0.6958, StDev = 0.5363, 95% CI 0.6636 to 0.7281), and Human Resource workers (n = 38, mean = 0.7077, StDev = 0.4871, 95% CI 0.6676 to 0.74767).

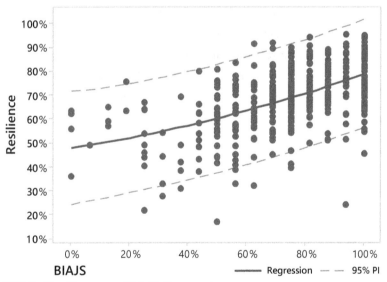

FIG 3: Resilience vs BIAJS Regression

Age grouping indicates an overall increase in resilience as age increases. While female resilience increases over age is relatively consistent, male resilience rates appear to decline somewhat past ages 45 through to 64. Males aged 18 – 24 had insufficient data to plot (Fig 1 and Table 1). Additional data is required to further validate.

BIAJS analysis

As an affective job satisfaction scale, the BIAJS provides insight into relationships with resilience and the individual domains of resilience, as well as resilience overall. Analysis of BIAJS results across the PR6-50 population (n=426) provided a mean of 0.7372 (between 0 and 1) with a StDev of 0.2099. Alpha for the BIAJS was high at 0.9174.

TABLE 3: Summary of Occupation by BIAJS and PR6-50 scores

Occupation	N	PR6-50			BIAJS		
		Mean	SE Mean	StDev	Mean	SE Mean	StDev
Education & Training	147	0.6715	0.043	0.5208	0.7623	0.0145	0.1752
Healthcare & Medical	69	0.69585	0.0646	0.5363	0.7781	0.0225	0.1871
Human Resources & Recruitment	38	0.70765	0.079	0.4871	0.6842	0.0357	0.2199
Professional - Other	155	0.70615	0.0414	0.5156	0.721	0.0194	0.2413

Regression analysis of PR6-50 to the BIAJS (Fig 3) yielded an R-Sq of 29.1% (S = 0.115). Correlation result is 0.536, indicating an overall positive relationship between resilience and job satisfaction. Domain-level analysis showed that the strongest relationship between resilience domains and the BIAJS is VIS (correlation = 0.607). Following that, MTM correlated at 0.490, followed by TEN at 0.418. VIS to BIAJS regression showed an R-Sq of 36.9% (S = 0.148).

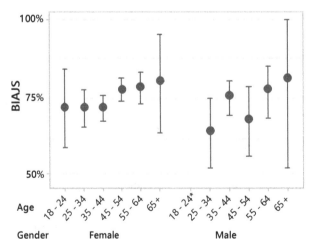

FIG 4: Interval plot – BIAJS by age group and gender.

*Insufficient data to plot

Occupation analysis shows that Education and Healthcare workers have proportionately higher job satisfaction than Human Resource workers. Education workers had a mean of 0.7623 (StDev = 0.1752, 95% CI 0.7337 to 0.7909). Healthcare workers had a mean of 0.7781 (StDev = 0.0225, 95% CI 0.7332 to 0.8230). Human Resources workers had a mean of 0.6842 (StDev = 0.2199, 95% CI 0.6119 to 0.7565) (table 3).

Age grouping indicated an overall upwards trend in job satisfaction over age. Trending is similar to resilience scores, with males showing a reduction in job satisfaction scores at ages 45 – 55. Males aged 18 – 24 had insufficient data to plot (Fig 4).

Consistency analysis

Consistency scores were generated by calculating the absolute value of the first consistency item minus the second, after reversing the negatively scored item. This produced a measure of inconsistency between the items. Dividing results by low inconsistency scores (0, 1, 2) produced an alpha for PR6-50 of 0.9378 (mean = 0.68325, StDev = 0.5488, 95% CI 0.6681 to 0.6984), compared to high inconsistency scores (3, 4) producing an alpha of 0.9356 (mean = 0.6997., StDev = 0.5331, 95% CI 0.6744 to 0.7250).

Consistency measures showed no direct relationships to any of the domains, nor BIAJS. Correlation with resilience was 0.063 (P value = 0.195), indicating no immediate relationship. The consistency measure yields a difference in mean resilience scores, however, analysis of the individual items provided greater clarity regarding underlying relationships. The first item (alcohol consumption) had no correlation with resilience (correlation = 0.005, P value = 0.916), while the second item (worry about alcohol consumption) had a minor inverse relationship with resilience (correlation = 0.114, P value = 0.018).

DISCUSSION

Building on the original PR6 research, this study showed the development of individual scales for each resilience domain alongside a scale for MTM. The combination of the domain scales gives rise to the full 50-item PR6-50, intended for further research purposes. From these scales, revisions to the OPR6 resulted in the revised 16-item PR6, intended for continued practical use in organisations and clinical practice as a fast resilience measurement that provides insight into each domain of resilience, as well as a forward-looking component through MTM. Domain-level scales may be used together as the full PR6-50, or separately to investigate specific areas.

These scales represent a refinement of the PR6 and the resilience domains, allowing more accurate measurement of the individual aspects that contribute to overall psychological resilience. Following a multi-stage testing format, all scales show strong internal consistency. Consistency between the OPR6 and revised PR6 allow for continuity of measurement, while providing a slight increase in overall accuracy for future results. In particular, revised COM and COL domain item combinations provide a stronger correlation to the full domain scales. Building on previous research, the COL items now focus on social skills and willingness to invest in new relationships, showing a higher relationship than prior items. Ongoing research indicate further potential neurobiological factors that contribute to certain domains, such as NPY acting through skills within RES, and also HLT factors.

Within the HLT domain, initial PR6 research indicated that sleep quantity may not be most directly related to resilience. Through this study, additional sleep factors were investigated, including ability to fall asleep, perception of sleep quality (being able to sleep well), and also waking up rested. Our analysis showed that the single sleep factor that most contributed to resilience is waking up rested, while the other factors did not significantly contribute. The overall HLT domain thereby now provides an insight into overall perception of health, nutrition habits, exercise regularity, and restfulness of sleep.

PR6 correlation with BIAJS provides evidence of a positive relationship between resilience and job satisfaction. In particular, the VIS domain showed the strongest relationship with job satisfaction.

A potential relationship may exist between age and resilience, showing that resilience improves with age. However, differences between male and female audiences suggest that additional data is required to draw conclusions. Lower participation at the early and later age groups limit analysis, while some dips through the age ranges were observed. A similar trend was observed with job satisfaction, including differences in gender behaviour. However, overlapping CI ranges preclude any meaningful conclusions thus far. Overall, individuals at any age may exhibit high or low resilience as indicated by current measurements.

In line with the previous paper, there appears to be little difference overall in resilience across gender. Similarly, no statistically significant differences were found in any domain for gender. Occupation does appear to have more significant differences, such as Human Resource workers having more resilience, though lower job satisfaction. Contrast with Education and Healthcare workers (possibly more direct services), where job satisfaction is higher though resilience is lower. Differences between geographical regions provide no conclusive results.

Consistency scores provided a negative result, showing no clear benefit in subdividing responses by low to high consistency ratings. However, differences in items showed that worry about alcohol consumption may have a slight negative relationship with resilience.

CONCLUSION

This research further adds to the validity of the PR6, and also enables further research through the more comprehensive PR6-50. HLT continues to show a strong correlation with resilience, improving internal consistency while showing additional theoretical mechanistic connections through NPY. This highlights that HLT isn't simply about maintaining physical appearance, but strongly about maintaining a healthy environment for the brain and mind to enable effective functioning of the resilience domains, acting as a foundation for resilience.

The relationship between resilience and job satisfaction may indicate that resilient people enjoy their work to a greater degree than less resilient people. Mechanistically, resilience may assist in creating a mindset through which an individual may derive greater satisfaction from their job, compared to someone with lower resilience. In particular, the strong relationship between VIS and job satisfaction suggest several possibilities. First, an individual who has more clarity on their own sense of purpose and goals may be more adept at choosing an occupation aligned with their own goals.

Second, an individual with this clarity may be able to better connect the goals of their occupation with their own goals, even where an intrinsic relationship might not directly exist.

We note that two VIS items (ability to stay motivated, and belief in ability to achieve goals) provide a 0.764 correlation with the PR6-50, providing a useful proxy for overall resilience purely from the VIS domain. Bandura (1988) viewed self-efficacy as one's belief in their own ability to do well, indicating that this might lead someone to put in greater effort to succeed. This, alongside the high correlation of VIS to job satisfaction, led us to propose that VIS is the most critical domain of resilience. Purpose, meaning and clear goals can therefore be seen as central to the implementation of the other domains of resilience, providing direction and guidance to navigate uncertainty. Difficult decisions and adverse situations can be managed through having greater clarity of personal goals and purpose, which is what VIS would provide. Therefore, all the other domains of resilience effectively work in service of the VIS domain, enabling the realisation of one's own raison d'etre. This is further supported by the basic needs, where VIS plays a role in all four of the basic needs – a greater influence than any of the other domains. The other resilience domains thereby provide additional skills and techniques through which an individual can realise their own purpose and goals, fulfilling the basic needs. Acceptance & Commitment Therapy (ACT) developed by Hayes (1999) aligns with the importance of VIS. To this effect, ACT incorporates the concepts of determining what is most important (Harris, 2006), followed by goal setting in alignment with values (Robb, 2007).

Bandura's (1988) work on social cognitive theory identifies factors influencing self-efficacy that connect to the resilience domains, further showing how interaction between the domains contribute to a belief in an ability to succeed. This fuels self-efficacy, underscoring the high correlation of the 'belief in ability to achieve goals' item to overall resilience. The first factor influencing self-efficacy is *experience*, relating to achieved skill mastery through practice. Experience bears close relation to the RES domain regarding mastery of planning for various challenges, COM in relation to practicing emotion regulation skills, TEN in practicing being persistent. The second factor is *modelling*, relating to how seeing others succeed increases our own self-efficacy. Seeing others fail then reduces our self-efficacy. Here, people within our proximity affect our own resilience, where seeing others with low resilience may reduce ours, or vice versa. The third factor is *social persuasion*, relating to direct encouragement or discouragement from others. Support networks that we build through the COL domain therefore needs scrutiny to determine the constructive nature of the network, screening at least for the removal of discouragement. The fourth factor is *physiological factors*, relating to the stress response (sweating, shakes, shallow breathing) and health factors (pain, fatigue), and how they influence our willingness to strive. These are present in the COM and HLT domains, providing a path to manage these symptoms proactively through focused training. All these factors affect self-efficacy, leading back towards the VIS domain supporting a healthy self-image and ability to achieve goals through a deep sense of resilience.

The positive relationship between age and resilience may suggest that wisdom gained over time aids in building the various skills that contribute to the resilience domains. It is not a given, however, that age necessarily increases resilience. The possibility exists that people from previous generations have higher resilience due to cultural differences at the time. A longitudinal study is required to confirm that age is a causative factor in increasing resilience, and not generational differences. In addition, an individual at any age can show high or low resilience. There is no linear path that individuals progress on. Rather, someone may develop resilience at an early age, or they may never fully develop resilience. This highlights the critical need for resilience education across all the domains to build skills within those who may not build these skills naturally.

We note that the inability of the consistency measurement to provide a meaningful way to adjust for positive impression management may be in the item interpretation. However, the negative result does provide an interesting insight into the relationship between alcohol consumption and resilience. The total lack of relationship between alcohol consumption and resilience indicates that amount of alcohol consumed appears to not affect resilience (precluding alcoholism, which was not measured), while *worrying* about alcohol consumption appears to have an effect. Some level of anxiety or concern about one's level of control over alcohol consumption may indicate broader concerns about one's sense of control (as a basic need), affecting confidence as well as the implementation of the domains of resilience. However, the intention of this research was not specifically set out to measure the effects of alcohol consumption on resilience, so additional research is needed to investigate.

Further research is being conducted with younger age participants, which also includes intervention testing to validate ability to improve resilience early in life. Other future research includes deeper investigation into occupational and gender differences, as well as digital intervention methodologies for various cohorts. Ongoing testing of the six domains of resilience and their contribution to various improved outcomes are of interest. We propose the PR6 be adopted to a greater extent in organisational and clinical application, alongside the PR6-50 for further research application.

REFERENCES

- Allport, G. W. (1961). *Pattern and growth in personality.* New York: Holt, Rinehart, and Winston.
- Bandura, A. (1988). Organisational applications of social cognitive theory. *Australian journal of management,* 13(2), 275-302.
- Bowlby, J. (2008). *A secure base: Parent-child attachment and healthy human development.* Basic books.
- Cannon, W. B. (1916). *Bodily changes in pain, hunger, fear, and rage: An account of recent researches into the function of emotional excitement.* D. Appleton.
- Critchley, H. D., Wiens, S., Rotshtein, P., & Dolan, R. J. (2004). Neural systems supporting interoceptive awareness. *Nature neuroscience,* 7(2), 189.
- Crowne, D. P., & Marlowe, D. (1960). A new scale of social desirability independent of psychopathology. *Journal of consulting psychology,* 24(4), 349.
- Crowne, Douglas P. (1991). From Response Style to Motive - A Citation-Classic Commentary on The Approval Motive - Studies in Evaluative Dependence by Crowne, .P., and Marlowe, D., *Current Contents,* 16 (August 5), 18.
- Davidson, R., Begley, S. (2012). *The emotional life of your brain.* Hachette UK.
- Dollard, J., & Miller, N. E. (1950). *Personality and psychotherapy; an analysis in*

terms of learning, thinking, and culture.

- Duckworth, A. L., Peterson, C., Matthews, M. D., & Kelly, D. R. (2007). *Grit: perseverance and passion for long-term goals. Journal of personality and social psychology*, 92(6), 1087.

- Epstein, S. (2003). *Cognitive-experiential self-theory of personality.* Handbook of psychology.

- Freud, S. (1909). The Interpretation of Dreams (Part One). 1900. Vol. 4 of The Standard Edition of the Complete Psychological Works of Sigmund Freud. 24 vols. Ed. and trans. James Strachey. London: Hogarth, 1953-74. *Analysis of a Phobia in a Five-Year-Old Boy (Little Hans)*, 10, 3-149.

- Frey, C. B., & Osborne, M. A. (2017). *The future of employment: how susceptible are jobs to computerisation?.* Technological Forecasting and Social Change, 114, 254-280.

- Frey, C. B., Osborne, M. A., Holmes, C., Rahbari, E., Garlick, R., Friedlander, G., ... & Wilkie, M. (2016). *Technology at work v2. 0: the future is not what it used to be.* CityGroup and University of Oxford.

- Harris, R. (2006). Embracing your demons: an overview of acceptance and commitment therapy. *Psychotherapy in Australia*, 12(4), 70.

- Herrman, H., Stewart, D.E., Diaz-Granados, N., Berger, E.L., Jackson, B., Yuen, T. (2011). What is resilience? *Canadian Journal of Psychiatry*, 56(5):258-65

- Jackson, C. J., Hobman, E. V., Jimmieson, N. L., & Martin, R. (2009). Comparing different approach and avoidance models of learning and personality in the prediction of work, university, and leadership outcomes. *British journal of psychology*, 100(2), 283-312.

- Keller, A., Litzelman, K., Wisk, L. E., Maddox, T., Cheng, E. R., Creswell, P. D., & Witt, W. P. (2012). Does the perception that stress affects health matter? The association with health and mortality. *Health Psychology*, 31(5), 677.

- Kohut, H. (1971). *The Analysis of the Self* (Madison, CT.) International Universities.

- Lewis, D. E., Shellard, L. Y. N. D. S. E. Y., Koeslag, D. G., Boer, D. E., McCarthy, H. D., McKibbin, P. E., ... & Williams, G. (1993). Intense exercise and food restriction cause similar hypothalamic neuropeptide Y increases in rats. *American Journal of Physiology-Endocrinology And Metabolism*, 264(2), E279-E284.

- Lomazzo, E., König, F., Abassi, L., Jelinek, R., & Lutz, B. (2017). Chronic stress leads to epigenetic dysregulation in the neuropeptide-Y and cannabinoid CB1 receptor genes in the mouse cingulate cortex. *Neuropharmacology*, 113, 301-313.

- Lundberg, J. M., Martinsson, A., Hemsén, A., Theodorsson-Norheim, E., Svedenhag, J., Ekblom, B., & Hjemdahl, P. (1985). Co-release of neuropeptide Y and catecholamines during physical exercise in man. *Biochemical and biophysical research communications*, 133(1), 30-36.
- Mickey, B. J., Zhou, Z., Heitzeg, M. M., Heinz, E., Hodgkinson, C. A., Hsu, D. T., ... & Stohler, C. S. (2011). Emotion processing, major depression, and functional genetic variation of neuropeptide Y. *Archives of general psychiatry*, 68(2), 158-166.
- Morgan, C. A., Rasmusson, A. M., Wang, S., Hoyt, G., Hauger, R. L., & Hazlett, G. (2002). Neuropeptide-Y, cortisol, and subjective distress in humans exposed to acute stress: replication and extension of previous report. *Biological psychiatry*, 52(2), 136-142.
- Morgan, C. A., Wang, S., Southwick, S. M., Rasmusson, A., Hazlett, G., Hauger, R. L., & Charney, D. S. (2000). Plasma neuropeptide-Y concentrations in humans exposed to military survival training. *Biological psychiatry*, 47(10), 902-909.
- Morris, M. J., Russell, A. E., Kapoor, V., Cain, M. D., Elliott, J. M., West, M. J., ... & Chalmers, J. P. (1986). Increases in plasma neuropeptide Y concentrations during sympathetic activation in man. *Journal of the autonomic nervous system*, 17(2), 143-149.
- Neuendorf, K. (2011). *Internal consistency reliability: Can Cronbach's alpha be too high*. COM 631-Multivariate analysis.
- Odendaal, A. (2015). Cross-cultural differences in social desirability scales: influence of cognitive ability: original research. *SA Journal of Industrial Psychology*, 41(1), 1-13.
- Olsson, C. A., Bond, L., Burns, J. M., Vella-Brodrick, D. A., & Sawyer, S. M. (2003). Adolescent resilience: A concept analysis. *Journal of adolescence*, 26(1), 1-11.
- Perroud, N., Rutembesa, E., Paoloni-Giacobino, A., Mutabaruka, J., Mutesa, L., Stenz, L., ... & Karege, F. (2014). The Tutsi genocide and transgenerational transmission of maternal stress: epigenetics and biology of the HPA axis. *The World Journal of Biological Psychiatry*, 15(4),
- Peterson, B. S., Wang, Z., Horga, G., Warner, V., Rutherford, B., Klahr, K. W., ... &

Hao, X. (2014). Discriminating risk and resilience endophenotypes from lifetime illness effects in familial major depressive disorder. *JAMA psychiatry*, 71(2), 136-148.

- Preston, A. R., & Eichenbaum, H. (2013). Interplay of hippocampus and prefrontal cortex in memory. *Current Biology*, 23(17), R764-R773.

- Robb, H. (2007). Values as leading principles in Acceptance and Commitment Therapy. *International Journal of Behavioral Consultation and Therapy*, 3(1), 118.

- Rogers, C. R. (1951). *Client-centered therapy; its current practice, implications, and theory.*

- Rossouw, P. J., & Rossouw, J. G. (2016). The Predictive 6-Factor Resilience Scale: Neurobiological Fundamentals and Organizational Application. *International journal of neuropsychotherapy*, 4(1), 31-45.

- Rutter, M. (1985). Resilience in the face of adversity. Protective factors and resistance to psychiatric disorder. *The British Journal of Psychiatry*, 147(6), 598-611.

- Schoenbaum, G., Takahashi, Y., Liu, T. L., & McDannald, M. A. (2011). Does the orbitofrontal cortex signal value?. *Annals of the New York Academy of Sciences*, 1239(1), 87-99.

- Schore, A. N. (2000). Attachment and the regulation of the right brain. *Attachment & human development*, 2(1), 23-47.

- Sijtsma, K. (2009). On the use, the misuse, and the very limited usefulness of Cronbach's alpha. *Psychometrika*, 74(1), 107.

- Tavakol, M., & Dennick, R. (2011). Making sense of Cronbach's alpha. *International journal of medical education*, 2, 53.

- Thompson, E. R., & Phua, F. T. (2012). A brief index of affective job satisfaction. *Group & Organization Management*, 37(3), 275-307.

- Windle, G., Bennett, K. M., & Noyes, J. (2011). A methodological review of resilience measurement scales. *Health and quality of life outcomes*, 9(8), 1-18.

- Zhou, Z., Zhu, G., Hariri, A. R., Enoch, M. A., Scott, D., Sinha, R., ... & Hodgkinson, C. A. (2008). Genetic variation in human NPY expression affects stress response and emotion. *Nature*, 452(7190), 9

Appendix B – 2016 Research

The Predictive 6-Factor Resilience Scale - Neurobiological Fundamentals and Organizational Application

Rossouw, P. J., & Rossouw, J. G. (2016). The Predictive 6-Factor Resilience Scale: Neurobiological Fundamentals and Organizational Application. International journal of neuropsychotherapy, 4(1), 31-45.

Pieter J. Rossouw, Jurie G. Rossouw

Abstract

Psychological resilience is currently viewed as being primarily a mental construct, with few measurement scales explicitly considering health hygiene factors as an integral component that facilitates healthy adaption to adversity. Ongoing research has provided greater clarity on the neurobiological nature of psychological resilience, suggesting that health hygiene factors affect mental wellbeing on a neurobiological basis. **Objective:** We describe the neurobiological fundamentals of a brief psychological resilience rating scale called the Predictive 6 Factor Resilience Scale (PR6) consisting of 16 items. Using the PR6, we test the hypothesis that health hygiene factors correlate with psychological resilience domains. In addition, we measure forward-looking elements to contrast with point-in-time measurements and check for consistency with the resilience construct. **Methods:** An existing neurobiological model was used as the basis for PR6 resilience domains which was then compared to other resilience scales for similarity in domain coverage. The PR6 was developed and subsequently applied using two modes (digital delivery, paper-based) to groups of working professionals (Healthcare, Finance). Internal consistency of the PR6 was tested, along with correlation between health hygiene factors and current resilience domains. Differences in resilience between industry, gender, and age groups were considered. **Results:** PR6 resilience scores showed good internal consistency over 16 items and, alongside correlation studies, confirmed that health hygiene factors have a statistically significant relationship with psychological resilience. Domain variances in groups indicated lower health hygiene scores in the Finance industry group, as well as with males. Emotion regulation (Composure domain) was found to be higher in the Healthcare industry group. Forward-looking items were also found to improve consistency and correlate with higher levels of resilience. **Conclusions:** We conclude that health hygiene factors should be considered in conjunction with traditional psychological resilience domains, and that the PR6 is a valid psychometric scale through which measurement can be applied. Forward-looking items (approach, avoidance motivation schemas) were found to have a strong positive correlation with overall resilience scores, suggesting approach motivation schemas favourably impact healthy adaptation to difficult circumstances and stress management. The foundations of each resilience domain measured by the PR6 provides for targeted treatment to improve holistic resilience capacity, and industry application in this study shows efficacy for both point-in-time and forward looking psychological resilience assessment.

Mental health disorders are estimated to cost US$800 billion annually in lost productivity and this amount is expected to double by 2030[1]. By extension this projected escalation prompts increased attention on preventative and protective measures as a potential long-term avenue to improve mental wellbeing. Research over the last three decades into psychological resilience has indicated that it may be a key component to attenuate the trend of mental health disorders[2]. In short, resilience can be described as the ability to positively adapt and thrive in the face of risk and adversity[3,4]. As a construct, resilience exists across multiple domains[5,6], which are changeable and dynamic at all stages of the lifespan[7]. Rutter has noted that the focus is on individual differences, indicating the importance of accurately measuring variances within groups for efficacious intervention[8].

While a host of resilience measurement scales have been developed in the last two decades[9], adaptation of scales to findings from neurobiology research and related findings in research on physiological wellbeing has not been readily apparent. Deeper integration of these fields with resilience measurement can assist in moving research beyond primarily phenomenological observations toward a mechanistic understanding of resilience capacity[10]. This may further reveal methods of intervention that are not currently in the arsenal to combat the projected rise of mental health disorders. Recognising this need, the World Health Organisation has set a target of a 20% increase of the service coverage for mental disorders by 2020[11]. The broad applicability of resilience across the lifespan as a protective measure against depression[12] places it as a valuable intervention avenue not only for clinical applications, but also for the workplace, schools, and other organisations across which the wider population can be reached.

In this paper we investigate theoretical connections between the domains of resilience and a neurobiological model to establish a new resilience measurement scale[13]. We also examine the implications of this. For example, given the importance of adaptation to the concept of resilience alongside the role of neuroplasticity to facilitate adaptation, we hypothesise that a correlation exists between health factors that promote neuroplasticity and psychological resilience.

As noted by Fredrickson, "the broadening and undoing effects of positive emotion might together account for the salutary effects of positive emotions on health, physical functioning and longevity". This may in turn be a bi-directional relationship in relation to resilience where positive health promotes feelings of confidence and ability to deal with adverse situations[14]. An analysis of the major resilience scales indicates that this potential relationship between resilience and health factors has not been incorporated into their fundamental design. In conjunction, we further explore the potential of psychological approach and avoidance patterns to have a predictive quality in determining future direction of psychological development, particularly in relation to resilience and wellbeing outcomes[15]. The culmination of these factors is the Predictive 6 Factor Resilience Scale (PR6) of which the theoretical framework and data analysis is explored.

METHOD

Development of the scale

Drawing on the wealth of research conducted in the development of existing resilience scales, particularly the higher scoring scales in Windle et al.'s review alongside their assertion that as of yet there exists no gold standard for resilience[9], allows the PR6 to be developed in a harmonious manner. Domains established in the PR6 are therefore in alignment with domains in the literature and existing scales. This alignment provides a foundation from which we connect a neurobiological model with the purpose of establishing a resilience scale that is more holistic and inclusive in scope. Measurement is at an individual level and aims to examine protective factors to mitigate risk and adversity, leading to thriving and resilient outcomes beyond what would normally be expected.

As a mental construct, resilience is underpinned by neural networks and neurobiological functioning[10]. Resilience is noted to change dynamically through various stages of life[7], and as a function that helps individuals adapt, psychological resilience itself adapts over time[16,17,18,19]. This adaptive capacity is enabled through well-established concepts of neuroplasticity as influenced by environmental factors[20,21]. Plasticity mechanistically functions via brain derived neurotrophic factor (BDNF) which elevates neural production and in turn neural proliferation to either strengthen healthy approach patterns or maladaptive avoidance patterns, depending on current neural activation[22,23]. Given the crucial role of BDNF in neural development on a temporal scale, it follows that factors that positively affect production of BDNF, such as physiological health hygiene, would positively correlate with the construct of resilience and thus introduce a new domain, Health. This domain may indicate a virtuous interplay between traditional markers of psychological resilience and physiological health factors that positively influence BDNF and neural proliferation. Next we investigate this domain alongside traditional domains of resilience as proposed by existing scales and literature.

Domains of the PR6

Domains are formed due to the expansive nature of traits within the construct of resilience, allowing for more insightful thematic trait-groupings that share neurological underpinnings. A neurobiological model that has previously been explored in the context of resilience is Davidson's six dimensions of emotional styles[13,24]. Theoretical analysis and comparison of this model with existing scales indicate a synthesis of interpersonal and intrapersonal protective factors that can be adapted into five domains of psychological resilience. These five domains are complemented by a sixth domain relating to physiological health. Interpretive and grouping differences between approaches result in domain sorting to be subjective, however we hold that sufficient thematic alignment exists to analyse and categorise. Note that some resilience scales did not clearly represent every domain described below as indicated in Table 1.

TABLE 1: Domain alignment between PR6 and existing resilience scales

PR6 domains	Davidson Styles	RSA	CDRISC	READ	RS	ARS	RASP	DRS	YRADS	CYRM	CHKS
Vision	Outlook style	✓	✓	✓	✓	✓	✓	✓	✓		✓
Composure	Self-awareness style	✓	✓	✓	✓	✓	✓		✓		✓
Tenacity	Resilience style		✓		✓		✓				
Reasoning	Attention style		✓		✓	✓	✓	✓	✓	✓	
Collaboration	Social Intuition style Sensitivity to context style	✓	✓	✓	✓*		✓		✓	✓	✓
Health	-										
Windle et al. Score		7	7	6	6	4	4	4	3	3	2

*Existential aloneness
RSA = Resilience Scale for Adults, CDRISC = Connor Davidson Resilience Scale, READ = Resilience Scale for Adolescents, ARS = Adolescent Resilience Scale, RASP = Resilience Attitudes and Skills Profile, DRS = Dispositional Resilience Scale, YRADS = Youth Resiliency: Assessing Developmental Strengths, CYRM = Child and Youth Resilience Measure, CHKS = California Healthy Kids Survey

The first domain includes concepts of self-efficacy and goal setting. The Resilience Scale for Adults (RSA), as well as the Resilience Scale for Adolescents (READ) indicate 'Personal competence' as a factor that aligns to this trait-group[18,25]. Likewise, review of the Connor Davidson Resilience Scale (CD-RISC) included 'personal competence', 'sense of control', and 'high standards' as related characteristics[26]. The Dispositional Resilience Scale (DRS) also include 'control' alongside 'commitment'[27]. The Resilience Attitudes and Skills Profile (RASP) scale describes 'creativity' in relation to goals, alongside 'initiative' and 'values orientation'[28]. The Youth Resiliency: Assessing Developmental Strengths (YRADS) aligns with 'self-concept' and 'empowerment'[16]. Likewise, the California Health Kids Survey (CHKS) includes 'goals and aspirations', alongside 'self-esteem'[29]. The Resilience

Scale (RS) 'meaningfulness'[30], reflecting a sense of purpose and long term goals, aligns well with 'positive future orientation' described by the Adolescent Resilience Scale (ARS)[17]. Conceptually these factors align to the 'Outlook Emotional Style' identified by Davidson, referring to the ability to maintain a positive outlook and allowing positive emotions to persist[24] which involves a positive self-concept, a proclivity to set goals as a pathway to meaning and belief in self-worth. This sense of hopefulness, planning and positive outlook is what we summarise as the 'Vision' domain. Neurological structures involved in the Vision domain include the ventral striatum through its role in higher order decision-making and risk/reward cognition[24]. The interplay of memory storage and retrieval by the hippocampus and meaning assignment by the prefrontal cortex (PFC) play a part in maintaining a hopeful sense of the future which is reinforced through goal-directedness[31].

The second domain is primarily about emotional regulation and the ability to recognise, understand and act on internal prompts and physical signals. The RS reflects this as a sense of 'equanimity'[30], alongside 'emotional regulation' in the ARS[17]. The RSA and READ include concepts of 'personal structure'[18,25] while the 'control' aspect of CD-RISC may also serve in the sense of self-control[26]. On the youth resilience side, RASP describes 'humour' and 'creativity' in the context of feelings[28], YRADS speaks of 'self-control'[16] and CHKS includes 'empathy'[29]. These align well to the 'Self-awareness Emotional Style' as described by Davidson which neurologically relates to the ability of the insula to effectively interpret signals to enable regulation of the hypothalamic-pituitary-adrenal (HPA) axis[24]. Self-awareness manifests through increased emotional granularity where an accurate and positive disposition has been shown to improve physiological health through the broaden-and-build effect and the undoing effect[14]. We group these as the 'Composure' domain.

The third domain centres on the concept of perseverance and hardiness, which to many is the main aspect that determines resilience and is the main aspect measured by the Brief Resilience Scale[32]. The CD-RISC describes 'tolerance to negative effect' and 'tenacity'[26], while the RS includes 'perseverance'[30]. Representation of this aspect is less clear on the youth measurement scales, however the RASP is supportive through their concept of 'independence'[28]. The 'Resilience Emotional Style' from Davidson's model presents clear alignment and points to the ability of the PFC to effectively regulate limbic and HPA activation[24]. Here linkage to self-awareness can be observed through its role to inform the PFC of the need for HPA regulation. More broadly, while hardiness may be a key component to aide in bouncing back from adversity, the other domains have crucial protective roles to play. Of interest in this domain is that perseverance has been shown to be more important than IQ as a predictor of long term goal outcomes[33]. Considering that broader psychological resilience is inclusive of this ability to persevere, we termed this the 'Tenacity' domain.

The fourth domain involves a wider range of higher-cognitive traits such as problem-solving, resourcefulness and growing through adversity (thriving)[34]. The ARS includes 'novelty seeking'[17] in this light, alongside an aligning concept of 'self-reliance' in the RS[30]. CD-RISC describes the 'positive acceptance of change' and the 'strengthening effect of stress'[26], while the DRS has a concept titled 'challenge'[27]. RASP includes 'insight' and 'creativity' in relation to resourcefulness[28]. Other youth scales such as YRADS include 'commitment to learning'[16], while the Child and Youth Resilience Measure (CYRM) summarises these as 'personal skills'[35]. The 'Attention Style' from Davidson's model is of interest here in its role to screen out distractions and stay focused when facing risk or adversity[24]. Left and right PFC activation functions in conjunction with the anterior cingulate cortex (ACC) to rapidly screen for errors and optimise subsequent responses[36]. Executive functioning here is enabled following the downregulation of the HPA axis through the Composure and Tenacity domains, and functions in the broader context set by the Vision domain. The ability to effectively regulate limbic functions is supported by strategies such as interpretation bias which has been shown to have a protective effect in the resilience construct, though must be grounded in a realistic sense of optimism[37,38,39]. We group these traits as the 'Reasoning' domain, reflecting its executive functioning and cognitive nature.

The fifth domain relates directly to psychosocial interaction, including secure attachment, support networks, context and humour. This domain is common among resilience scales with some scales focusing more heavily on this aspect. For example, the RSA and READ include 'social competence', 'family coherence' and 'social resources', making up the bulk of these surveys[18,25]. CD-RISC contains 'secure relationships'[26], while the RS contrasts with 'existential aloneness'[30]. Youth scales are also heavy on this aspect, with YRADS listing 'parental support / expectations', 'peer relationships', 'community cohesiveness', 'school culture', 'cultural sensitivity' and 'social sensitivity'[16]. RASP describes 'relationships' and 'humour' in this context[28], while CYRM includes 'social skills' and 'peer support'[35]. Finally, CHKS aligns with 'help seeking' and 'communication and co-operation' in this group[29]. These align with two of the Davidson styles, namely the 'Social Intuition Style' which refers to the ability to accurately read people through body language, emotional tone and needs, and the 'Sensitivity to Context Style' which involves being able to accurately discriminate between social context and adapt approach accordingly[24]. Schore noted in 2000 that the right prefrontal cortex (RPFC) plays a key role in secure attachment[40] which receives cues interpreted by other regions. It has been suggested that fusiform gyrus plays this interpretive role through facial expression recognition and has been shown to be able to affect the amygdala in response to emotional faces[41]. Healthy RPFC interpretation and accurate facial recognition is thus crucial to appropriately regulate amygdala activation for constructive reaction when faced with risk and adversity. On a broader level, secure attachment is well documented as a key component of resilience[42,43]. This positive impact of the social framework continues through adolescence and into adult life, where research has shown social influence affects BMI and weight loss outcomes[44,45]. Of particular interest is that it is not received support, but rather the perception of support that is the key enabler of resilient outcomes[46]. This reinforces the importance of healthy neural activation in the PFC to regulate triggers that may otherwise cause distress and thereby maintain wellness through positive interpretation and perception management. Multifaceted and complex, we title this the 'Collaboration' domain.

Proposed domain – Health hygiene factors

The sixth domain concerns physiological health and is the proposed addition. While the other five domains are heavily informed by current resilience scales, this sixth domain has received little attention likely due to a focus on the psychological aspects of resilience. Work by Tugade et al. clearly indicated a link between emotional experience and health, for example, calling on the effect of higher resilience to quell autonomic arousal in the HPA[14]. This type of arousal increases cortisol levels which in turn reduces BDNF thereby reducing potential for positive neural adaptation[47]. Evidence of chronic health issues affecting mood and the relationship between post-traumatic stress disorder, anxiety and negative health outcomes strengthens the hypothesis of a link between positive health and resilience[48,49]. This is especially relevant as resilient individuals have been shown to be better at coping with serious health issues such as cancer[50]. We turn now to the positive effect of BDNF on resilience and find three physiological factors that affect production. We also find further indication beyond BDNF as to potential interconnection with resilience.

The first factor is regular exercise which has been shown to increase BDNF and hippocampal function[51,52]. In the short term, exercise improves cognitive and memory functions, as well as ACC activation, key for the Reasoning domain[53]. Benefits also extend into the long-term to maintain cognitive capacities and serve a protective factor from future adversity in the form of mental decline[54].

The second factor is nutrition, as a diet high in sugar, dietary fats and alcohol has been show to downregulate BDNF[55,56]. More broadly, the psychological link between the broader influence of nutrition and wellbeing is well established, such as strong relationship between obesity and depression[57].

The third factor is sleep hygiene where recent evidence points to a crucial interplay between stress, sleep and BDNF levels[58]. Lack of sleep has further been shown to degrade higher cognitive functioning, along with increasing impulsiveness which may lead to negative outcomes when faced with adversity requiring reasoned responses[59,60]. Suggested quantity of sleep is inversely related to age, and is currently recommended as eight to ten hours for teenagers, and seven to nine hours for adults[61].

In combination, these three factors indicate adequate health hygiene factors to include as items in the PR6. We include an item per factor as well as an item for overall health, as even the best hygiene may not protect against all physiological problems, such as chronic pain where a general health self-report survey showed high correlation[62].

Approach, avoidance motivation

Motivation in terms of approach and avoidance suggests a distinction between behaviours of approach where reward is expected or avoidance where there is a fear of loss[15]. In the context of high resilience, one would expect the approach-avoidance conflict to result in constructive outcomes. Approach and avoidance models have been suggested to show "considerable promise as a predictor of work and educational outcomes as well as dysfunctional outcomes"[63]. Continued goal striving during adversity is a constructive product of resilience. As Elliot and Thrash summarise, a goal is "a concrete cognitive representation of a desired or undesired end state use to guide behaviour" going on to connect an approach temperament to positive prediction of goal outcomes[64]. Two items are included in the scale to measure approach and avoidance schemas in terms of a sense of direction and openness to new challenges. This is measured in conjunction with the other six domains as 'Momentum'.

Survey design

The survey was envisioned as a shorter form self-report questionnaire to increase applicability to broader contexts and appetite for re-testing over time. This follows precedent and pre-empts the path followed by previous scales[32,65,66]. Items are rated on a five point Likert scale ranging from "1 - Not at all like me" (most negative), "2 - A bit like me", "3 - Somewhat like me", "4 - Often like me", and "5 - Very much like me" (most positive). Two of the Health domain questions have more specific answers again ranging across five points. Two items were selected per domain which were informed by a review of existing scales as well as additional literature on the subject of resilience. Item revision was also conducted via feedback from the first group of study participants, resulting in minor revisions of wording for items related to Composure. Each domain and the Momentum items contain one reverse-scored question, except for the Health domain which comprises four positively scored items. Table 2 expands on descriptions of each item within PR6.

TABLE 3: Statistics summary of resilience scores within groups

Industry	N	Mean	SE Mean	StDev	Minimum	Q1	Median	Q3	Maximum
Healthcare	111	0.697	0.011	0.116	0.3929	0.6161	0.7054	0.7857	0.9464
Finance	76	0.6842	0.0133	0.1157	0.2857	0.625	0.6786	0.7679	0.9911
Education	8	0.6908	0.0295	0.0833	0.5804	0.6094	0.692	0.7366	0.8393
Not specified	9	0.6052	0.0493	0.1478	0.3393	0.4955	0.6339	0.7143	0.8214

Age	N	Mean	SE Mean	StDev	Minimum	Q1	Median	Q3	Maximum
21-30	15	0.656	0.0179	0.0691	0.5357	0.5804	0.6696	0.6875	0.8036
31-40	56	0.688	0.0161	0.1203	0.2857	0.6183	0.7054	0.7589	0.9911
41-50	61	0.6852	0.0155	0.1212	0.3929	0.6027	0.6786	0.7857	0.9107
50+	60	0.7027	0.0161	0.1244	0.3393	0.6339	0.7054	0.7835	0.9464
Not specified	12	0.6682	0.0263	0.091	0.5179	0.6049	0.6518	0.7612	0.8036

Gender	N	Mean	SE Mean	StDev	Minimum	Q1	Median	Q3	Maximum
Female	131	0.6823	0.0101	0.1151	0.3393	0.5982	0.6786	0.7679	0.9464
Male	62	0.6983	0.0161	0.1267	0.2857	0.6339	0.7054	0.7857	0.9911
Not specified	10	0.7	0.0274	0.0866	0.5	0.6674	0.6964	0.7723	0.8036
Other	1	0.6696	N/A	N/A	0.6696	N/A	0.6696	N/A	0.6696

TABLE 2: The Predictive 6 Factor Resilience Scale

Item	Description	Scoring
1, 7*	Tenacity domain	1 2 3 4 5
2*, 8	Vision domain	1 2 3 4 5
3, 9*	Collaboration domain	1 2 3 4 5
4, 10*	Composure domain	1 2 3 4 5
5, 11*	Reasoning domain	1 2 3 4 5
6*, 12	Momentum	1 2 3 4 5
13, 14, 15, 16	Health domain	1 2 3 4 5

*Reverse scored

Study sample

The overall sample (n=204) consisted of two groups of professionals recruited to complete the survey. The first group (n=128) was primarily Healthcare and Education professionals contacted during workshops in the following cities; Sydney=29, Dunedin=14, Brisbane=26, Melbourne=59. Surveys were completed on paper sheets handed out and then handed back to the facilitator once completed. Of this group, 80% were psychology clinicians or counsellors. Males accounted for 13%, females for 78%, with the remaining 9% marked either as 'other' or left blank. Age representation was broad, with 9% between 21 and 30, 18% between 31 and 40, 27% between 41 and 50, and 44% were 50 and over.

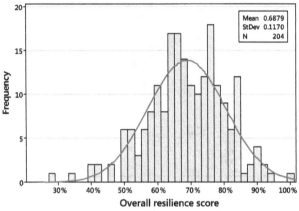

FIG 1: Histogram of Overall resilience scores across all groups

The second group (FIN, n=76) was financial services professionals recruited from a major bank. The survey was offered to the organisation in the form of an online device completed confidentially by each staff member. Individual results were not made available to management. Respondents all resided in Sydney (100%). Females accounted for 41%, and males 59%. Age representation was again broad, with 5% between 21 and 30, 43% between 31 and 40, 34% between 41 and 50, and 5% were 50 and over.

RESULTS

Scoring was completed by first reversing the negatively phrased questions, then summing each item pair together per the first five domains and for the momentum score. Health has four positively scored items which were subsequently summed to complete scores for the six domains. Each domain was averaged to produce a comparable score per domain. An Overall Resilience Score (PR6 score) was calculated as an average of each of the six domains, ranging from 0 (lowest resilience) to 1 (highest resilience).

The distribution of PR6 scores for n=204 (figure 1) resulted in a mean of

0.6879, standard deviation of 0.117 and a 95% confidence interval of 0.67178, 0.70409. Results primarily followed the standard deviation, with additional clustering around the 75th and 85th percentiles. Normality was confirmed with an Anderson-Darling test of 0.440 and a P-value of 0.289 for the full population. Floor and ceiling effects were not encountered as no responses reached the lowest level, while only one response reached near the upper bound with a score of 0.9911.

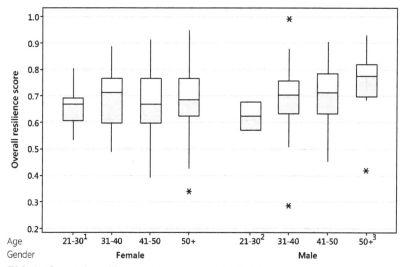

FIG 2: Overall resilience scores per gender and age group
[1] n=13, [2] n=2, [3] n=12

Group analysis

Table 3 summarises scores for the different populations across Industry, Age, and Gender. Industry-grouped PR6 scores for Healthcare at mean = 0.697 was slightly higher than Finance at mean = 0.6842, though both fall within the 95% CI, indicating no statistically significant difference, while Education and Not Specified scores at the time of measurement did not have sufficient data to draw meaningful conclusions. Similar results were observed within Age, Gender, and Location whereas once a sufficient number of responses has been received, no statistically significant differences were noted within groups for overall scores. Domain analysis indicated one statistically significant difference between Finance and Healthcare. Composure scores (95% CI 0.6262, 0.6863) for Healthcare were significantly higher (mean = 0.6971, p = 0.027). Health scores (95% CI 0.6047, 0.6613) for Finance were lower, however the difference was not statistically significant (mean = 0.5921, p > 0.05).

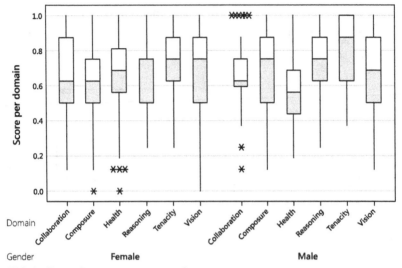

FIG 3: Domain scores per gender

Overall, mean PR6 scores for females were 0.6823, with males scoring slightly higher at 0.6983. Males had higher variability, ranging from a minimum of 0.2857 to a maximum of 0.9911, compared to females with a minimum of 0.3393 to a maximum of 0.9464. Further investigating scores, Figure 2 shows PR6 scores by gender and age group. Initial results indicate stability among female age groups, while males appear to have an upward trajectory over time. However, low number of results for males ages 21-30 (n=2) and 50+ (n=12) suggest additional data is required before significance can be validated.

Figure 3 shows gender differences by domain of resilience. This analysis indicated an area of statistically significant difference between genders. Within the Health domain (95% CI 0.6047, 0.6613), compared to females, males were noted to score much lower (mean = 0.5696, p = 0.012). Conversely, within the Tenacity domain (95% CI 0.7407, 0.7875), males scored higher (mean = 0.7944, p > 0.05), as well as in the Reasoning domain (95% CI 0.6694, 0.7203) where males also scored higher (mean = 0.7440, p

> 0.05). However, the high P-values for the differences noted in the Tenacity and Reasoning domains indicate statistical significance was not reached.

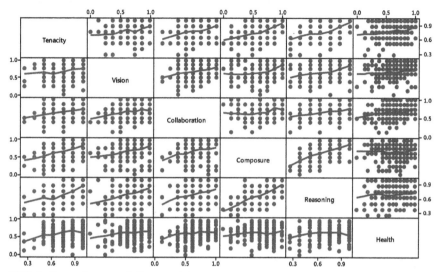

FIG 4: Domain correlation matrix

Domain correlation and consistency

Domain correlation (figure 4) shows relationships between the five Davidson styles (Vision, Composure, Reasoning, Tenacity, Collaboration) and the proposed Health domain. The Composure and Reasoning domains displayed the strongest relationship, while relationships were also evident between other Davidson styles as is to be expected as part of traditional resilience factors. Of interest is the hypothesised correlation between the five Davidson styles and the proposed Health domain. Pearson correlation between the Health domain and five Davidson styles was found to be positive at 0.169 with a p-value of 0.016. While the Pearson value in the lower range, the < 0.05 p-value result indicates the relation is of statistical significance. Additional analysis was conducted to confirm the relationship through Chronbach's α.

Item analysis yielded a Chronbach's α of 0.7364, indicating good internal consistency and validity as a psychometric tool. Table 4 details the item analysis and α if removed from the survey. Of note are items 3 (openness to working with others) and 14 (sleep hygiene) which have a slight negative effect on α. The first 12 questions (excluding the four Health domain questions) yields an α of 0.7491.

Addition of the Health domain retains the α above 0.70, indicating high internal consistency and a meaningful relationship between traditional resilience domain measurements and the Health domain. In particular, three of the questions improve α significantly. Exercise frequency (item 15) had the strongest effect (α = 0.719 if omitted). Adherence to healthy nutrition (item 16) had the second strongest effect (α = 0.7295 if omitted). And general perceptions about health (item 13) and the third strongest effect (α = 0.723 if omitted).

Forward-looking Momentum items (6, 12) were found to have a strong positive correlation (figure5) with resilience (Pearson = 0.642, p-value < 0.001). These items also had a positive effect on α, with items 6 (reverse scored) and 12 reducing α to 0.7251 and 0.7173 if omitted. No significant differences were found in Momentum scores between industry, gender, or age groupings.

TABLE 4: Item analysis

PR6 Cronbach's α = 0.7364

Item	Mean*	StDev	Cronbach's α if omitted
1	4.064	0.871	0.7185
2	3.539	1.142	0.7241
3	4.206	0.852	0.7411
4	3.603	0.928	0.7131
5	4.064	0.837	0.7212
6	4.333	0.76	0.7251
7	4.049	0.858	0.7159
8	3.794	0.956	0.7239
9	3.118	1.226	0.7221
10	3.647	1.176	0.7209
11	3.495	1.048	0.7137
12	3.549	0.943	0.7173
13	3.784	0.844	0.723
14	3.598	1.334	0.7478
15	3.245	1.251	0.719
16	3.5	1.201	0.7295

*1 to 5 Likert Scale

DISCUSSION

We have developed a new holistic resilience scale (PR6) that includes health factors through which we tested the hypothesis that these health factors are an integral component of psychological resilience. The PR6 was primarily tested within Healthcare and Finance industries to validate the hypothesis and potential for individual and workplace application of the scale itself.

Statistically significant positive correlation between Health and the five Davidson styles supported the hypothesis that health hygiene factors function together with traditional resilience constructs. Furthermore, good internal consistency measurements support this hypothesis and confirm that the PR6 represent a valid psychological resilience measurement tool that incorporates health hygiene factors. The PR6 unifies domains measured by other resilience scales across five distinct neurobiological schemas, and effectively incorporates Health as the new sixth domain of psychological resilience. The positive relationship between Health and the other five domains of resilience is of interest as it is not currently measured as standard in any of the scales considered. As the current view is that resilience is mainly a psychological construct, the data from this study supports the hypothesis that resilience is a wider phenomenon that also relies on or manifests as a tendency to maintain healthy habits in terms of exercise frequency, adherence to health nutrition, and sleeping patterns. We note that this research does not make a determination if there is a causative relationship between Health and the other five resilience domain, or if one precedes the other. Interpretation of previous research for the neurobiological foundations of the PR6 indicate mechanistic factors that may explain these relationships in a causative fashion.

Testing of the scale on a population of professional workers presents a useful application in measurement and treatment of specific resilience factors. Diverging industries (Healthcare and Finance) displayed no statistically significant differences in overall PR6 scores. On a domain level, some differences were noted, significantly in the Composure domain, and to a lower extent in the Health domain. Composure was noted to be higher in the Healthcare industry, while Health was noted to be lower in the Finance industry.

Momentum items were noted to be highly consistent with the resilience construct, suggesting that psychological approach and avoidance schemas may play a functional role in the ability to manage adversity. This suggestion fits with current models as approach motivation towards changing or adverse circumstances suggests healthy adaptation. Non-Momentum items are designed to quantify resilience primarily as a point-in-time measurement, while the Momentum items through approach and avoidance schemas contrasts with a forward-looking element. This allows particular usefulness in workplace applications where the Momentum scores may serve as a leading indicator to future direction of resilience and wellbeing.

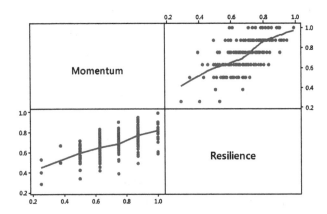

FIG 5: Momentum/resilience correlation matrix

Furthermore, mapping the PR6 resilience domains to neurobiological structures indicates more direct potential brain-based treatment. The addition of health factors as an integral component of maintaining a healthy brain and its subsequent effect on the overall resilience construct further bolsters a holistic resilience treatment methodology.

CONCLUSION

The PR6 is a holistic resilience measurement scale that reaches further than traditional scales by incorporating health hygiene factors as a fundamental component of psychological resilience. Reflecting eventual use of existing scales, the scale itself is short and simple to administer. Application through paper-based and electronic administration has been shown to have no significant deviation, allowing multiple modes of delivery.

In consideration of differences in scores observed, we note the following speculations. Higher Composure scores in the Healthcare population is likely related to 80% of the group being psychology clinicians or counsellors who have received specific training through their education. Differences found in the Health domain, particularly lower scores in Finance, is suspected to be largely related to gender differences given that a large percentage of the Healthcare group was female, and female participants overall had higher Health scores than males.

The significantly lower Health scores of males, accompanied by slightly higher (though not significant) scores in Tenacity and Reasoning, suggests that males may sacrifice Health in favour of domains that are more directly perceived as pursuant to current goals. These findings suggest an area for further research to determine validity and motivation. Upward trending resilience scores as age increases in males noted in figure 2 is expected to stabilise towards the mean once larger sample sizes are obtained.

Items noted to be less strongly consistent with resilience in particular were sleep hygiene and openness to working with others. It may be the case that more resilient people are better able to stay focused during periods of varying sleeping patterns, however the effects of chronic sleep disturbance are well documented and are expected to have an effect on long-term wellbeing. For the second item, resilience often relies on the assistance of others, but may not necessarily require one to actually prefer the company of others. However, there may be a longer-term relationship between the desire to be around others and protective resilience factors over time. The authors plan to monitor variated versions of these items in order to further investigate and refine their relationship with resilience.

Ongoing application of the PR6 is planned in younger age groups as well as in clinical settings. This will be contrasted with treatment as well to determine effective methods of resilience modification, particularly focusing on digital delivery methods. The current test across wide-ranging age groups allow for application within the broader application as an individual and workplace resilience and wellbeing measurement scale, indicating specific strengths and weaknesses across the holistic six domains of resilience. We propose that the six domains of resilience present discrete neurobiological components that allow for effective treatment to improve overall resilience and wellbeing by focusing on individual areas as highlighted through PR6 measurement.

References

1. World Health Organisation. (2014). Out of the Shadows, Making Mental Health a Global Development Priority. Retrieved from http://www.who.int/mental_health/WB_WHO_meeting_2016.pdf?ua=1

2. Edward, K. L. (2005). Resilience: A protector from depression. *Journal of the American Psychiatric Nurses Association*, 11(4), 241-243.

3. Masten, A. S., Cutuli, J. J., Herbers, J. E., & Reed, M. G. (2009). 12 Resilience in Development. *Oxford handbook of positive psychology*, 117.

4. Kong, F., Wang, X., Hu, S., & Liu, J. (2015). Neural correlates of psychological resilience and their relation to life satisfaction in a sample of healthy young adults. *Neuro Image*, 123, 165-172.

5. Rutter, M. (1985). Resilience in the face of adversity. Protective factors and resistance to psychiatric disorder. *The British Journal of Psychiatry*, 147(6), 598-611.

6. Olsson, C. A., Bond, L., Burns, J. M., Vella-Brodrick, D. A., & Sawyer, S. M. (2003). Adolescent resilience: A concept analysis. *Journal of adolescence*, 26(1), 1-11.

7. Herrman, H., Stewart, D.E., Diaz-Granados, N., Berger, E.L., Jackson, B., Yuen, T. What is resilience? *Canadian Journal of Psychiatry*, 2011 May;56(5):258-65

8. Rutter, M. (2012). Resilience as a dynamic concept. *Development and psychopathology*, 24(02), 335-344.

9. Windle, G., Bennett, K. M., & Noyes, J. (2011). A methodological review of resilience measurement scales. *Health and quality of life outcomes*, 9(8), 1-18.

10. Russo, S. J., Murrough, J. W., Han, M. H., Charney, D. S., & Nestler, E. J. (2012). Neurobiology of resilience. *Nature neuroscience*, 15(11), 1475-1484.

11. World Health Organisation. (2014). 2014 Mental Health Atlas. Retrieved from http://apps.who.int/iris/bitstream/10665/178879/1/9789241565011_eng.pdf?ua=1&ua=1

12. Elisei, S., Sciarma, T., Verdolini, N., & Anastasi, S. (2013). Resilience and depressive disorders. *Psychiatr. Danub*, 25, S263-S267.

13. Rossouw, P. (2015). Resilience: A neurobiological perspective. *Neuropsychotherapy in Australia*, (31), 3-8.

14. Tugade, M. M., Fredrickson, B. L., & Feldman Barrett, L. (2004). Psychological resilience and positive emotional granularity: Examining the benefits of positive emotions on coping and health. *Journal of personality*, 72(6), 1161-1190.

15. Elliot, A. J., & Covington, M. V. (2001). Approach and avoidance motivation. *Educational Psychology Review*, 13(2), 73-92.

16. Donnon, T., & Hammond, W. (2007). A psychometric assessment of the self-reported youth resiliency: assessing developmental strengths questionnaire 1, 2. *Psychological reports*, 100(3), 963-978.

17. Oshio, A., Kaneko, H., Nagamine, S., & Nakaya, M. (2003). Construct validity of the adolescent resilience scale. *Psychological Reports*, 93(3f), 1217-1222.

18. Friborg, O., Hjemdal, O., Rosenvinge, J. H., & Martinussen, M. (2003). A new rating scale for adult resilience: What are the central protective resources behind healthy adjustment?. *International journal of methods in psychiatric research*, 12(2), 65-76.

19. Windle, G., Markland, D. A., & Woods, R. T. (2008). Examination of a theoretical model of psychological resilience in older age. *Aging and Mental Health*, 12(3), 285-292.

20. Kandel, E. R. (2014). A new intellectual framework for psychiatry. *American Journal of Psychiatry*, 155, 457-469.

21. Kandel, E. R., Schwartz, J. H., & Jessell, T. M. (Eds.). (2013). *Principles of neural science* (Vol. 5). New York: McGraw-Hill.

22. Lu, B., Nagappan, G., Guan, X., Nathan, P. J., & Wren, P. (2013). BDNF-based synaptic repair as a disease-modifying strategy for neurodegenerative diseases. *Nature Reviews Neuroscience*, 14(6), 401-416.

23. Castrén, E., & Rantamäki, T. (2010). The role of BDNF and its receptors in depression and antidepressant drug action: reactivation of developmental plasticity. *Developmental neurobiology*, 70(5), 289-297.

24. Davidson, R., Begley, S. (2012). *The emotional life of your brain*. Hachette UK.

25. Hjemdal, O., Friborg, O., Stiles, T. C., Martinussen, M., & Rosenvinge, J. H. (2006). A New Scale for Adolescent Resilience: Grasping the Central Protective Resources Behind Healthy Development. *Measurement and evaluation in Counseling and Development*, 84-96.

26. Connor, K. M., & Davidson, J. R. (2003). Development of a new resilience scale: The Connor-Davidson resilience scale (CD-RISC). *Depression and anxiety*, 18(2), 76-82.

27. Hystad, S. W., Eid, J., Johnsen, B. H., Laberg, J. C., & THOMAS BARTONE, P. A. U. L. (2010). Psychometric properties of the revised Norwegian dispositional resilience (hardiness) scale. *Scandinavian Journal of Psychology*, 51(3), 237-245.

28. Hurtes, K., & Allen, L. (2001). Measuring resiliency in youth: The Resiliency Attitude and Skills Profile. *Therapeutic Recreation Journal*, 35(4), 333-347.

29. Stewart, D., Sun, J., Patterson, C., Lemerle, K., & Hardie, M. (2004). Promoting and building resilience in primary school communities: evidence from a comprehensive 'health promoting school'approach. *International Journal of Mental Health Promotion*, 6(3), 26-33.

30. Wagnild, G. M. Young, H. M. (1993). Development and Psychometric Evaluation of the Resilience Scale. *Journal of nursing measurement*, 1(2).

31. Preston, A. R., & Eichenbaum, H. (2013). Interplay of hippocampus and prefrontal cortex in memory. *Current Biology*, 23(17), R764-R773.

32. Smith, B. W., Dalen, J., Wiggins, K., Tooley, E., Christopher, P., & Bernard, J. (2008). The brief resilience scale: assessing the ability to bounce back. *International journal of behavioral medicine*, 15(3), 194-200.

33. Duckworth, A. L., Peterson, C., Matthews, M. D., & Kelly, D. R. (2007). Grit: perseverance and passion for long-term goals. *Journal of personality and social psychology*, 92(6), 1087.

34. Carver, C. S. (1998). Resilience and thriving: Issues, models, and linkages. *Journal of social issues*, 54(2), 245-266.

35. Ungar, M., & Liebenberg, L. (2011). Assessing resilience across cultures using mixed methods: Construction of the child and youth resilience measure. *Journal of Mixed Methods Research*, 1558689811400607.

36. Peterson, B. S., Wang, Z., Horga, G., Warner, V., Rutherford, B., Klahr, K. W., ... & Hao, X. (2014). Discriminating risk and resilience endophenotypes from lifetime illness effects in familial major depressive disorder. JAMA psychiatry, 71(2), 136-148.

37. Kleim, B., Thörn, H. A., & Ehlert, U. (2014). Positive interpretation bias predicts well-being in medical interns. *Frontiers in psychology*, 5.

38. Clarke, P. J., Nanthakumar, S., Notebaert, L., Holmes, E. A., Blackwell, S. E., & MacLeod, C. (2014). Simply imagining sunshine, lollipops and rainbows will not budge the bias: The role of ambiguity in interpretive bias modification. *Cognitive therapy and research*, 38(2), 120-131.

39. Oettingen, G., & Wadden, T. A. (1991). Expectation, fantasy, and weight loss: Is the impact of positive thinking always positive?. *Cognitive Therapy and Research*, 15(2), 167-175.

40. Schore, A. N. (2000). Attachment and the regulation of the right brain. Attachment & human development, 2(1), 23-47.

41. Pujol, J., Harrison, B. J., Ortiz, H., Deus, J., Soriano-Mas, C., Lopez-Sola, M., ... & Cardoner, N. (2009). Influence of the fusiform gyrus on amygdala response to emotional faces in the non-clinical range of social anxiety. *Psychological medicine*, 39(07), 1177-1187.

42. Svanberg, P. O. (1998). Attachment, resilience and prevention. *Journal of Mental health*, 7(6), 543-578.

43. Blaustein, M. E., & Kinniburgh, K. M. (2010). *Treating traumatic stress in children and adolescents: How to foster resilience through attachment, self-regulation, and competency*. Guilford Press.

44. Leahey, T. M., Kumar, R., Weinberg, B. M., & Wing, R. R. (2012). Teammates and Social Influence Affect Weight Loss Outcomes in a Team-Based Weight Loss Competition. Obesity, 20(7), 1413-1418.

45. Leahey, T. M., LaRose, J. G., Fava, J. L., & Wing, R. R. (2011). Social influences are associated with BMI and weight loss intentions in young adults. Obesity, 19(6), 1157-1162.

46. Wethington, E., & Kessler, R. C. (1986). Perceived support, received support, and adjustment to stressful life events. *Journal of Health and Social behavior*, 78-89.

47. Issa, G., Wilson, C., Terry, A. V., & Pillai, A. (2010). An inverse relationship between cortisol and BDNF levels in schizophrenia: data from human postmortem and animal studies. Neurobiology of disease, 39(3), 327-333.

48. Eckenrode, J. (1984). Impact of chronic and acute stressors on daily reports of mood. Journal of personality and social psychology, 46(4), 907.

49. McWilliams, L. A., Cox, B. J., & Enns, M. W. (2003). Mood and anxiety disorders associated with chronic pain: an examination in a nationally representative sample. Pain, 106(1), 127-133.

50. Min, J. A., Yoon, S., Lee, C. U., Chae, J. H., Lee, C., Song, K. Y., & Kim, T. S. (2013). Psychological resilience contributes to low emotional distress in cancer patients. Supportive Care in Cancer, 21(9), 2469-2476.

51. Cotman, C. W., & Berchtold, N. C. (2002). Exercise: a behavioral intervention to enhance brain health and plasticity. Trends in neurosciences, 25(6), 295-301.

52. Cassilhas, R. C., Lee, K. S., Fernandes, J., Oliveira, M. G. M., Tufik, S., Meeusen, R., & De Mello, M. T. (2012). Spatial memory is improved by aerobic and resistance exercise through divergent molecular mechanisms. Neuroscience, 202, 309-317.

53. Chapman, S. B., Aslan, S., Spence, J. S., DeFina, L. F., Keebler, M. W., Didehbani, N., & Lu, H. (2013). Shorter term aerobic exercise improves brain, cognition, and cardiovascular fitness in aging. Frontiers in aging neuroscience, 5.

54. Colcombe, S. J., Erickson, K. I., Scalf, P. E., Kim, J. S., Prakash, R., McAuley, E., ... & Kramer, A. F. (2006). Aerobic exercise training increases brain volume in aging humans. The Journals of Gerontology Series A: Biological Sciences and Medical Sciences, 61(11), 1166-1170.

55. Molteni, R., Barnard, R. J., Ying, Z., Roberts, C. K., & Gomez-Pinilla, F. (2002). A high-fat, refined sugar diet reduces hippocampal brain-derived neurotrophic factor, neuronal plasticity, and learning. Neuroscience, 112(4), 803-814.

56. Heffernan, T. M. (2008). The impact of excessive alcohol use on prospective memory: a brief review. Current drug abuse reviews, 1(1), 36-41.

57. Simon, G. E., Ludman, E. J., Linde, J. A., Operskalski, B. H., Ichikawa, L., Rohde, P., ... & Jeffery, R. W. (2008). Association between obesity and depression in middle-aged women. *General Hospital Psychiatry*, 30(1), 32-39.

58. Giese, M., Unternaehrer, E., Brand, S., Calabrese, P., Holsboer-Trachsler, E., & Eckert, A. (2013). The interplay of stress and sleep impacts BDNF level. *PloS one*, 8(10), e76050.

59. Kerkhof, G. A., & Van Dongen, H. P. A. (2010). Effects of sleep deprivation on cognition. Human Sleep and Cognition: *Basic Research*, 185, 105.

60. Greer, S. M., Goldstein, A. N., & Walker, M. P. (2013). The impact of sleep deprivation on food desire in the human brain. *Nature communications*, 4.

61. Hirshkowitz, M., Whiton, K., Albert, S. M., Alessi, C., Bruni, O., DonCarlos, L., ... & Neubauer, D. N. (2015). National Sleep Foundation's sleep time duration recommendations: methodology and results summary. *Sleep Health*, 1(1), 40-43.

62. Mäntyselkä, P. T., Turunen, J. H., Ahonen, R. S., & Kumpusalo, E. A. (2003). Chronic pain and poor self-rated health. *Jama*, 290(18), 2435-2442.

63. Jackson, C. J., Hobman, E. V., Jimmieson, N. L., & Martin, R. (2009). Comparing different approach and avoidance models of learning and personality in the prediction of work, university, and leadership outcomes. *British journal of psychology*, 100(2), 283-312.

64. Elliot, A. J., & Thrash, T. M. (2002). Approach-avoidance motivation in personality: approach and avoidance temperaments and goals. *Journal of personality and social psychology*, 82(5), 804.

65. Burns, R. A., & Anstey, K. J. (2010). The Connor–Davidson Resilience Scale (CD-RISC): Testing the invariance of a uni-dimensional resilience measure that is independent of positive and negative affect. *Personality and Individual Differences*, 48(5), 527-531.

66. Carver, C. S. (1997). You want to measure coping but your protocol's too long: Consider the brief cope. *International journal of behavioral medicine*, 4(1), 92-100.

CPSIA information can be obtained
at www.ICGtesting.com
Printed in the USA
LVHW020827050222
710245LV00008B/141